1955

THE SUMMER WHEN...

VALERIE THORNHILL

Pergola Press

ALSO BY VALERIE THORNHILL

In Restoration
winner of the The People's Book Prize for Fiction 2012

The Children of Kumbhalgarh and Other Stories.

The Tycoon's Tale

Cynthia Loves her Fiat 500

Dedication

This book is dedicated to all my former students at
St. George's School in Rome

Acknowledgements

My heartfelt thanks to all who helped and encouraged me to write *The Summer When...* , in particular Sylvia Ashurst, Susan Cockcroft, Ben Gardiner, Judith Harris, Sascha and Lars Krückeberg, Gerald Onn, Sarah Morgan, Silvia Gavuzzo Stewart, María Dolores Sánchez Jáuregui and Catherine Roberts, and for my family's support and patience, especially my husband's.

A CIP catalogue record for this title is available from the British Library.

ISBN 978-0-9950335-2-0

First published 2013

Published by:
Pergola Press
1 Minster Moorgate
Beverley
HU17 8HP
U.K.

www.pergolapress.co.uk

Printed by:
Lavenham Press Ltd.
Arbons House
47 Water Street
Lavenham
Suffolk CO10 9RN

www.lavenhampress.co.uk

CONTENTS

'There is a tide in the affairs of men,

Which, taken at the flood, leads on to fortune;

Omitted, all the voyage of their life

Is bound in shallows and in miseries.

On such a full sea are we now afloat,

And we must take the current when it serves,

Or lose our ventures.'

Shakespeare *Julius Caesar* IV, iii, 217

CHAPTER 1

There is no turning back. Perched on a bench at the fore end of the promenade deck enjoying the sea air and swooping gulls, I'm starting to write my travel journal on the very first day of July, 1955. Ferries are fun, afloat to the unknown. Words seesaw on the page with each pitch and toss. Everywhere inside the ship is painted the same colour, a magnolia shade of distemper, the ubiquitous wartime colour for schoolrooms, hospital wards and station waiting rooms. Mother explained it was cheaper and easier for factories to produce gallons of the same hue. At least it's brighter than the utilitarian brown slapped over the wooden fittings on this boat taking me to France. I've been observing from the railings the sunburnt sailors tugging at ropes and coiling them, presiding over the throbbing heart of the ferry.

I'm a *tabula rasa*, a clean sheet, drifting with the flow of events into the unknown.

Two Americans on an adjacent bench are scrutinising me, unaware that I am about to slip this sensibly clad couple tracking seagulls through their binoculars into my journal. Thirsty, I follow them to the lower deck in search of the bar.

'Like a drink?' Why do they have to talk to me? There are two of them; they can chat to each other.

'No. Thanks all the same.'

'What's your name?' The sturdy husband in rather loud check trousers is balding before his hair goes grey.

'Valerie.'

'Val,' repeats the wife with curly blond hair and freckles, eyes and nose crinkling into a wide smile. Her body is round and bouncy, smaller than mine. 'Val, you must be thirsty. Have a coke. Do. On us.'

'Just a glass of water, please.' I don't like Coca Cola. Mother says it rots your teeth. I'm never called 'Val'. Why does she assume such familiarity? It's what Dad calls Mum.

'Only water?'

'Can't afford more. I'm a student.' A pause. 'My mother's name is Val, so –'

'So you're Val junior, or Val II.' Oh dear, he's trying to be jovial. 'That often happens in the States. I'm Charles Hammond IV! And this is Liz, my wife.'

'In my case they couldn't think of anything else. They were expecting Timothy, and here I came, another daughter.'

The barman, about my age, is eying me with interest.

'Do your parents let you travel abroad alone?' Liz asks. I don't want to speak, let alone think about them, my father's bankruptcy and their hasty departure from our last home to rent the ground floor of a house; owner above, tenants – us – below.

'I'm going to study in Paris. My Cambridge professor has invited me. The rest of July I'll be teaching English to a girl my age in the south of Spain. In Andalucía.'

'Fun, but hot. Olé!' She raises her glass of beer. 'Good luck, Val!'

Prying adults! I just want a simple glass of water and my own, uninterrupted thoughts. I admit I'm amused by the young barman who, eyes half closed, is scanning me with his head slightly tipped back. Then with, 'for a girl like you,' he plonks a glass of water down in front of me.

'Thanks.' A girl like me! He's probably a student as well, pretending not to glance at me while dealing with random orders.

'Disappointing,' Charles Hammond IV is saying, 'the dull food, rationing and slow service'.

'It's pointless to think back to the pre-war Cunard liners, or Harrods. Now the only place for a decent meal is the Lyons

Corner House, and that's not up to much,' his wife reminisces sadly, lips pursed behind a glass of tepid lager.

I pull myself upright and draw in my chin, ready to pounce in defence of the Corner House. Just before leaving London, I splashed out guiltily on 'all you can put on to a plate' using too much of the money I had just earned slaving away in a jam factory. It was fun to see how much from the cold buffet could be balanced in a pyramid. Mike, my student boyfriend with shaggy hair like a Newfoundland dog, piled up so much food on his plate that it collapsed all over the floor as we laughed at his audacity. We ended up sharing my food mountain. I smile at the American couple and escape to resume my quest for the French coastline. I must write about my solitary encounters with fate.

How come your parents let you travel alone? The Hammonds are too pushy by far. Or are they? That's a normal question, I suppose. My elder sister Rosanne jollied off to the continent on her first university vacation, and now she's in Finland or somewhere in north Europe. My family is always on the move. This is at least the fifth time our parents have changed house, and I've been to almost as many schools. The ground floor of the house in Godalming where they are now is no more a home than any of the other places.

A tentative line on the horizon. Eureka, France! Over it lie grey clouds. Soft, unfocused, the face of Uncle David, who was like an elder brother, appears as if hiding behind them. No, he didn't die near Calais. It was somewhere closer to Le Havre. He was blown up in France on D-Day 1944, whereabouts unknown.

The coast looms, the sky above clear in expectation. Time to disembark at Calais.

At the foot of the gangway porters jostle for custom from passengers straggling towards the Paris train. A porter in dark blue tunic and beret, a *gaulloise* on his lower lip, hoists my new suitcase onto his shoulders, legs bending under its weight. Trotting after him, I practise my French on the notices. *Pas plus* de 45 francs *par valise*. Easy. Forty-five francs for each suitcase. I've only one suitcase, a knap-sack and a shoulder bag holding valuables. Admittedly the case is heavy with the tomes to read during the long vacation. Poor old porter! But it is his job; he looks tough and keen. Not many travellers so he can't be earning much. I feel uncomfortably like Lady Bountiful, and smile at the Hammonds as I pass them in the wake of my speedy porter. They have a stouter one, who progresses at a statelier pace towards the train. One common goal: Paris.

Are French trains higher or platforms lower? Whatever the explanation, it's a big step up into the train. My porter grunts and curses as he heaves the case into a carriage towards the front, shuffles along the corridor to an empty compartment, hoists it on to the rack making the netting bulge dangerously under it and stands four square, expectantly. I open my purse confidently. Forty-five francs, the poster says. I count out forty. Then fifty. The bank hasn't provided anything in between. A pity. Still, the porter must have change. I smile, hold out the banknote, and turn to wriggle the knapsack off my back.

Sacre dieu! My case is hauled off the luggage rack and hurled out of the open window to land in front of the American couple. Catches snap open to reveal underwear wedged between shoes. Books skid along the platform. A battered alarm clock protests in a state of shock. The porter scowls: I freeze. What have I done? His departure is fuelled by a burst of incomprehensibly rude expletives referring to cul, bottom, as in *cul de sac*. All rather unnerving.

'A fine mess.' Charles Hammond IV is contemplating my exploded case prone on the platform. His porter stops, half-dropping their two fine leather suitcases.

'We'll be back in a moment.' Liz glances at me staring in horror from the compartment window, and pulls at his arm. They hurry off in pursuit of the bags that have resumed their progress

4

along the platform; I must deal with my shattered suitcase. Better to put the heavy books in my knapsack, and drag the case up myself. Better...

'Can we help?' Here they are again, like unsummoned guardian angels.

'Can cope, thanks!' I straighten up and grin my thanks. The husband insists on heaving my battered case into the carriage. They are so kind, but I want to be alone. I have so much to filter through my mind.

'We're in the next car if you need us.' Their porter is smiling and thanks them many times, exuding Gallic charm. Hardly surprising, since they confess they tipped him a hundred francs for each suitcase! Better not to understand French and ignore advice given on posters. Just blunder through and take the risk, though I can't pay that sort of money.

They itch to travel. So do I, but differently. I'm sailing out to improve my French and Spanish. A friend in Italy has also asked me to stay. All that my parents know. I'm free to go with the current, gathering material like a journalist over whatever remains of the summer vacation. A thrill or two lie ahead, I hope.

Leaving Calais, the train chugs over flat fields enlivened by sparks from scattered poppies. Some farmhouses are rebuilt; others still sit war-scarred on the edge of ripening wheatfields. I turn away, not to be reminded of my father's experience of the First World War, nor of the Remembrance Day service in church every November, overwhelmed by memories of Uncle David. 'At the eleventh hour of the eleventh day...' echo in my memory. Looking through the window again, I can't see any trace of the trenches where father had saved soldiers under fire. That's why he was awarded his Military Cross. Wrong part of France perhaps.

'You just can't imagine what I've been going through!' brought me downstairs when I was home last Christmas. The kitchen door was ajar. Dad, head in one hand, the other flat on the kitchen table, was mumbling about being too old for a free-lance writer. Paper is rationed. His wartime job in the Ministry of Information has ended. Similar positions are now filled by younger men back from the war. 'My wound and Military Cross from the First World War simply don't count,' he growled. 'Nor does my service as air raid warden and fire fighter in the second one.' Then came the confession. He had been catching the same commuter train to London for months, wandering in the streets or reading discarded newspapers, if he could find a warm place to sit. Then back on the usual evening train. The bank had just closed his account. Mother was staring at him in disbelief. There was no more money for fares.

I resigned myself to father's bankruptcy during my first year at university. The rented ground-floor flat removed them from their neighbours' inquisitive eyes. Rosanne had to study for her finals, graduate and get a job - quickly. I scraped savings from my university scholarship to send to them. When I was invited to stay in Paris and then found a summer job in Spain, I didn't ask my parents if I could travel on my own, being underage, as they had already a lot to worry about. I was, however, thrillingly aware that an innocent young girl travelling to the Continent for the first time couldn't fail to encounter adventures.

The suitcase is on the luggage rack with underwear hanging out where a catch won't snap shut. I'll have to buy a strap in Paris. String will do for now.

'OK?' Freckle-faced Liz Hammond pokes her head into the compartment, followed by an ample body. As she sits down, the upholstery puffs up on either side of her buttocks. Too close. Why does she have to come? She means well, of course. These adults seem to insinuate their way into my life just when I want to strike out on my own. If it isn't my parents, then it's some unwanted person trying to *in loco parentis* me, just because I'm under age, too young and vulnerable for the 'big bad ways' of the world. These are precisely what I want to confront. Secretly and alone.

'A nice girl like you travelling alone.' Along come the usual questions. I live in Surrey. Yes, south of London. With my parents. A pang as I picture the 1930s cottage-style house they had to sell, mother tending the flowers while father mows the lawn. Yes, I'm a student at Cambridge University. Sophomore year? Well, I've finished my first year. The second starts in October. I don't mention my secret mission to record Europe shaking off the war years. A scoop, perhaps. Who knows? It's a very personal quest in search of the indefinite. Open-ended. If I gaze out of the window, Liz might take the hint and leave me to my thoughts.

Instead, through lack of conversational fodder, she changes the topic into an account of London with rationing and bargains found in old bookstores and antique shops because no one seems to bother about such things. Quite right too, I think, mindful of the homeless, bombed out during the war and still living in prefabs. I turn my head firmly to survey the fields and the Hobbema avenues of Lombardy poplars.

That picture by Hobbema has fascinated me since I first saw a reproduction hanging behind the headmistress's chair on the same wall as Franz Hals' *Laughing Cavalier*. When Miss Green was sitting bolt upright in her most headmistressy mood, her bespectacled face topped by a tight bun of grey-streaked hair blocked the avenue. Hobbema's poplars sprouted behind each ear! It was reassuring for a chastened child like me to know that, when Miss Green relaxed and leant sideways with her bony hand over one side of the chair, I could walk my eyes up the dead straight avenue of poplars that faced me wherever I stood. Before leaving, I would turn and smile politely, when really I just wanted to run up the sunny avenue again, or shift to a much more disturbing proposition - those insolently attractive eyes of the *Laughing Cavalier*. If I had time, and didn't feel that Miss Green might interpret it as being rude, I could glance sideways from the safer avenue to check if the Cavalier was still looking at me. He was.

'- then we'll leave Paris for Rome. Next Athens,' Liz drones on, ' though we've seen an exact copy of the Parthenon in Nashville -' A light in a distant farmhouse. A small town flickers past. Dusk is blurring the edges of the world outside. Charles Hammond IV pauses at the door with three paper cups.

'Time to keep up your strength. We'll arrive in forty minutes.' My first taste of this fiery liquid, Bourbon, brings unwilling tears to my eyes.

'You're welcome to have it. I know you all have been deprived for so long. Bourbon is a horrendous price in London...'

It is decent of them to include me. I must try to be more sociable.

'I haven't been to Paris. Ever. My tutor, Madame Magny, has invited me to stay for a few days.' Charles laughs as he describes pre-war Paris, trying to tease Liz with sly allusions to the *Folies Bergères*. Fields give way to careworn 19th-century suburbs. The outskirts of Paris at last. The Hammonds stand up to return to their compartment, Charles worried about my suitcase. I insist I can manage on my own. At the Gare du Nord I lean out of the window and wave as they walk away. Really kind people.

As passengers flow past the compartment window, I note women are wearing longer and wider 'New Look' skirts. Wonderful to swirl round in, but I couldn't make myself one. Too expensive. They use up so much material.

How can I lug my battered suitcase to the metro? I must get off at Denfert-Rochereau. From there I've been given rough directions to find a street next to a cemetery. I'll retrieve Madame Magny's brandy-stained map from my handbag. It hadn't been the best moment to ask her for directions. A number of empty bottles graced the ledge outside her university room that morning, and another two, one unfinished, stood on her desk. Oh well, her map will have to do.

I try to lift the suitcase down from the rack without dislodging the contents. String? Only dry biscuits, sticking plaster, disinfectant, scissors, safety pins, lipstick, hankies, a sanitary towel, rubber bands and books in my knapsack - no string. Rubber bands for the catch. Quick, the cleaners are in the next compartment. Knapsack hitched on to back, handbag slung sideways over shoulder while dragging the case along the corridor, I feel people staring. I'm not used to being watched. Blond, leggy Scandinavians might top the desirability charts, but dark hair, blue eyes and a Celtic wiriness convey a more subtle charm – according to my boyfriend Mike. For an instant I wish him here; tall, shaggy and hugging me tight.

Peering through the window is a steely-eyed porter, beret pulled down over bulging forehead and inch-long eyebrows. I drag the case further along the corridor away from those predatory eyes and bump it down on to the low platform. The rubber bands snap off the catch shedding the contents. As I bend to gather them up, the knapsack, heavy with books transferred from the case, crashes against my head, half knocking me out. A hand pulls it back; another steadies my arm.

'*Voyons!*' It's the same porter who peered into the carriage; behind him the notice, forty-five francs for each piece of luggage. I point at it; he nods and heaves the half-open suitcase on to his back, just like in Calais.

'*Ecoutez. De la ficelle?*' Any string? Better a strap, but I can't remember the French word. He grunts, twists to one side, replaces the bag carefully on the ground, and flicks his hands round the innumerable pockets of his blue tunic. It's after eight. No shops will be open. Can I manage the metro, change station, and walk to the flat near Denfert-Rochereau without leaving my possessions in my wake? A taxi is the only solution I can think of, but it costs too much. My vacation is ending before it begins.

'*Voilà!*' His longish piece of string might be grubby but it's strong, resilient and full of hope.

'*Merci, ça va très bien.*' So far so good, but the dilemma remains. In the face of this gift, does forty-five francs increase twofold or more? How much does string cost? Direct method best. That's the way Miss Green managed her school, bobbing her bun up and down Hobbema's avenue while issuing orders. I try to help him tie one end on the broken catch and pull the string round so both ends just meet. Phew! One potential disaster averted. Another looms. I tap his shoulder to stop him swinging the case onto his back, and point again to the forty-five francs.

'Bah!' Is that *bon* or the sort of equivocal response that the downturned corners of his mouth seem to indicate? His shoulders are too weighed down by now with the case to be shrugged and his arms balancing it could hardly be shoved in my direction, palms upwards. Sign language is all, I'm thinking as I scuttle along the platform after him, especially in France.

How does he know where I'm going? Have I mentioned the metro? Which line is it? I must not panic. Only one option at this point: the end of the platform. There he carefully lowers my suitcase on to the platform and looks at me.

'*Alors?*' Please, to Denfert-Rochereau.

He's carrying my case right to the metro, each step making me more and more nervous. The case can't stand another thud. The other catch will break. A cab? Impossible. Better to ask him straight out.

'*Combien, s'il vous plaît?*'

'*Comme vous voulez, m'selle.*' I'm to decide. Help! forty-five for one case. Then something for the string and more for going right inside the metro? Fifty francs? Anything to get out of this without a fuss, and to salvage the suitcase. The porter smiles, pats my shoulder and disappears into the evening crowd.

The metro ticket first. Direction Porte d'Orléans. The string is holding but, alarmed the suitcase might be jostled open, I keep apprehensively to one side out of the main rush down the stairs. At the sound of a train arriving people begin to run. The less mobile travellers are flipped back by two metal barriers with leather flaps that swing down when the train reaches the far end of the platform. To prevent people crowding others on to the rails, I suppose. Curious - perhaps effective in the rush hour. There is no need to hurry. Better not to. The evening is yet young and Madame Magny didn't fix any arrival time. The reek of cigarettes explains the general grime of the pitted platform. Discarded packets have landed with apple cores and spittle beneath the rails. Unshaven workers returning to the suburbs gape through puffs of smoke at the monochrome posters, while couples clutch and giggle, oblivious.

Out on Place Denfert Rochereau, lights, voices, a shiver of expectation. The brandy-stained scrap of paper has a rough circle for the square and a squiggly line for the road alongside the cemetery with an unpronounceable name. No way of telling which side of Place Denfert Rochereau I'm on in relation to the cemetery. Where to start? A *bar-tabac* would be the place to enquire. I deposit the case by a tubular stand plastered with posters and, careful not to forget the slip of paper, make for the nearest bar. On my return two figures are contemplating the suitcase. A whiff of sweat and beer, a glimpse of dark stubble, whites of eyes; faces scoured by despair. Panic. I must grab the handle and flee - never mind the weight - to the far side of the square. At the end of a street, a dim outline of trees. The cemetery. Turn right there. Decipher the numbers. Thirteen. Unlucky? No choice. That's where Madame Magny lives. Don't look behind; they might, may, will be following me. The door pushes open in answer to my prayer. Dumping the case just inside the entry, I peer out into the now dark street. Silence. A siren wails in the direction of the square. Not a soul in sight.

11

The *concierge* emerges from her cubicle, eyes narrowed in professional suspicion, knitting dangling, and a shawl over her grey dress on a warm July evening.

'Madame Magny?'

'*Troisième.*'

Madame Magny mentioned there was a lift, but where? No sign of it in the panelled vestibule. I don't dare ask. Too stupid a question. One foot shoves the case past the concierge's snugly lit cubicle to reach the curved end of the vestibule. Mirrors confuse the space. A wave of sleepiness swamps me; all I want in the world is to slump down right here. A light shines though some stained glass, a whirr, and the panelling opens to scatter two figures into the dimly lit hall. Foot out to keep the door open, back aching but grimly determined, I tip the case inside, swing round to close the door and thud the knapsack against the side almost knocking myself over. Nothing broken, but unsettling. *Troisième.* I press button three rapidly before anyone else enters. There's hardly room to spare. The lift opens on to a dark landing. Three doors. To the right, Soulages. To the left, Moquet. Opposite, *voilà!* Magny.

The old apprehension is returning, a gut reaction as I recall skirting those bottles in the college corridor before confronting a brilliant mind swooping and scoring. 'Stand up straight, Valerie, draw in your breath...' I miss my mother's cup of chocolate and company when situations twist my stomach. A step backwards and a glance at the lift, still open. I could ask for the date on my return ticket to be changed. Green fields and horseriding, the cinema, tennis... but without my childhood home and friends. All have vacation jobs. I might even meet some of them on my travels. Breathing deeply and with sudden misgivings, I ring the bell, ready for the unknown.

A middle aged, whiskery man opens the door. People are sitting around the high-ceilinged room and I panic. Where is she? Have I mistaken the door, invitation, date, time? There she is ensconced on a faded flower-patterned sofa, holding court. I suppose this is a modern version of those 18th-century salons of *Mesdames de Quelquechoses*!

Funny the way tiredness engulfs you unawares, just when you want to make an impression. I am introduced around as '*mon étudiante assez douée*', but to be frank I'm so worried about what exactly the *assez* means that I can hardly rub one word of French against another. I must be letting her down 100%, since she thinks I am either 'quite' or 'very' gifted.

Who are these people? All middle-aged or more; definitely old. The whiskery man is Maxime something. He seems to be paying attention to a wild-looking woman called Claudine; she has round eyes of unfocused brown depths and her wavy greying hair is all over the place. A sort of *gamine* charm, I suppose. She doesn't look well-to-do. Nor does anyone for that matter. Then there is a Count Guy de something or other. I blurt out 'Maupassant' and everyone titters. Fool I am. At least he comes over to me smiling, squeezes my arm and offers me some dried-up bits of cheese - or meat - on a stale biscuit and a glass of vinegary wine. As soon as I can, after a brief visit to a bathroom without a proper bath tub, I'm shown to a couch under a sort of inside balcony. I'm sticky, smelly and exhausted. But above all, excited.

Here I am - actually in Paris! What will happen now?

CHAPTER 2

I'm woken by a snuffling noise soon after dawn. My eyes stray from the back of the green-striped sofa by my bed to the one facing it, where Madame Magny sat enthroned the previous evening. Spreading upward out of sight is a strange, mottled grey and yellow rough-weave curtain. More snuffling. I hadn't noticed an animal. It sounds like a snub-nosed pug.

Feet firmly planted on the floorboards, I check that my cotton nightie decently covers me. The mottled grey and yellow isn't a curtain or huge canvas. It's a window spreading up two storeys; busybodies could be peering in at me from the building opposite. Number 13 is the first door after turning right into the road edging the cemetery. I expected to peer down at its funerary monuments since Madame Magny had once recounted strange rituals there while offering brandy to a select group of students. Instead, this room faces an anonymous block with mean windows gaping at me, at least four to my huge solitary one. How can I dress under their scrutiny?

The snuffles are increasing in vigour and number to turn into a sequence of short tenor snores, rising in volume until a final crescendo smashes them into silence. Springs complain above me on the balcony as I grab random garments, scurry across the room to creep up the spiral staircase and into the bathroom. I've never seen a hipbath before, its enamel crazy-paved with grime. It must be a historic fitting that has seen its day. I try the taps. The system shudders, spewing out a rusty trail of water, and expires. Hardly encouraging. The basin? Only one tap functions, predictably the cold one. Not to worry. It's July and hardly chilly. A catlick will suffice. I must get dressed and ready for Madame Magny and her faceless neighbours across the street. I scrub my face, amazed at the bloom, as my mother would have put it, on my cheeks, given how late I had gone to bed. Makeup? A bore, but perhaps it helps when one faces the unknown and needs to impress. A touch of blue shade to match my eyes and pink summer lipstick? I suspect Mike rather likes me to heighten the effects, though he protests that he loves me *au naturel*. There's little 'natural' left, I think as I brush my now regularly spaced teeth that had tortured my early teens. A huge upper jaw plate had to be screwed wider every day and then forced in to make the teeth lock correctly. I've inherited my father's determined lower jaw. Ugly in a girl, people say.

With men you never know what they really think. The yellow cotton blouse and green skirt hardly match my eye shadow. Too bad. The pink rosebud skirt pattern echoes my lipstick. It will have to do. At least I can tighten the skirt having lost weight after exams on a diet of strawberries and bread during my two-week jam factory slog.

As I return from the bathroom across the wooden floorboards, leaping from one scrap of carpet to another to avoid the splinters, the hem flaps against my calf. Damn it! I've forgotten that I've started letting my skirt down to give it some semblance of the New Look. To be in fashion is to be free! I take it off in the safety of the alcove, find my emergency sewing kit and settle on the bed to finish lengthening the hem.

'*Alors, qu'est-ce qu'on va faire?*'

A bespectacled moon face is peering down from the balcony, two elegantly tapering fingers balancing a cigarette, a half-full glass in the other slender hand. The face appears disconcertingly expressionless beneath Madame Magny's dangling blond hair. Strange. She's asking me what's to be done.

'*Il faut prendre du café. Allez-y!*'

Coffee? I shrink back, startled by a black object that hurtles down from the balcony to land just in front of me. Madame's purse. I secure the last stitch, wriggle back into my now fashionable rosebud skirt, pick up the purse and make for the door, lift and mirrored hall to run the gauntlet past Madame la Concierge, the

Knitting Tigress with narrow eyes. Safely outside, I pause to savour the anticipated nine o'clock Parisian smells: the seductive aroma of coffee, the heady impact of freshly-baked *croissants*, sensuous odours from oyster-laden fishmongers to the strident appeal of *gaulloises* hanging from a hundred lips. Instead there is only an empty street along the cemetery wall. A few blocks away I find another crammed with pavement cafés, food shops of every possible variety, street vendors and vegetable carts. Besides the coffee and *croissants* for breakfast, I buy myself two rolls, two fat slices of *gruyère* and a peach, carefully paid for out of my own money.

Madame is heating water in a coffee-making contraption inside the minute kitchen. Her eyes loom emotionless from behind the glasses; her attenuated hand reaches out for the coffee. Mission accomplished, she retreats to recline on the faded flower sofa, draws the pale-blue flannel robe around her, lights a cigarette and waits for coffee to be served. I meanwhile rootle around the kitchen cupboards to find plates for the *croissants* and matching mugs. Drat it! I've forgotten the milk. *Il n'y a pas de quoi.* Madame Magny doesn't want any, just black coffee and plenty of sugar to jolt her mind into thought. She has to review a recent edition of Baudelaire's poetry as well as a new book, written by a girl my age and attracting much attention. I want to find out more about her, but Madame is ignoring my questions. She's busy thinking and withdrawing behind her bespectacled mask.

With the hostess too preoccupied to talk, it's better to retreat.

'I'm going to explore Paris, and won't be back till late. I'll buy a map to find my way around.'

'*Allez-y!*'

Evidently Madame has no intention at all of introducing her student to the city.

With a dramatic amount of freedom to go wherever I wish, I decide to walk all the way to the Seine to save money and see life.

I buy a map at the first bookshop. It takes longer than I realised to reach the Jardin du Luxembourg with children babbling and bustling around under the plane trees hosting gossipy sparrows. It is hot by mid-morning; the flowers round the formal ponds and statues are already drooping. I stop near the Palais du Luxembourg at the centre of a vast gravel semi-circle, thrilled at being right on the axis: behind me the long avenue, before me the main garden of the august palace. It's looking sternly at me; I return the stare with interest and admiration. That is, until I feel a tap on the shoulder and turn to see a scrawny hand emerge from a grubby shawl. I offer the smallest coin I have and am rewarded with a scowl and a grunt.

Perusing a map in the middle of a public space invites attention.

"Vere to go? You want help?" No peace for the wicked, I object silently and turn away to head for the *Rive Gauche*, intending to explore the Sorbonne on the way, and whatever else takes my fancy. The young man trying his English out follows at a discreet distance though I pretend not to notice, stopping nonchalantly to buy a red rose from a young gypsy with a baby. I try tucking it jauntily behind my ear; it keeps on falling down so I have to stop and stoop - a natural way to note the developments in my wake. The young man stops when I do, keeping his distance. What's he plotting, I wonder, but don't care.

Leaving the gardens, I'm lured by a domed building in the distance. Scattered figures are mounting the steps to disappear under the portico. It must be open, whatever it is. The nearer I go, the more imposing it is until, as I too scale the steps, the dome seems to tip over to peer down at me. Inside, coolness and stark splendour. Arches and domes, edged in dusty gold and cream, echo my steps onwards towards the apse. It's the Pantheon, shrine of the Great and the Good, of the nation's heroes. Any heroines? Madame Curie? She's here, though she wasn't French. She had married a Frenchman and they did discover things together.

Chopin? Another Pole, though always associated in my mind with France - perhaps because of his preference for French women? Not buried here. I purse my lips and pick my rose up from the marble paving. Why not place it to honour the monument or grave of a genius who died young? I'm feeling young and vulnerable. Where is Chopin buried? Doesn't France have a Keats or Byron, or a Raphael? It must have, but I'm too ignorant to know. A chance look at a monument reveals it is Rousseau's. Hardly a young martyr to fate.

I don't feel like bestowing my rose on Rousseau, because he lived a long and contentious life. I'll keep it until inspired.

My thoughts slide into my future novel, and I wonder what my heroine should do next. Madame is at this moment writing a review of the first novel by an author my age while I'm having fun in Paris. I'll sit under the portico, eat my lunch and decide where to go next.

As I munch, I'm aware that someone's eyes are travelling all over me. Dammit. Why not satisfy my curiosity? Straight ahead down the flight of steps there's only an old man with a white stick, another beggar probably. To my right, a few individuals on their various ways along the far side of the square. Am I mistaken? Oh no! I might have guessed. Peering out from behind the nearest pillar, too close not to be disturbing, a handsome face with laughing eyes above wide, muscled shoulders - that laughing cavalier from the headmistress's study? More precisely, the young man who spoke to me in the gardens.

No, don't get entangled. That is that, thank you very much, *monsieur* whoever you are. I wrench myself away from the come-hither look of the young man who is too handsome for comfort, jump nonchalantly down the steps two at a time - now that our eyes have met I can't ignore him – and veer right in what I hope is the direction of the Sorbonne.

Its courtyards are only patrolled by two plump cats. Maybe they were sent over with the Americans' Marshall Plan to solve the problem of rat-infested Parisian sewers? Probably not. Not ferocious enough. The long vacation has started here too. I like the feel of the place, even though all doors are closed and most windows shuttered. Further on towards the Seine, where Boulevard Saint Germain bisects Boulevard Saint Michel, an old building lies hidden behind creepers - the Musée de Cluny.

It is cool, deserted and free for students. I wish my follower would come to talk to me in the safety of a museum and deter the warders who tend to emerge like wraiths from behind the display cases just when you least expect it.

Settling on a worn bench in a hall of tapestries, I contemplate the famous *Dame à la Licorne*. The maiden stands on a flower-strewn meadow between the lion and the unicorn, attended by a young woman offering her something in a chalice – a love potion? In another section she is framed by a tent held open by the attendant lion and unicorn, with the motto *Mon seul désir* above her, the servant now offering her something from an open jewel chest – a love token? The tapestries are bafflingly silent, telling of a faraway world with calmer rhythms. The few other visitors are equally absorbed in unspoken fellowship. I linger in delight to emerge into the afternoon shadows as they lengthen towards evening. There are more passers-by making me less conspicuous. Where now?

My map shows that one of the oldest churches in Paris lies directly opposite Notre Dame, but on this side of the Seine. Halfway down a street leading to the Seine is an unexpected patch of green; a place for yet more children to play. Madame Magny has informed me with disdain that the French government is paying the wrong sort of mothers to repopulate the land. What a silly state the world is in! Too many births in famine-stricken Africa and not enough in France.

At last here in front of me is the view from my French grammar book. Across the river, beyond the mass of Notre Dame, beats the heart of medieval Paris – the Île de la Cité.

I expect a small, simple church interior, with heavy piers supporting the roof beams. Inside Saint-Julien-le-Pauvre the profuse decoration overwhelms. I move from the numerous hanging lamps with what seem to be red nightlights glowing inside, to the screen dividing the worshippers from the altar. It is laden with icons that I imagined were only found in Greece or Russia. Eyes of saints and the Virgin Mary are watching me; so many eyes and such deep blue, green, red robes all edged in gold that increases in lustre as I slowly walk up and down the screen, looking at one, then another and another and another.

I've done enough looking for the day. Time to immerse myself in street life.

Should I return in time to eat with Madame Magny? Would I be expected to cook a meal? Would Madame have any food, and when do the shops shut? It's nearly six, too early for much to happen in the cafés at the Seine end of the Boulevard Saint Michel, or 'Boul Mich' as Madame calls it. Though it's a warm evening, I shiver, half wishing I had encouraged that young man. I pause under a striped canopy to consult the map. A waiter by the café door looks quizzically at me. Should I sit down? It wouldn't be much fun on my own. I head for the nearest metro and beat a retreat to Denfert-Rochereau. Today's adventure has ended.

Madame opens the door looking grumpy. Why hadn't I taken a key? Returning to slump down on the flowered sofa, she informs me she has written the review on *Bonjour Tristesse*, but hasn't yet been able to arrange an interview with the young author, Françoise Sagan. She's evidently the flavour of the month and hard to track down, even for someone as influential in the intellectual world as Madame appears to be. She sinks further into the cushions, sips her brandy and lights a cigarette.

I feel a twinge of uneasiness. What's my role here? At university it is clear: there's *Madame le Professeur*, and Valerie the student, mindful of her professor's brilliance, of someone who stems from France's intellectual élite, a graduate of the *Grandes Écoles* no less. Can I just admit that I'm hungry and don't know what to do about it? Should I go out and eat on my own? Or offer to get something for both of us? I can't afford to pay for both of us to dine out.

A bang on the front door. Madame nods at me. As I open it, the corner of a huge canvas peeps in supported by a large hairy hand,

'*Vite! Aidez-moi!*' A dark-haired, middle-aged man with brawny shoulders in a navy cotton shirt appears behind it. I stare, hand on doorknob, not knowing how to react.

The removal man - who else can this be? - motions me to hold one end, while he hitches up the other. Pain drags down my shoulders as I shuffle half of the canvas back nervously into Madame's living room, unsure how far I can and should retreat towards the far wall.

'*Ça va.*' No introductions, so Madame obviously knows the tall, well-built individual at the other end of the canvas. He's holding out his hand, though mine are still holding my part of, I reckon, a two metre square canvas. Hardly a work one can lean against a wall and forget, even in this most informal of places! As I look at him, unable to free a hand to grasp his, he laughs and moves towards me. Carefully checking the frame is resting against the green-striped sofa, he reoffers his hand with,

'Pierre Soulages, *enchanté.*' He has the ruddy complexion of a countryman, and a broad, confiding smile. Though he must be nearly forty, there's an air of youthful confidence about him. His sudden entrance drove away the pangs of hunger. Now, the drama over but still unexplained, I'm desperately hungry again. All the while Madame has remained impassive with an enigmatic smile on her face. She begins to speak to him in a low purr.

'*Cher ami,* is this the only one you need to save? You can leave as many as you like. When are the dealers coming?' So that's the problem. He has painted this canvas and has just won a *prix d'estime,* so is being plagued by sudden, unaccustomed publicity. Just like that Françoise woman - the novelist my age, and so famous. I feel dizzy, whether through hunger or the unexpected proximity of famous people, and move away to sit on the green-striped sofa.

'*Qu'avez-vous?*' Pierre is leaning over me, making me feel tiny and insignificant. He probably thinks I'm sitting down because of inherent female frailty, a male-defined combination of monthly adversities and a weak frame. I straighten my spine in an effort to give some semblance of self-control, and explain I'm hungry.

'*Je le comprends bien.*' He tells me to wait a moment, glances at Madame, and disappears through the door across the landing, to reappear two minutes later and call out that a scratch supper will be ready in half an hour.

Succour for me. For my body, my eyes, my soul. Here we sit, Pierre, his wife Colette, as tiny as he is tall, Madame, and me. All inside Aladdin's cave, Parisian style. The flat is almost a mirror version of Madame's, except it overlooks the cemetery and is glowing in sunset light. Of course, these are artists' studios. Why haven't I realised before? Embarrassed by my ignorance and intrigued by the canvases stacked against the walls, I gaze around me. Two of the largest finished paintings hang near the top of the only unencumbered wall to the left of the window; another two smaller ones lie next to the spiral staircase, presumably to be placed higher up the studio wall. The balcony above the entrance door must be their bedroom, so Pierre and his wife can lie in bed and contemplate the sunset over the trees in the cemetery. Her kitchen, directly opposite me, is well lit and filled with a familiar jumble of implements, peelings, fruit, vegetables, spices and herbs that promise tasty fare.

'It's nearly midnight before we leave Pierre and Colette, and an evening of super food served around a monologue from Madame - less good. Probably because I have heard it before or I didn't bother to follow it all or I couldn't understand her French. There also seemed to be a lot of what I assume must be *argot*. I must pick up some slang. We've drunk a lot and I can't remember what I ate. Or much of what was said, except, I think, Pierre doesn't want the dealers to carry off the canvas I had helped into this flat. Or Madame's studio, as I shall now call it to disguise my earlier mistake. To be accurate, we are now hosting another two canvases. He talked of putting them on the wall, as I seem to have shown interest in them. Amazing. I'll learn what it's like to live with works by a famous contemporary painter. As I'll never be able to afford them, I'll savour the experience right now while I can. I think I must have muttered something of the sort to him. He's coming over tomorrow, when he can escape from the dealers, to talk to me about his work.'

A lot else I could add to my journal, but I'm too tired. To be honest, I have to say that Pierre is one of the most likeable men I've ever met. It's exciting when he talks, not just to me, but to anyone. I like Colette a lot too. She doesn't speak much, but smiles, has curly brown hair and a happy feel about her. In all, I am lucky to have met them. Things are looking up.

CHAPTER 3

Pierre's presence obsesses me. I wake up and contemplate the huge canvas leaning against the bookcases to my left. The surface of luscious black paint splashed up and down and across the canvas, in five or even eight inch stripes, makes me feel I am peering out into newly created space. Beyond these black bars lie opalescent swirls of colour, creamy white tinged with green. Focusing on the background propels the bars on the canvas surface towards me. Every time I sit and dream my way into the work, it looks strangely different.

Pierre appeared this morning before Madame descended from her balcony. I made him some coffee and asked how long it took to produce such a large work.

'Il faut du temps. Assez...' Some time, because one had to do a lot of thinking. The actual painting - though he had never timed himself - took less long but much physical effort. He smiled at that. Colette was a great help in mixing paints, but couldn't physically manage the brushwork though she too is a trained artist. He uses wide housepainter brushes which are heavy for accurate wrist work, especially when the drips have to be controlled.

'I wanted Colette to be included as joint author, but the gallery wouldn't have it. They told me,' and here he looked away, as if bracing himself against the memory of distant battles, 'that nobody would accept a work being by two artists. Raphael, David, Watteau, Turner. Just imagine Picasso, the wiliest of all, successfully selling works by him and another! People want to associate with individuals, geniuses, whatever you understand by the term, and the buyer needs to feel a sort of communion with the lone creator.' He added with a tinge of bitterness, 'I hate the word "genius". It seems to hold connotations of ease, of divine intervention, of...' His voice trailed off in embarrassment. He smiled, got up, said he had work to do and Colette was waiting for him.

No space for a child in a studio flat. No space for a family in Pierre's life, perhaps? Maybe Colette is deprived of another choice too. She's the handmaiden of his success. I shall never let my life be taken over by anyone, I declare to the studio window and blank panes on the other side of the road while imagining the vivacious young woman who married her handsome fellow art student. They started life together as equal artists. Instead, history played its old tricks on her, the female side of the equation. A chance came. A prize, publicity, a presentation... but if two people win it, producing works of art together? Somehow that waters it all down.

'*Ça fait plus de dix ans* ... They've been struggling for over ten years,' Madame Magny comments, clambering down the spiral staircase as Pierre closes the door. 'Any coffee left?'

I go off dutifully to my new domain. Instead of making for her throne of faded flowers, Madame installs herself on the green-striped sofa where her student has been sitting next to the painter. Returning with the cup of coffee prepared just as Madame likes it, I wonder whether I can sit on her sofa throne instead, but think it might be interpreted as an act of impudence if I did. So I perch on the sober stripes with my coffee, this time next to my professor.

'The studio was bought for them by Pierre's father, a farmer in Rodez, Aveyon. More a gentleman farmer,' she adds while drawing the coffee through her lips. I've forgotten the biscuits which Madame sometimes, in the capricious way she treats food, likes to dip into her coffee. As I return to the sofa with the biscuit tin, I note that Madame has inexplicably moved to the centre. Perhaps it's more comfortable for her, though I'm now squashed against an armrest. Sensing I'm fascinated by Pierre, Madame continues,

'They're both about thirty-five. Young, but it's a long time to struggle without recognition until now.' Her delicately-veined hand is now on my knee as if to explain,

'I did my best. Introduced him to all my friends with influence. They came over to meet him for cocktails, and he would

25

leave, to return a little later and invite everyone to a drink in his studio. It was all arranged between us. He soon found a dealer, and then went on to win a significant prize. Again, that was through my contacts...' I'm suitably impressed, but uncomfortably pinned down by the hand now pressing my thigh. I've an uncontrollable urge to wriggle, but reason that Madame will soon need her left hand to hold a cigarette lit by the right one, and so it turns out.

'Have you managed to finish the articles?' I enquire politely, thinking how to make the best use of my time. I'm becoming interested in the Parisian art world and want to explore some of the smaller galleries, especially the one that promotes Pierre.

Madame blinks in what looks like slow motion, eyelashes magnified in her round, blue-frame spectacles. She contemplates two centimetres of ash hanging dangerously, and taps her cigarette with slow and elegant deliberation on the edge of her saucer.

'Vas-y!' She's pointing at an unruly pile of papers on a table by the window that serves as her desk. Glad of an excuse to leave the sofa, I go over to gather the pages as directed, tapping them together on the edge of the table. An antiquated typewriter with two of its many arms still elevated lies surrounded by three overflowing ash trays and a scatter of pens, one a quill lightly resting in its pot on an ancient inkstand. A creative jumble; very Madame Magny. I return with the twenty or so sheets in what I hope is some sort of order to find Madame's arms outstretched for them, her current brainchild.

'Voilà! This is on Baudelaire. A new interpretation. I thought of it when sipping brandy with Pierre and Colette last winter. It was dusk; there were lights in the cemetery. Their studio overlooks it, as you know. We opened the kitchen window and heard intoning somewhere near Baudelaire's grave. Then I began to think. The date when Baudelaire was born, the precise time. It has taken me over two years, but the theory holds.'

'What theory?' I'm ever curious.

'His astrological sign, how it shaped his life, and so his poetry, of course.' I feel uncomfortable about outside forces located in the heavens - stars, planets or whatever - that might be pushing people around willy-nilly. Now Madame seems to be bringing all that into literary criticism. I pluck up courage to ask,

'What about the article you're writing on the new novelist, Françoise somebody? I don't recall her surname.'

'It's supposed to be an interview as well as a critique of the novel. She's difficult to pin down. She's got an agent.' Madame leans back, crosses her spindly legs and looks knowingly through the dirty window panes into the blank gaze of the windows opposite. She doesn't like to be interrogated. She has to be the one to initiate any exchange of ideas. 'I'm concentrating on Baudelaire for now.'

That is that. It's Sunday, so Madame is up early for her. She is going to church and announces she will take me with her.

'Pas loin. Only a couple of streets away. Maxime's brother is the Russian priest in charge. He's a Bishop in the French Orthodox Church.'

I remember people asking Maxime, the whiskery man who opened the door the evening I arrived, about 'Père Evêque'. Curious. It sounds like 'father bishop'. It's a lovely morning, my plans are flexible, and I quite like the idea of drifting to church with Madame. We cross one of the wide boulevards spinning off Place Denfert-Rochereau to take a street into a tunnel of unpollarded plane trees. Someone at the end of the last century had shoved a neo-gothic church into what may have been a communal garden between two 19th-century blocks of flats. Since the start of World War II it has been leased on a peppercorn rent to a group of Russian refugees. So this is the French Orthodox Church.

Behind the iron railings edging the pavement knots of people are conversing outside the church. No sign of Dior's New Look here. Unmemorable clothes clad assorted shapes and ages, from the children dodging hither and thither in an endless hide-and

seek, to grannies with similar faces, puckered lips and eyes wrinkled into pinpoints. Deprived of their contemplation of endless space on the Steppes, they have assumed a suburban inconsequentiality. Younger dark-robed women look wintry in their ankle-long dresses and cheerful pinafores all hanging from their shoulders, their hair plaited into pigtails or wound into tight little buns. Round-faced and jollier than their men folk, they are busying themselves with their families. This generation fits in better. The men particularly are indistinguishable from their French social counterparts, apart from the high Slav cheekbones and defensive look of refugees set adrift by war. The younger unmarried women still tend towards the pinafore and plait, but wear brighter colours and ribbons - one or two are even clad in a smart number that could double for office on weekdays.

Are they all Russian? Madame isn't, and I suspect there are other true tricolour French here, gradually drawing this traumatised community into mainstream Parisian life. When Madame Magny descends the steps into the forecourt, the groups draw back, eyes on us. Almost like royalty, a trace of a smile crosses Madame's face as she bends her head very slightly and stops to talk here to an elderly, narrow-eyed man and a younger woman with thick blond plaits, there to a dark handsome man with sprawling black hair and beard next to an older woman with grey-streaked beribboned pigtails and doll-like face.

A familiar face appears at the open church door to ring a bell. Time to start. Maxime, clad in long white robes, is swinging a tasselled brass bell.

'The deacon,' whispers Madame. *'Il est beau, n'est-ce pas?'* Handsome? I hadn't thought of whiskery Maxime like that. Stepping over the threshold into the darkly-incensed interior, I'm painfully aware of my own stupidity. Old, I had thought him, not handsome. Hitherto I had been consigning him, Madame, my parents, everyone older than, say, Pierre and Colette, into a prosaic world of friends

and loyalties, but with little passion and even less lust. I had never thought about this because it had never occurred to me, preoccupied as Mike, me and my friends have been with self-discovery. I unexpectedly yearn for them all and my familiar stamping-ground.

'*Attention!*' Madame is nudging me to sit down in a pew near the *iconostasis*. It's like the church by the Seine, with all those eyes of the Virgin and saints looking unflinchingly at the congregation, ready to tick them off, but with compassion. Madame sinks down beside me, head lowered, eyes closed. Enthralled by the flickering lights and the clearing of throats at the back of the church, I sit bolt upright in excited anticipation.

A strong baritone, rich as dark chocolate, starts at the top of the scale and descends in different patterns of notes, welcoming the congregation into the parameters of redemption. Between the notes, the chain holding the censer clinks as it swings intoxicating aromas that tickle the nostrils and stun the brain.

'*Alleluia, alleluia, adorons la Christ...*' intones a slight figure in a dark robe under a red and cream embroidered cope, his dark, grey-streaked hair falling over his collar and ears to join his long unkempt beard. He stands tall in sacramental dignity at the entrance. '*Alleluia...*' Followed by Maxime the deacon, other dignitaries and a straggle of choirboys chanting, he processes up the small nave to open the gate in the *iconostasis* and disappear out of sight. As the ceremony continues, the gates are frequently opened by Maxime who intones what has, I think, already been said at the altar. It is a familiar ritual to all present, and must give comfort in an alien land.

Outside in the courtyard afterwards everyone chats around a makeshift table. I'm surprised to see the Claudine I met with Madame's friends on my first evening in Paris. She's helping the pig-tailed ladies offer tepid lemonade and dry little biscuits speckled with seeds. They are strange but tasty. Madame is mixing and talking, so I feel stranded. Who do I know? Claudine, but she's too busy. I try to glance round without looking like an outsider. Père Evêque - it must be him - stands at the church door surrounded by a crowd. Had I heard correctly? Did he say *la* Christ? Where is Maxime? Nowhere to be seen.

'*Comment t'appelles-toi?*' A voice to my right. I turn to see the woman with two brightly beribboned pigtails who was talking to Madame before the service.

'*Je m'appelle Valérie.*' I smile back.

'You must be Dominique's friend,' the doll face with pigtails continues, 'and you're coming to lunch with us.' I smile again, to show how pleased I am. I might find out more about this community and how it spills over into Madame's other sphere of the *Rive Gauche* intellectuals. I imagine them putting the world to rights in the *Quartier Latin,* ensconced in the Deux Maggots or Café de Flore. I can hardly dare to pass through those august portals on a meagre student grant, though I dream of doing it. When I hinted as much, Madame mumbled something vague about going there to do her writing - the background noise helped concentration and provoked new ideas! Little likelihood of her inviting me. I'm adopting a 'wait and see' policy.

Only then do I realise 'Dominique' refers to Madame Magny. The name sounds masculine to me, somehow related to the Dominican religious order and the Latin word for 'master'. Upon further reflection, as I wait for Madame to signal departure, I think the name suits her. Madame does want to teach, or rather inform, though she also needs to dominate. She exudes a female rather than feminine softness, not gentle at all; she talks and argues with sharp male incisiveness. Her hands become the eloquent bridge between these two selves, writing or praying, describing or in repose.

'*Je m'appelle Ludmilla. Viens!*' Doll-faced, pig-tailed Ludmilla takes my hand to lead me up the steps and out through the open gate in the railings. She lives a few blocks away in a large, dilapidated building behind a shaggy privet hedge. To the left of a cat-smelling wooden staircase is a dark corridor cluttered with bicycles and a huge pram. Ludmilla shows me the way, followed by Madame and the dark-bearded man with two small girls holding his hands. Maxime and Claudine bring up the rear, stopping and turning, as if expecting yet another guest.

The door at the end of the corridor opens into an even more cluttered passage with clothes hanging on pegs or piled on top of bookcases. An indefinable sadness haunts the stale air. At last a larger living area, dominated by a worn dark-green sofa, matching armchairs, some kitchen chairs and a scrubbed table at one end. Ludmilla is bustling to and fro through a doorless opening, handing a tasselled tablecloth and plates to a tall, fair boy called Michel, while the two little girls with dark curly hair, almost like twins though of different ages, hover waiting to arrange the knives and forks. Ludmilla has her helpers well trained. A huge steaming bowl is placed at the centre of the table to an accompanying hush. A hand appears from the kitchen area waving a *baguette*. Dark-bearded Alexandre, Ludmilla's husband, cuts the bread while Ludmilla seats the children round the table. She serves the last arrival, Père Evêque, after his blessing, then the children, leaving the adults to help themselves and find chairs to pull up to the table.

It's a kind of goulash soup with dumplings, the sort of food kept hot at one side of a fireplace, waiting from century to century for men to return hungry from their labour in the fields. Hot, tasty, filling and ready to order. Madame sits next to the priest at the head, while Alexandre squeezes in beside me.

'It's a special day for us,' he says. I'm in awe of him, and of Père Evêque who looks as if he has stepped out of an icon, and am apprehensive of being drawn into their strange world.

'Once a year Père Eugraph comes to paint some more of our shrine. I'll show you.' I'm relieved. Nothing to do with me. But I also feel a bit stupid, as the priest's name sounds different.

'I didn't quite catch his name?' I look at Alexandre anxiously. 'Eugraph, not "évêque"'. Is he a bishop? Have I got everything wrong?'

Alexandre patiently spells the name and explains that it means 'writer' in Greek, and was the priest's choice when he entered the Orthodox Church. Everyone did this. He is a bishop. Père Eugraph's pronunciation in French is a bit odd. Yes, he does sometimes forget and say la Christ. He was quite old when he took refuge in Paris. Because the feast of St. John the Baptist falls on the 24th June, he always comes as soon as he can afterwards to continue painting the shrine.

The meal over, Alexandre takes me through the girls' room into what had once been a smaller bedroom. The bed is covered with a white and gold cloth, and along the ledge behind it nightlights shiver in their shallow red jars. Starting from the top of the wall above the bed Père Eugraph has written in Greek and French with gold lettering on a blue background: 'In the beginning was the word...' As if springing from the words themselves, up and over the ceiling rise figures in resonant tones of crimson, green, ultramarine and a range of browns, the spiky folds of their garments trimmed in gold.

'Père Eugraph has devoted half a day to this task over three years, and look how much he has already completed!' Two walls and part of the ceiling are glowing with colour.

'Where will he start this afternoon?' Alexandre doesn't know. He says Père Eugraph isn't the sort of person you ask that kind of question. God's spirit moves him as he paints. Ludmilla, herself a painter of Russian wooden dolls, provides everything he needs. He comes, paints, intones prayers and sings Russian folk songs. When he stops, he leads a short service and they eat supper together. Just Père Eugraph and the family. It is a day they remember and look forward to all year.

'What's your birth date?' he asks me as we leave the little shrine in the making. I hesitate.

'December 29th. Capricorn. A rather boring sign, as I understand it.' Alexandre is excited.

'No. You're wrong!' His eyes flash as he strokes his beard. 'It's the sign of philosophers. And politicians. But a lot depends on what your ascendant is, and which planets are in which house.'

'What does that mean?'

'Well, for example the ninth house is the one governing intelligence. Perhaps I'll do your horoscope one day,' he says, interrupted by Ludmilla bearing a plate piled high with éclairs dripping cream and chocolate.

'Maxime brought these,' she explains.

Madame still hasn't moved from her place next to Père Eugraph. I sense she is avoiding Maxime. There's an atmosphere I can't fathom.

On the way back I tell Madame that Alexandre might do my horoscope.

'*Tu as de la chance!* He usually charges - it seems to be the only money he earns. You're lucky. You won't have to pay.'

'Why do people have them done? I wouldn't, if he hadn't offered and I didn't want to offend him.' Madame stops in her tracks.

'But don't you know? We're all influenced by our horoscopes. He married Ludmilla after he had done both their horoscopes and found they were compatible. He mostly provides them for people thinking of getting married.' This is one of the most informative short talks I have ever had with Madame who usually looks wise, but communicates little except about herself. And no wine had flowed at lunchtime!

Apparently Ludmilla had been widowed for about a year when she met Alexandre at church. She already had two sons. Although she is about ten years older, they married; two daughters were born. They have to share the big bedroom with their half-brother Michel, while Jean had the tiny bedroom to himself, being the eldest. Both Ludmilla and Alexandre were born somewhere in Russia, she can't remember where.

Then Jean, Ludmilla's eldest child, '*beau comme un ange*', had to leave school at sixteen to go to work. There wasn't much he could do without qualifications, however intelligent he was. Père Eugraph paid for him to attend evening classes, but in the daytime he laboured on a building site. A few months later he fell from scaffolding and was killed. He would have been nineteen now.

My age. I wish I could have met him.

So that's why Père Eugraph has been creating a shrine to Jean and his patron saint, John the Baptist.

'We all helped them in any way we could when Jean died, Père Eugraph most of all. The shrine does console Ludmilla. Père Eugraph often slips in there and prays with her and Alexandre.'

So Père Eugraph had drawn Madame Magny into the church. She praises his brother, the deacon Maxime who sings so well, yet clearly finds Claudine irritating.

'*Claudine n'est même pas propre. Elle est même "scary"...*' Madame has this odd way of dipping into the bran tub of Babel and picking out a word in any language that neatly fits the situation, whether her audience can understand it or not. At first Claudine seemed like a breath of fresh air, cycling everywhere, running errands for people on the way, tousled, unkempt even. According to Madame, she lives in a tiny room and has nowhere to cook or wash. So she's always out and about on her bicycle, picking up a sop from someone here, a crust there. Then she found the French Orthodox Church.

That's that. Madame Magny slides back into her own preoccupations. On our return to the studio apartment, she busies herself opening drawers and shifting piles of papers, to stuff a wad of them into a scuffed leather case and indicate a book on the latest philosophical theory she thought I should read.

'*Je pars au café Flore. Il faut che je finisse ce que je suis en train d'écrire sur Baudelaire.*'

Five minutes later she leaves, after a preliminary sip of brandy, to write up her article on Baudelaire. Sunday is over, the part of Sunday devoted to abstinence. Now her *Rive Gauche* persona emerges. The intellectual Madame Magny with a vengeance: Dominique dominant. I resent not having been invited to accompany her, but am too overawed to suggest it. I should attempt to read the philosophy book as well as some other set texts still in my knapsack, but they don't appeal. All Paris seems to be out socialising on this fine Sunday afternoon in early July except me. I'll go out too. A walk in the park.

In the Jardin du Luxembourg I wander, happily immersed in my own thoughts until I become aware of probing eyes. I imagine what passers-by must be thinking,

'A girl like her... Out on a Sunday afternoon and no boyfriend. Not even friends. Alone.' Everyone else is strolling past in pairs or foursomes. I'm isolated, rejected. Why hadn't I let that student speak to me on the first day? On other occasions I have spurned male interest by ignoring remarks aimed at me or averting my eyes. Do they now think me prim? Ugly? Am I spotty? Not really; the main crisis in skin blemishes has passed, but I do still bite my nails. My fingers make my hands ugly, but Madame's hands are no better; her long pointed, crimson nails are tinged with nicotine.

I think of Mike, regretting I haven't yet written. At home we would phone. It's too expensive here, and anyway it will be hard to find him in the Weymouth hotel where he's working. I begin an imaginary conversation, telling him what I've been up to. It's a reassuring way to occupy my mind, and oddly enough makes me hungry. I turn back to the flat to find something to eat. On an impulse, I overcome shyness and knock on the door opposite. Colette opens it and smiles.

'*Viens, Valérie...*' The studio is stacked with even more paintings. Orders have indeed overwhelmed Pierre after winning the prize. Colette sits me at the table and gives me a glass of wine. Unfortunately they're invited out to dinner. I feel destined to spend the evening alone. Pierre leans over the balcony inviting me to look in again when they have more time.

Rummaging around in Madame's kitchen I find just enough for a scratch supper. Pierre's huge painting is still leaning against the bookcases. My thoughts float round the dark glistening bars into the heavens behind.

I leave the striped sofa to sit at Madame's table desk, push the papers to one side, and firmly open my journal.

'Ludmilla's eldest son, Jean, haunts me. *Beau comme un ange.* He haunts Ludmilla, and Père Eugraph. Also Madame, to a lesser degree. Did he fall because he had too little to eat, or was it despair at the sort of work he had to do, a no-hope job? Perhaps not, because youth means hope, and he was going to evening classes. Père Eugraph with his deep-set eyes and powerful presence seems to help everyone. Was Jean in the state of resigned submission that I sense among the older members of the Russian community at the church?

A pause to look up at Pierre's paintings again. I imagine a face emerging from the pearly green background: pale, fair tousled hair, blue eyes wide open, vacant. I start to weep, blotching the sheet.

When there is an accident in a mine, I was told the convention is for the youngest to be saved first. They still have the right to a life span, while the last to be saved are the ones who have already lived the longest. But Jean was my age, and I'm only just beg...'

I stop writing, finding the thought of Jean's death brings back memories of my uncle David that I have been trying to forget. Another useless death of someone, admittedly sixteen years older than me and Jean, about Pierre Soulages's age, but still with a large lifespan owed to him. Turning from the diary, in an effort to block out those thoughts, I start reading the first volume of Proust's *A la Recherche du Temps Perdu*. When Madame Magny returns after midnight, the completed Baudelaire manuscript in her battered leather bag, I am still reading and making notes. Madame pulls the manuscript out with her nicotine-stained fingers, like eagle talons.

'*Lis-le!*' I smile and thank her. I had better read it in the morning. It's past midnight and I'm not in the mood to entangle my mind in Madame's brilliant but arcane analysis. Tomorrow, another day.

CHAPTER 4

Madame's article on Baudelaire has to be submitted now so I can only skim through it. The editor of a prestigious literary magazine is holding up publication, so she informs me. This impresses me more than the actual contents. Madame is demonstrating, in consummate detail, how the imagery in Baudelaire's poetry was dictated by the conjunctions of wayward planets in various houses of his horoscope. A *tour de force*, I think, magnificent perhaps? But isn't it constructed on an unproven premise? If that founders, the whole elaborate structure topples down. As I hand back the manuscript, my bitten nails almost brushing the professor's talons, I determine not to speculate, and murmur,

'*Très intéressant. Unique même.*'   My command of French improves every day I spend in Paris. Madame has been unfailingly kind in matters linguistic and the more she encourages me, the more confident I become. Feeling guilty I haven't shown my appreciation, I've rashly offered to cook a dinner for her friends. Later in the week, after Madame Magny has spruced herself up to go and interview Françoise Sagan at her publisher's, I am to prepare a literary reception for the young novelist in Madame Magny's studio flat. I am very apprehensive about my offer, but consider it can be safely shunted out of my mind until the day before. I need to plan my departure for the summer job in Spain, but that too can wait.

I shall spend the next few days walking the streets looking for inspiration for my own novel, visiting any historic building that is open or museum that catches my fancy. But this morning when Madame is about to take the eagerly awaited manuscript to her editor, Alexandre appears triumphantly waving my horoscope.

'*Beaucoup de surprises*! A lot's going to happen to you. You'll get involved emotionally...You'll start writing - poetry? A book? I'm not sure what, but your creative abilities will be stimulated. Soon you'll have an amorous entanglement to unravel...' I gasp, thrilled by the prospect of multiple adventures. Up to now the four days in Paris have been an emotional desert, if partly by my own choice.

Alexandre is persuasive; force of conviction animates his frail body. His pale olive skin appears almost translucent framed by his jet black beard and hair, peaking on the forehead but slowly receding on either side. It would be churlish to show scepticism. He's gentle and friendly, welcoming the coffee and biscuits I offer, but never following up any allusion to his wife, or Jean or even his children. Instead Alexandre talks about the spiritual warmth of Père Eugraph who does so much, but always has time left over for his parishioners. I picture the lean, middle-aged priest with grizzled hair and beard, his deep-set eyes, piercing and powerful in a tightly lined face. He looks like a Christ Pancreator gazing down over the faithful from the apse of an early Christian basilica. I can feel his presence as Alexandre talks.

This evening Madame Magny is in a confidential mood. As she speaks from her sofa, she looks beyond me into the shadows under the balcony, eyes round and mysterious behind her glasses, hands crossed and limp in contrast to her taut body. She recounts how Alexandre has drawn up the horoscopes of most of the congregation including her own, and Maxime's. When she sought advice of a practical kind about him, Alexandre pointed out that the conjunction of planets governing stable relationships and emotions in her horoscope were in harmony with similar aspects in Maxime's.

I find all this confusing. Madame is surely past the age when such matters are important? I'm sort of uncomfortable and embarrassed. She picks up my horoscope and studies it in silence.

'*Rien dans la neuvième. Pas bien... La mienne en est pleine...*' She points to my ninth house, the seat of intelligence; it is empty. Uranus nudges close, but no, it's definitely empty. Madame's, it seems, is predictably cluttered. I'm tired of it all. How can planets determine one's life? Recovering my free will, momentarily lost whilst Alexandre was explaining my horoscope, I decide to disregard it.

৩৯৫

On the morning of the reception, after I have taken the post and a bundle of magazines up to Madame, still in bed and wearing a very light silk negligee, she yells and hurls a journal from the balcony, narrowly missing me. I'm busy worrying about the food and drink. It is only later, after returning with coffee and croissants, that I learn the prestigious literary journal has appeared without her article on Baudelaire. When Madame phones her friend the editor, he delegates one of his assistants to tell her that the astrological approach doesn't suit the publication's style and content.

Madame is raging. No literary freedom! A clampdown on originality! The editor's mind addled by self-importance...

'Shall we cancel the reception this evening?' I ask tentatively.

'*Que'ce qu'on va faire?* People are coming. They can't all be put off.' Madame is pacing up and down between the two sofas, fuming as she smokes endless cigarettes and spits out venomous comments. I retreat to my alcove to watch, intrigued by the width of her body seen straight on. It's like one of those Cycladic figures with widely-spaced, small pointed breasts and hips branching out from the waist to curve generously down to tiny forward-pointing feet. Only Madame doesn't have a waist to speak of. From the side she's flat, as if she had spent a lot of time squashed between two publicity boards like the London 'sandwich men' that intrigued me as a child. I smile at this humble comparison. Madame prides herself upon how distant she is from the masses, light years away, in fact, because she has been to the *Grandes Écoles* and is of the *élite*! She is about to leave for her interview with Françoise Sagan. Now I must focus on the reception. The wine has to be be fetched, and the titbits laid out before people start arriving. It's like planning a social campaign, and I haven't ever done this before.

Later when gingerly steadying the two bags holding the wine bottles as I look for my key, a lean hand reaches out to grasp one of them. I glimpse a bicycle balanced against the kerb, and a tall tousled figure pushes past to open the lift door for me. Claudine.

'*Ça commence dans une heure!*' I look at her anxiously, aware there is barely more than an hour for my preparations, afraid I have mistaken the time and that everyone is about to arrive.

'*Je viens t'aider!*' Claudine has come to help. It is soon evident, however, that her presence is not welcome. Madame, already back from the interview and ensconced on her sofa, uncharacteristically sways on to her feet, cigarette and glass in hand, and a rapid exchange follows. It seems that Claudine is not invited. Claudine retorts that Maxime said she was. In any case she wants to help Dominique's student. Me!

And so she does, while Madame retreats upstairs, ostensibly to get dressed.

It is the first time I have seen Claudine in a dress rather than a shabby blouse and skirt. I suspect the strong whiff of perfume is to disguise her lack of bathing facilities. Not to dwell on such unkind thoughts, I busy myself arranging the titbits on the biggest plates I can find. Claudine, gently brushing me aside, suggests I might instead deal with the glasses and drinks instead.

Ten guests have been invited, plus Madame and me, making twelve in all. Or thirteen, with Claudine if she really wasn't invited. How many more gatecrashers might there be? There are eight plates with about fifteen mouthfuls on each. That should do. After all, it's a reception, not dinner! I look anxiously in the kitchen cupboards to see if there are enough glasses. There are, just, but a motley collection which has to be augmented by the three I retrieve from Madame's bedroom. She is lying on the bed, pouting and reading a book, a half-filled glass of brandy next to her and a cigarette poised dangerously close to the pages, certainly not dressing. She acknowledges me with a grunt, still sulking at the rejection of her article and Claudine's unwelcome presence. I have been trying so hard to show my appreciation of Madame's hospitality, but the omens are not looking good.

Back downstairs, I cast my eyes casually over the plates. They look different. Claudine is bent over the largest one, pushing the titbits into another design.

'*C'est plus beau!*' she explains.

'*Ça va très bien.*' I disappear into the kitchen, reappearing with the clean glasses. There are now just fourteen. That allows for only two gatecrashers, one already here! I shall have to ask Madame to bring down the glass she's using. Should I go and borrow some from Colette? No, I can always ask at the last moment. There is too much still to do, and only twenty minutes left. Claudine is now leaning over another plate. Why is she taking so long, I wonder, as I change my dress in the alcove.

All I have to do now is to put on some make-up. I miss Mike, shocked to realise I have only written a couple of letters. Already forgetting him, and I haven't even found someone else! I head for the bathroom and a mirror, only to step back as Madame descends, transformed into the epitome of voluptuousness, her blonde hair combed back with a black velvet ribbon disguising the grey roots. My professor has emerged as daring Dominique in a deep décolleté 1930s black satin dress, all the more alluring for that. 'Gosh!' I think, 'I'd never have imagined...'

'It's super!' I say in English, not being able to find the equivalent in French without sounding trite. Madame smiles her loveliest smile. The omens are more favourable now, I reckon, as I spiral up to the bathroom and make a rapid attempt on my face.

Madame is back enthroned on the usual floral sofa, while Claudine prudently makes herself scarce in the kitchen. Time to spare. What a relief! Anxiously I survey the plates. Eight with... not fifteen pieces on each. My memory must be at fault. I look at the ingenious new patterns, very different from the ones I started with, and found fourteen morsels on one dish, twelve on another, ten even on a third... Panic. Will there be enough? Never having prepared such an occasion before, I thought that ten mouthfuls each would be sufficient. Now there can hardly be six! I suspect what has happened but do not want to admit it, still less act on it. Will there be time to rush out for some more?

The door bell rings. Guests are arriving exactly five minutes late, the height of civility as mother always says.

Colette and Pierre cross the landing and bump into Maxime stepping out of the lift. All familiar faces. This is a relief as Madame seems to expect me to be on door duty. As it is opened, Dominique the seductive hostess rises to her feet and assumes a stately pose in the centre of the room, glass in one hand, a Thirties style cigarette holder in the other. Her courtiers make appreciative noises as expected, followed by an embarrassing pause as Madame looks around for me and enunciates silently '*à boire?*' Now the waitress, I pour two glasses of red, two of white, and place them on a small tray. Balancing it on one hand and a dish with diminished titbits in the other, I circulate the company assembled in animated conversation around Madame. Others have arrived and someone else, I note with relief, has let them in - Claudine.

More wine poured, more glasses needed as everyone seems to be choosing white. The nibbles have been cleared off two of the eight dishes and the party has hardly started! 'Don't panic!' I say out loud by mistake. I have poured too many glasses of red. Can I sneak into the kitchen, tip the wine back into the bottle, rapidly rinse the glasses out and refill them with white wine? Claudine has let in people I've never seen before: a dark-haired man, just thirty perhaps, and a strongly-built woman in her forties, too old to be Françoise Sagan. Maxime and the dark-haired man gravitate away from Dominique towards this imposing female, Simone something or other, a famous author who lives in the studio below us. Only the loyal Pierre and Colette remain by Madame.

'*Calme-toi!*' whispers a voice from behind my left shoulder. I turn to see the count Guy something-or-other I met on my first evening in Paris raising his glass and telling me not to panic.

'*Tout va fort bien.*' Guy is the only member of the company who acknowledges my presence. Grateful for this scrap of attention, I return with more white wine and a plate where I've assembled the odd bits left on others. I observe with a novice's satisfaction, that Dominique has moved over to the Simone woman's circle of admirers.

A loud knock. Everyone stops mid-sentence to look at the latecomers. A young girl, scarcely out of her teens, enters with an older woman following her. Here are the gatecrashers.

'*Ah, Françoise!*' Madame sweeps forward to grasp her hand and the others follow suit. How strange. This girl, hardly older than me, is the literary taste of the moment on the Paris circuit. She has made a fortune with *Bonjour Tristesse* and is about to publish her second novel. I shall have to hurry up with mine. Brains and ingenuity don't always inhabit a striking body, I observe. Françoise is slender, with mousy hair and a pale skin. There's nothing racy about her, such as I would have expected from her novel and reputation. The older woman with her, immaculately groomed in a neat black number and white embroidered blouse with crisply-cut chestnut-brown hair, is a delight to see.

Looking round imperiously for me, Dominique commands drinks for the new arrivals. Still no attempt to introduce me, but perhaps that is just as well. I'm annoyed with myself at feeling both envious of Françoise's success and disappointed at her lack of presence. Is it because she doesn't really want to be here and deliberately dresses in a drab blue-striped frock? The new arrivals take their drinks and a titbit or two, while the strong-faced, older

Simone does most of the talking though the fashionable companion is trying to interrupt her.

I am so peripheral that I don't catch much of the exchange, but imagine they must inhabit the unknown world of the *Rive Gauche* that I long to enter. Dominique is asserting her position as hostess, abandoning her usual throne to avoid being marginalised. Simone moves over between Françoise Sagan and Dominique, while the woman in the dark suit hovers in and out of the gaps between them, sometimes breaking the circle to nod at me to refill glasses or bring over another plate.

Down to the last plate but one, and the door bell rings again. No Claudine to help out this time, so I open it to find Alexandre and Ludmilla waiting outside. As I pass the main group, I turn to see if Guy is with them. He is standing by the window next to Maxime poring over a manuscript score with the dark-haired young man, another Pierre somebody, who is humming and talking animatedly.

Alexandre and Ludmilla don't fit in. Guy and Maxime are too deep in discussion over the score to help out. Where is Claudine? I take the Russian couple to the drinks table, find with relief they choose red wine, and assure them the few titbits left are vegetarian. Then I look around for Claudine, to find her lying on my bed in the alcove.

'Are you asleep?' I whisper.

Claudine's eyes open, 'Definitely not. Only bored.' She's nothing if not direct.

'Who are all these people?' I ask her. 'Do they know Alexandre and Ludmilla? They've just arrived and are standing together like wallflowers at a dance?' She sits up and shrugs her shoulders. Claudine can be kind, but is never communicative. It's part of her elusive feline charm.

I observe Claudine's green eyes staring out from the alcove like beacons controlling Maxime's every movement. The literary coterie has drifted away from Françoise who hardly seems to say anything - the dark-haired woman is in some strange sort of control - back to the older Simone, who is declaiming something. Dominique seems uncomfortably aware of herself as only a listener, so she poses drawing elegantly on her cigarette holder with only a stub in it. The atmosphere is impregnated with smoky passion of a literary, musical, or visual variety, as Pierre turns to his painting and points out something I can't hear. The last plate is almost empty, but bits remain on the others. I gather them onto one plate without anyone noticing. Glasses have now been abandoned to leave damp circles on the tables or floor, and I sense with relief that they will all soon be leaving. It's past nine; surely they're hungry?

All in all, Françoise's has been a limp performance, I think as I clear up the plates. She probably couldn't be bothered. I should finish her novel, but how can I find the time, with all I must read for my university courses? And now that philosophy book as well. Most of the guests have left. Maxime, therefore Claudine, and Guy show no intention of following. Madame has retired with relief to the floral throne to kick off her shoes and extend her legs elegantly along it. She might do better to leave space for someone to sit by her, either Guy or, astrologically, Maxime, but then I catch my breath, wary of a new flavour spicing my thoughts.

Claudine's voice floats over my shoulder,

'*On va manger?*' How I hate the French '*on*'. 'One is going to eat,' meaning, 'You're going to get us some grub, aren't you?' Is that also part of my remit?

'I'll help you,' Guy offers.

In the event he is worse than useless, but provides an avalanche of information strewn with gossip. I know there's some spaghetti, so I fill a pan with water, chuck in salt and rummage around for something to make a sauce out of.

'Why did Dominique,' (I judge it wise to show familiarity, though Madame has never invited me to do so), 'ask Ludmilla and Alexandre? They seemed so uncomfortable'.

Guy focuses on me attentively, evidently imagining he holds an irresistible fascination for women. He assiduously cultivates a youthful wistfulness as well as a slim, taut frame.

'She thought Alexandre might meet people who would pay him to do their horoscopes. But he just doesn't know how to deal with social or literary types. Hopeless,' Guy sighs without really caring one way or another. He usually assumes a *c'est la vie* opt-out attitude. That's life.

I prompt him as I cut up some shrivelled tomatoes, and start to fry them while looking for onions.

'Et Françoise Sagan?'

'Reined in by her agent, who is minding her. Anyway, it was probably a mistake to confront her socially with not only a famous writer, but also one who's celebrated for her heroic exploits in the Resistance.'

I stop chopping and wipe my eyes with an oniony hand.

'I didn't know Dominique had been in the Resistance! She never mentions anything about the war years.'

'Don't you know? She also has famous neighbours. Opposite, Pierre Soulages, now a famous painter, and he really deserves to be,' but so does Colette, I think bitterly, 'and on the ground floor a celebrated writer and philosopher. I suppose Dominique had to invite Simone de Beauvoir...'

So she is the strong-faced woman, Madame's rival. Claudine pokes her head into the kitchen.

'Elle a faim!' Madame might well be hungry, I mutter to the water which still isn't boiling. She'll just have to imbibe yet another glass of brandy and puff through her sixtieth cigarette!

'*Comment?*' Guy thinks I'm saying something about him; he's gossipy about others, but sensitive when he imagines he is the subject of comments.

'*Rien.* And the dark-haired man?' I didn't have the chance to talk to him, which I would have liked to do, especially as he looked quite toothsome and my horoscope is favourable. He slightly resembles the Laughing Cavalier in Miss Green's study, I think as I hurry to finish chopping the onions and toss them in with the fried tomatoes.

'That's the young composer Pierre Boulez. He's already made his mark on the *avant-garde* and might win a prize for the poems he's set to the ground-breaking music he was showing us. He's really original, so it depends if they want new music, or more of the same. Dominique thinks he has a good chance, and she yearns to manipulate new talent.' He pauses, 'But I'm not sure about Françoise Sagan. Her agent annoyed Dominique, while Françoise was upset by Simone. After all, she can't compete with two older women bearing a triple reputation as philosophers, writers and war heroines. Hard to beat,' he adds winking at me.

Manipulate? That worries me. I'm trying to get the onions to cook amid the tomato slush. I dislike tasting what I'm cooking, especially when my mind has other matters to brood over, but I force myself to try it. The would-be sauce is too bland. I shake in more salt and search fruitlessly for the pepper.

'Does Dominique,' I'm relishing the assumed familiarity, 'really manipulate people?'

'*C'est la vie!*' That horrible let-out phrase again with a very Gallic shrug. I balance a strand of spaghetti on a fork and poke it in Guy's direction. He has offered to help, and so he shall!

Claudine again appears at the door, but seeing my fraught glance, beats a rapid retreat.

'*Cuit. Presque...*' Guy announces confidently. It still looks a bit stiff to me, so I'll leave it a few seconds longer. I taste the sauce.

The onions are almost cooked, but the mixture is still flavourless. Desperately I put in a generous amount of salt. I have just found an elderly *baguette* and some Camembert which isn't completely dried out, but they will not be produced until after the main dish, together with the apples and a couple of peaches I've found lying around.

I tip the steaming spaghetti into a bowl, add a dash of olive oil, and then the sauce to top it all. It looks appetising to the hungry threesome irritably waiting. Plates and forks are handed out by Claudine - I wonder when she has last eaten a square meal - and people start tucking in.

'What is Françoise Sagan's *Bonjour Tristesse* like?' I ask to break the unusual silence. No one seems inclined to comment. 'I've only found time to read a few pages.'

'*C'est une nouveauté,*' Maxime pronounces, looking to Madame for more comments. She puts her plate down decisively with most of the spaghetti still on it.

'*Elle est le dernier cri.*' The flavour of the month. Madame leans back on the faded flowers and lights up. She still has no shoes on but her feet slip to the ground to let Maxime sit beside her, after he has taken his plate with hers out to the kitchen with food on them. She warms to her subject as the others clear their plates away with spaghetti still on them and a strange eagerness to help in matters domestic.

'There's plenty more,' I say, having doled out medium-sized portions.

'*Merci, main je n'ai plus faim...*' Only Guy requests more. As he follows me to the kitchen he puts his arm round me and gives my bare shoulder a squeeze. I don't react or spurn his advance. I'm not quite sure of the turn events are taking. A low-key response will be the best way to wait and see.

While Guy and I are coping with the spaghetti and talking of Françoise and why she is just what literary Paris currently needs,

Claudine has taken clean plates and small knives to the cheese and bread on a side table. She has also washed a few glasses, just enough to go round, not one more nor one less, and is serving the remains of the half-used bottles. I don't know whether to be pleased I'm being helped, or to feel mightily annoyed at the way I'm expected to prepare the essentials and then clear up when the others can't be bothered to help. Madame is excluded, of course, because I'm repaying hospitality.

Guy is eating a second helping while the others seem keen enough to chew on chunks of stale *baguette,* cheese and fruit. He at least appreciates my efforts.

❧

It was past midnight when all finally left after much drinking, punctuated by Madame's frequent jibes at Claudine - to go and see if her bicycle was still there, or leave to feed her cats, if she still had any. I wearily cleared the studio, washed up most of the glasses from the party as well as supper, put the lid on the jar of salt, and... On an impulse, I stuck my index finger in it and tasted the white granules. Sugar!

It was an effort to reach my bed, head throbbing, back aching. I opened my journal, then yawned and leant back. It fell on the lamp flex and the light flickered out. In my drowsiness I thought I heard the heavy tread on metal of Madame descending the spiral staircase. But then, maybe not.

CHAPTER 5

What happened is hazy, disturbing.

A whisper, '*Valérie, c'est Dominique. Je viens...*' together with a whiff of lilies-of-the-valley and warm breaths of brandy. I began to sweat, my nightdress clinging to me. I pulled back the bedclothes to alight on something warm and soft. Now stark awake and frozen in terror, what was I touching? A soft hand stroked mine, the other travelling up to my shoulder and throat. I turned my head away, aghast, but the fingers were moving down. Nauseated, I rolled round, my teeth clenching. What could I do? It made my flesh creep; then a quiver followed by a shudder and tremors through my body.

I couldn't escape into the street early in the morning in my nightie. Where could I go?

The hands were insisting. Not a word uttered. That relieved me of one type of response. How could I escape from these embraces without offending? The soft body shifted closer to my back. I was dissolving into rivulets of physical and emotional agitation. In desperation I pushed my wrists and knees forward and levered myself to the side of the bed, creating space between me and the other body. A hand held on to my hip, and determined breathing accompanied a shift in my direction. I eased my body further towards the edge, inevitably followed by a similar move. A third attempt forced me to yield my side of the bed to the intruder as, crab-like, I lay suspended with arm and leg on the floor in an absurdly uncomfortable position. It was so ridiculous that I nearly started giggling, but the breathing increased its rhythm and an intrusive hand moved out over my shoulders.

Enough! I abandoned my last narrow strip of the bed and crouched for a moment on the floor. It was cool and welcome. Creeping stealthily as far as I could from the bed, I lay on Madame's sofa, a cushion for a pillow, and waited. Nothing. No movement. The heavy breathing subsided into snores.

Chapter 5

When my heart stopped rattling away so fast that I couldn't think or react, I tried to get some sleep, disturbed as I was by the close proximity of the brandy-stained floral pattern and the stench of cigarettes suffused with Dior's new perfume. The only alternative was the green-striped sofa, but it was closer to my bed. I shouldn't be silly; the sounds under the alcove were hardly threatening. She had been imbibing alcohol of one sort or another for over half a day, so wouldn't wake up until late in the morning. I'd sort things out before then. But...

What should I do? Where else could I go?

CHAPTER 6

Waking, I'm confused. Why am I on Madame Magny's sofa? Then I remember. Facing the blank gaze of the windows opposite, chilled by the light of dawn, I resent the trendy openness of studio flats and the pretensions floating around in the lofty spaces designed to display the art of inflated egos. More importantly, the shape on the alcove bed is breathing regularly. No time to be lost.

All my possessions are there in my suitcase under the bed. Stealthily I creep over, slip the suitcase out, shove my clothes into it and hurriedly check that money, travellers' cheques, passport and student's card are in my handbag. Should I leave a note?

'Dear Madame Magny,

I've suddenly realised I must leave for a job I have found in Spain. To improve my Spanish. You have been so kind, introduced me to many people, and helped me improve my command of French...' It all sounds rather strange and abrupt, yet Madame has abused the laws of hospitality. Who can I trust? Distressed by thoughts of predatory adults, I dress hurriedly. With painful concentration I gently close the door. Too late I realise I still have the keys. No letter box except down in the entrance hall. With suitcase now well-strapped, books in knapsack and vital documents safe in handbag, I take the lift. The keys clang into the post box marked 'Madame Magny' with a sad finality. Then out on the pavement to join the wide open world. The morning is damp and discouraging.

I choose the largest bar in Place Denfert Rochereau, the most anonymous place I can find to plot my next move and attempt to capture in words what happened last night. I have just enough money for a large mug of coffee, and that's it. I must find a bank. How many francs do I need? Panic swirls in the pit of my stomach at the stark realisation I shall have to pay for a room for five days. Five full days! My ticket to Spain can't be changed because it's linked to when I'm expected in Andalucía, though now Carmen's family wants me to arrive later than originally planned. I could return and stay with to my parents in their new flat. That prospect so early in my first long vacation devoted to studying the ebb and flow of life and languages, seems singularly unalluring. I toss it out of my mind as tantamount to defeat.

I must take the current where it offers new experiences. They can't all be bad. I look into the dregs of my coffee as if they might tell me what to do next. The church? No, I would have to explain something at least of what has happened to make me leave Madame so suddenly, and it wouldn't be fair to tarnish my professor's reputation where, by all accounts, she has been helping people. Ludmilla and Alexandre, for example.

I begin to weep. Tears fall silently at the thought of Jean, *beau comme un ange*. If he were alive, then we could explore Paris together. I could help him. Two vulnerable young people united in the face of an alien world. I have only met adults so far, and a fat lot of good that has done me! Here I am, homeless in Paris, without enough money even for a garret. Far easier if I had someone to share my predicament.

Few of the adults I've met have been unfriendly. Colette and Pierre I trust, but they could hardly risk upsetting such a close neighbour as Madame Magny. Claudine? I haven't a clue how to contact her. Through Maxime, but I don't have his address either. People at the church would know, but I might even bump into Madame there! Or, a sudden stabbing thought: will those adult minds suspect me of fancying him? I'm fluttering around in a spider's web, drawn into the world of adult machinations through my own incompetence. No, worse, my ingenuousness. That's too uncomfortably close to the 'silly little girl' image I detest. My silent flow of tears turns into sobs of frustration and self-disgust.

A waiter is eyeing me at a discreet distance, wanting to collect payment and fearing there won't be a tip. He's also curious, as are others snatching glances at this dark-haired girl, so alone, so sad. I resent their ideas travelling all over me, speculating about what hidden defect has made me so rejected and unloved. Asking the waiter to take care of my suitcase, I flee to the WC to wash my face and find some privacy for thought.

The face looking out is thinner, eyes rounder and skin pasty. Altogether an unappetising appearance. Young and already disgusted with Parisian life. Or more accurately, with whatever propels these ageing, self-seeking intellectuals, all lusting after someone who is inevitably lusting after someone else. There seems to be a chain of passion. If I can, then so-and-so; if so-and-so isn't available, then that other one might do, if not, what about thingamabob? Thus they dance down the scale of desirability. How high or low do I come in Madame's? If not Maxime, then Guy - or perhaps it's the other way round? If not Guy, or Maxime, then any available victim. Or me? It's disturbing, distressing and vaguely disgusting. I have never bothered to imagine these elderly people still having love lives. A sudden revelation. Perhaps my friends' parents, even my own, do as well?

I return slowly to my table and sit down to open my purse. The waiter moves closer and I hand him the entire contents. He peers at me though his professional reserve and returns a heap of coins. The other tables are filling up; no one now is paying me any attention. That's just what I like, anonymity in crowds. I contemplate myself as if in a film walking along a silvery strand, alone, buffeted by wind, the sea greying from blue as I shiver. On and on I walk along the endless stretch; the faster I walk the longer it spreads out before me. I begin to trot, then run, then look behind as the rising wind tugs at my hair which seems to grow longer as I run...'Hold on to yourself, Valerie!' I clutch the table. The waiter has returned with his baleful look implying I have imbibed, paid and should go. I nod and force a smile, tap my watch and allow myself five minutes to decide on a tip and a plan of action.

What are my options? I try to relax and not focus my mind too much so that a solution can float up from my subconscious. I've taken to this way of making choices, my subconscious usually being wiser than my rational self. Especially in matters emotional. I breathe deeply to a slow regular beat, look out of the café window at the peeling trunk of the nearest plane tree, and let it slip out of focus. Nothing. Then the face of Christ on an icon floats towards me; penetrating eyes of authority, and of calm. Père Eugraph! The one adult I can trust. How could I find him without setting the cat among the pigeons in the church community? Impossible. What a shame. I return to my reverie. No image, but words this time,

'Si tu veux quelquechose, téléphone-moi, je t'en prie...' If in need, call me. Guy. I recall his hand on my shoulder but in a protective, fatherly way, giving me his card. Clutching at the only straw, I indicate to the watchful waiter that I'll just make a phone call, and leave.

I'm irritated to find my hand trembling as I lift the receiver. Guy's family are at the château in the vacation and he goes back and forth. Might his Parisian flat be empty for the five days I need it? Nothing venture, nothing win.

Guy answers the phone. His family is away and he is about to join them. The concierge will have a key for me. Just to say I'm a friend of the family, and all will be well. He'll call to see everything is all right in the next day or so.

I let my imagination wander back to the strand; the sea has turned blue, the sand golden, the sun shines down, and a house now stands on the cliff. That's where I see myself heading.

The waiter jolts me out of my reverie. He ostentatiously moves the ashtray and condiments to one side of the table. I have enough money left, I think, for a taxi ride, and if not, who cares! I'll manage. What use being young and in search of adventure, if I'm not optimistic, and Guy is proof of this. Caution advises me to replenish my store of francs from a bank in my new quartier, the Seizième, the poshest part of Paris. My affairs are taking a turn for the better. I can't wait to park my belongings and embark on a new exploration of Paris, this time north of the Seine. I know the *Rive Droite* has always been for the wealthier, the *Rive Gauche* for the less affluent, the literary crowd, artists and workers. I need a change of ambience.

The taxi flees through my old stamping ground near the Jardin du Luxembourg, speeding past the Invalides on the right, with me gaping at the Tour Eiffel before crossing the Seine into the leafy 19th-century *Grands Boulevards* of the Seizième - and Guy's pad.

Jumping from the taxi, I pull the luggage out and push my last francs into the driver's hand, turning away quickly, afraid they will not be enough. He waits ominously. I hurry my case towards the entrance which I would never have found without his help, and turn back apprehensively. He waves, and drives off. Relief.

It's only when I've chosen one of the children's rooms to sleep in and am sitting on the bed under pictures of horses and Gérard Philipe, my favourite actor, that I realise the waiter has virtually paid for my taxi. I check the receipt from the café and estimate the change left. As I look out on to the quiet, elegant tree-lined street, I glow with gratitude for a person I wrongly thought despised me. Not all humanity is lost, I muse, as I unpack trying to disturb the child's bedroom as little as possible.

Next I should change the sheets, hang my clothes over the back of the chair, and use the desk to write my journal. Instead I wander around the apartment. It's larger than I imagined. The sitting room appears vast; most of the furniture is covered in dust sheets. I lift up a corner and find what looks like damask upholstery and light-coloured wood, some of it finely carved. The dining room is the same. Twelve curve-legged chairs and two at each end with armrests. A heavy gilt framed mirror makes the room seem larger. Other doors are ajar. I peep round one of them, fearful of finding some forgotten relative amid the pink and white muslin over a four-poster bed. Heavy cream taffeta curtains surround a large window, its shutters open as if someone is about to return to her boudoir. At last I find the kitchen and maid's room. Perhaps I should take it instead of the child's bedroom? No, better the one I have. I return to sit on the bed and plan the day ahead. Closing my eyes to rest, head on hands, an image floats up of my mother in her garden with a floppy straw hat, so familiar, so reassuring. The flow of time is hammering at my temples and I need a familiar refuge: my room at home, though I don't have it any more; my desk at school; Miss Green's study (any reproach from her always gave you hope and new energy); my room at college, and... No, I must not start crying again just because it's hard to cope with all I have to do - getting to the bank on time, studying, learning languages, experiencing people...Perhaps I'm not doing so badly after all.

'Don't be too hard on yourself, Valerie.' I'm contemplating Gérard Philipe, fearful he will lure me away from that self-imposed straight and narrow path. Like Hobbema's avenue.

'Ideas, Valerie,' Miss Green advised me not long before I left school, 'you have plenty of them. An ingenious mind. There aren't many around,' and she turned away after mumbling about the 'future potential' of television. I knew it was time for me to glance at Hobbema's avenue, perhaps for the last time, to wink at the Laughing Cavalier, and not to admit I rarely saw television. My family couldn't afford a set.

Something strange is happening. I swing my legs up on to the bed and lie on my stomach, head projecting over the end. Small rugs are scattered over the once elegant, now unpolished parquet floor. I put my right hand down to steady myself and scrutinise the boards, aware of movement but not certain where it's coming from. Suddenly I see them, hop-scotching from one join in the wood to another, averaging a leap of four to six inches. That, I conjecture, would put them in the Olympic category, if one considers the leap in proportion to their size. My ankles tickle and burn. Something must be done, but I have no idea what. Fleas and lice were, I was told, brought back by the 'brave soldiers'. We queued at school to have our hair parted with a knitting needle to check if any had deserted the train upholstery. Something has to be done. A close survey of the rugs convinces me they are unaffected, so I grab my bag, check the key is in it and, using the rugs as stepping-stones, jump to the front door.

Outside the leafy boulevard is quiet and deserted. The men are at their jobs in the City, or whatever the financial district of Paris is called, the children at school, and the housewives shopping. There's no-one to ask where the shops are, so I turn left, hoping also to find the nearest metro station. The shops and banks are not gathered along roads with street markets and blocks of flats as on the *Rive Gauche* or around Madame's studio, which I'm already beginning to miss. I find them alongside the raised section of the metro in grubby, animated streets stubbornly unlike the secluded residential boulevards.

The assistant in a hardware store with the fascinating name of *quincaillerie* – it would sound rather nice as a surname - stares at me grumpily, eyes glazed. I summon up my best French for a request I never thought in my wildest dreams I would ever have to make. I have found a bank and changed enough money, I think, to see me through, but I 'meet my Waterloo', as Madame would wryly say to tease a reaction from me, in trying to find '*poudre pour tuer les puces*'. My French is woefully inadequate for the task.

'*Lesquelles?*' from the mouth beneath the glazed eyes. Which ones? '*Pour les animaux?*' Then the glazing turns to an impatient expression of disgust, '*ou les êtres humains?*'

Ah, now I understand. Maybe they think I'm asking for flea powder for my filthy self. Apparently, there are two kinds of fleas needing different sorts of fleacidal powder. I didn't ask the fleas what sort they are. They could be either, as they are not actually on a human being until, that is, they nip my ankles. Better to plump for the least disgraceful, so the glazed-to-despising eyes will not think me unwashed and living in a grime-bespattered room.

'*Pour les animaux.*' I fear I'll be asked, 'cats or dogs?' and I'd have to answer on the hoof, not having noticed, yet, the trace of any animals. Disgusted glazed-eyes hands me a canister like a huge pepper-pot, with the end covered in paper to be perforated.

I hardly like to admit it, but I rather enjoy shaking it over the parquet, fanning outwards from the door, though the perfume added to disguise some venomous chemical tortures my nostrils. I scatter it all over the place as fast as possible, hoping no one will enter the rooms while the treatment is taking place.

Now to explore the *Rive Droite*! I bounce along to the metro station, leap up the steps two by two swinging my bag with two cheese and ham rolls and a bottle of water.

My plan is to go to the Louvre. It has a powerful royal presence about it, the wide, noble façade defiantly distant from everyday affairs, and the endless steps that aren't too high so one can glide up or down them in a long, elegant courtly dress, or so I dream as I stride up them. Postcards. I haven't sent any, not to my parents, friends, and above all not to poor Mike, still working away at his vacation job in Weymouth. Inside the entrance hall, another flight of steps to a landing where a statue I have long admired in my favourite book on art is revealed in all its glory. The Winged Victory of Samothrace is actually sailing out above me, headless and mostly armless, soaring on eternally through time. Postcards. I can afford six at the most, as there are the stamps to buy as well, and I'm on the straight and narrow, financially anyway. A bored middle-aged woman in a mangy shawl sits slumped in a shaft of dusty sunlight. There is hardly a soul, and she obviously doesn't want to drop her knitting. I offer a crisp banknote. She scowls and shakes her head muttering something about having no change, and returns to her knitting, ignoring me, my money and my postcards.

In a surge of anger I say, *'Que vous êtes con!'* (an expression I learnt from Madame Magny meaning the postcard seller is being silly), replace the cards and retrieve the offending note to use it for my entrance ticket. The clerk there presumably will have some change. This is the smallest note the bank has given me. Not my fault.

A shriek. *'Comment?'* Needles and knitting flung to the floor, the woman rises with unexpected agility from behind her stack of postcards to run across the hall in my direction, fist raised. I turn on my heels to flee towards the door, down the steps and across the forecourt at a rate of knots followed by the woman, shawl a-floating. I'm too scared to stop and look behind until I reach the Rue de Rivoli and take refuge behind a column in the arcade. Needless to say, youth has easily out-run middle age, which has returned disgruntled to knitting, and perhaps, if lucky, a customer or two. With small change.

I must have committed some gross linguistic impropriety in the postcard incident, but that will have to be sorted out by asking someone - Guy perhaps when he drops in to see how I'm faring.

Though I only left Madame Magny's studio this morning, I'm already out exploring the other side of the Seine. Claudine told me about some Turkish Baths. I'll try them out. The Rue des Rosiers is further along the Rue de Rivoli, not far on my map. So I set off briskly, munching the ham and cheese rolls as I go. I pass the Louvre on my right and the Palais Royale on the left. It's getting hot; the street goes on and on. The square with the Tour Saint Jacques appears to my right and the Boulevard de Sébastopol feeds into it from the left. Claudine confessed she loves to ride her bicycle down there *à toute vitesse* imagining it taking flight to cross the Seine and touch down on the 'Boul Mich'! It's fun to share another's fantasy world. I hurry on invigorated. The mysterious mad Claudine with her cats must live around here, and if she is as smelly as Madame hints, why does she know about, and presumably frequent, the Turkish Baths? It doesn't add up. Typical of these adults, 'confusionists' I call them all. My map is deceptively simplified, and the Rue des Rosiers isn't quite where I expect it to be. Irritating, for I pride myself on accurate map-reading, but the detailed ones of Paris are too bulky and expensive.

I choose the next small street on the left, plunging into the myriad smells of pastry cooks, bakers, furniture restorers, and kosher butchers, winding my way past women in shawls and dark threadbare dresses with men in worn black suits and wide-brimmed hats. I pause at one of the many projecting wooden shop fronts to savour the crisp aroma of loaves mottled with seeds or twisted and plaited into every shape or size that dough can take, and even different colours. Rye flour, perhaps, though I have never tried it. A plaque on a faded yellow wall commemorates the return of Jews to Paris in the eighteenth century; another mourns their descendants, seized during the Nazi occupation never to return from concentration camps. Ludmilla and Alexandre, and others, who live in the streets near their church, have something in common with the denizens of this district: the bitter taste of exile and the yearning for roots, for a past they know has gone. Here they seem more integrated; they speak fluent French, though there is writing in Hebrew on some merchandise and a nearby synagogue. When inside a café for a cup of coffee, I hear snatches of strange phrases.

There it is. A handsome building with a plain front on the ground and first floors, while the second one has carved flowing lintel decorations between two brackets swelling into scrolls like liquorice wheels. There are three windows, and between them project lion heads holding in their mouths two placards - BAINS and PISCINE - with another decorative form like an open fan with bobbins hanging below. Light plays across this storey, while the lower ones lie in perpetual shadow. There are three doors, but only one is ajar. To my relief, it has DAMES above it. I've happened to choose the right day.

It's clammy as soon as you step inside. The turnstile clicks heavily as I hand the same disputed bank note to a large woman perched in what strangely resembles a pulpit. She is perspiring, discreetly. Not a word, just sounds from behind doors of bumps and splashes. Some change is returned with a request for my bag so it will be kept safe; in return, a metal number hanging from a large curtain ring. The cashier or manageress indicates the changing rooms. I enter a cubicle and hop out quickly, not sure how much to take off and where to go next. Acutely self-conscious of how easy it is to look silly, I do a recce while still decently dressed. A door in the corridor outside the cubicles opens into a circular room. There before my eyes is a live version of Ingres' paintings of naked women in my art book, wide-hipped and generously proportioned. Seated or standing, some are looking vacantly at the different volumes of steam emanating from apertures to what I imagine are spaces heated to different degrees by huge furnaces somewhere below. Other female figures, rendered anonymous by their lack of clothes, are trying to read newspapers that flop damply from their hands. They come in all shapes and sizes, mainly large. It only confirms my lack of interest in the female body, hardly the right place to seek symbolical cleansing from my recent experience. Now I'm here, and have paid a fair amount, I must get on with it.

Each aperture is numbered. Only experience, or the reduced amount of steam issuing forth, will reveal the coolest room to start off. Claudine said one should do them all. I'm fascinated by three athletic figures that have just emerged from billowing steam; they are scraping themselves with what looks like the strigil used by the bronze Greek athlete illustrated alongside the Winged Victory. It must be satisfying to scrape the dirt off, to separate oneself physically from dross. One could associate it metaphorically with all one wanted to free oneself from, to slough it off as snakes do with their skins. I imagine myself emerging from a chrysalis, shining and newly born in body and soul. Room number one, next to number twelve that has just disgorged the three women with the strigils, isn't too hot. Just clammy. So far so good. Out when one can stand no more, and into the next. Longer rests in between one's progress round the increasingly hot and humid chambers.

I only make it to number eight, and can't find even one strigil lying around. I wonder if they're the personal property of the three muscular Amazons but don't dare ask the woman in the pulpit. My heart begins to pump rapidly. Lucky I remembered to weigh myself just after I stripped and entered the first 'caldarium'. From steam cauldron number eight I retreat to the large central area with a flickering blue pool and slump front down on a marble slab, hoping to calm my heartbeat. Lying inert on another slab, an Amazon is being pummelled by a small, energetic woman dressed only in a clinging tunic. The uniform graces the masseuse, marking her out as a staff member. Except for the three Amazons and me, the youngest, the other bodies all lie, lean or ponderously plod this steamy realm, graceless and unashamed.

Finally I've cooled down enough to swim, but the heat and effort to stay in cauldrons one to eight have left me little energy. Only two lethargic lengths from a former competitor in junior swimming competitions. Disgraceful! At least in compensation I will have lost a few ounces. Or kilos. I weigh myself. Eight hundred grams lost, not even a kilo! Dried and clothed, but still vaguely damp, I hand the manageress my number.

Crossing the street, I check the money is intact in my purse. It is. Over an hour spent opening my pores. The sun no longer illuminates the plaques on the third storey and I'm ravenous.

Something cheap to eat should be easy to find in Montmartre. There'll be a breeze on the hill where the vineyards once were, and I can continue rather belatedly my vacation reading. Proust. I'm only on the first volume of *A la Recherche du Temps Perdu*! And I had better hurry up, as I won't improve my command of Spanish if I'm still reading French when I arrive in Andalucía.

Leaving the metro at Place Pigalle, I stop to peruse my map. *'Mademoiselle!'* Ignoring the call, I turn off into a small street leading up the hill. Someone is breathing close behind me. I quicken my pace. So does my shadow. I slow down and swerve sharply. So does he, pulling back out of my reach. A curly-haired, olive-skinned man.

'Je suis votre ami. Je vais vous achêter à boire.'

Never! He's a stranger and pretends to be a friend wanting to buy me a drink. Never! The man grows bolder as I continue up the hill. Faster I stride, my anger and frustration increasing in time with my pace, but he stays breathing down my neck. I stop mid stride, turn, swipe him with Proust Volume One and flee, leaving the man crouching, one knee on the cobbles. Terrified he will seek rapid revenge – I'm now out of breath, the hill too steep for me to run any more - I bang on the nearest door.

'Un homme me poursuit. Aidez-moi. Je suis une étudiante anglaise!' Refuge for a student being chased! The man opening the door is as astonished as his wife hovering at the end of the narrow corridor.

'Entrez!' They couldn't have been more helpful, allowing me to stay for a glass of water and a moment's respite. He checks to see if all is clear on the pretence of watering the plants ranged in pots round the front door. From what the couple tell me, it seems there are pimps in the area notorious for its prostitutes. Nothing new in that. But he seems to be talking of a 'white slave trade' that I know nothing about. I don't want to show my ignorance or trespass on their hospitality, so I reassure them I will follow their advice and go up to Sacre Coeur, the big white basilica at the summit and only a stone's throw away, where there will be safety mingling with the crowds. 'Avoid the small streets,' they counsel anxiously as they squeeze my hand. *'Au revoir, Valérie. Faîtes attention!'*

Up by Sacre Coeur the first street lamps are blinking undecidedly. I deserve some cheap food. Algerian *cous-cous* perhaps?

I'm curious and have never tasted it. From under a tatty red and white stripe awning come American voices raised in protest, then -

'Valerie. Thank goodness you're here! Can you help us?' It's Charles Hammond IV and Liz, an amazing coincidence. I thought they had long since left to travel south to the Mediterranean. They are sitting at a pavement table and a young waiter, who looks as if this is his vacation job, is standing perplexed beside them, pen poised over a small pad.

'Please join us.' Liz motions for another chair to be drawn up. 'He doesn't understand a word, and we are trying to speak slowly,' she explains in exasperation.

'What's up?'

They have ordered the very best French steak, slightly rare, with string beans, roast potatoes and a large glass of milk each. The waiter says they can only have one vegetable, either roast potatoes or the beans. They don't want the bread that comes with everything, and he is insisting they should have Beaujolais or Burgundy with their steak. He snorts in disgust as he repeats their request for milk, *'une abomination, pour insulter la cuisine française...'* I must prevent any disagreement over a simple culinary preference! Actually, after my recent experience, I'm finding this fun. A bit of education all round, I think, then free choice to be upheld.

So Liz and Bob have it explained to them that milk is rarely drunk in France on its own, and never ever with a meal. Just with coffee at breakfast. In France they consider it spoils the dish; red meat should be accompanied by a full-bodied red wine.

'We've each had a glass of wine while sitting here. Now we're hungry and want to eat. Doesn't he have any milk?' Liz insists. That's a thought. Perhaps not. Nobody in France takes milk with coffee after a full meal; it always comes black, often already sugared!

'Ecoutez...' I turned to the waiter, 'have you any milk at all?' He moves behind me to whisper that they certainly do but he is sick of these Americans fouling up the meal, that French cooking is the

best in the world and not to be insulted in this way. He is doing this job because he has to earn money for his studies, but it is more than even he can do to suffer such fools... I let him run out of steam. While my friends look on anxiously, afraid there will be yet another twist to the tale, I look up and smile with pleasure at the student turned waiter because he is handsome if haughty.

'Those are your opinions, not universal truths. My friends have every right, as you do, to eat what and how they wish, if it's available and they pay for it. As this is the case, you can advise them to take the Burgundy, and I happen to agree, because it suits my stomach, not because we are right and they are wrong. If they insist on milk, give it to them!' I have always distrusted fashions and fads foisted on others when whatever one chooses would not make the slightest difference to world injustice or things which really do matter. 'So?'

I'm really glad to see Bob and Liz, and pleased about the way I'm dealing linguistically with this minor international incident. Curious about what I've said, I explain to them that I've spoken out for tolerance, and he will bring the milk. They kindly ask me what I would like to eat, and I join them ordering a steak, showing them how to mop up the juices with bread and use it as a substitute for potatoes. Oh, and while they drink the milk, I'm enjoying a glass of Burgundy.

'Cheers!'

'A pity you weren't here earlier when we were having our wine.'

The sky is velvety and speckled with stars. The full moon is over and another lunar month on its way. I haven't had such a good meal since I came to France. They took a taxi and dropped me a short distance from my boulevard, chuckling over my experience with fleas. Their hotel is the best they can find and has no such problems, or they hadn't felt anything yet! Salt of the earth, I thought.

Inside Guy's flat I peer down at the trails of yellow powder. There doesn't seem to be any movement. Stalking from carpet to carpet, fearful of the first telltale itch, I leap on to the bed, turn and hang over the end. That's how I first noticed the acrobatic fleas. Nothing stirs. I take out my torch, always kept in my bag for emergencies, and shine it parallel to the parquet floor. Alleluia, nothing is moving!

In spite of the smell, less powerful by now, I decide not to open the windows to let the chemicals go on working till the morning. No one will return at this late hour.

Drowsily I sit down at the desk and open my journal to reread what I jotted down in the café this morning about the events last night, now so far away.

'Today I've spent time deliberately alone, among exiles - Jews, Russians, and the deserted or rejected flotsam and jetsam of this world. All through some form of intolerance it seems. And I end the day with a futile example of that same intolerance over food. I must think about this for my novel, and the need for roots, and how and why that has bred intolerance, particularly in my century. I wish I had more ideas. What would you do, Valerie, if you were driven out of your home and landed in Paris? You'd look for a small, manageable group, round a minority church perhaps? But the wheel of fortune turns, and if that group is seen as a threat, just because it keeps itself apart, or grows wealthy, or sets itself up as exclusive, helping only its members and shrinking from the mass outside, then persecution follows as night follows day...'

That glass of wine, this stifling room, a full stomach... I succumb.

CHAPTER 7

Anagging sense of insecurity pervades my final days in Paris. There isn't enough time for my tough self-imposed schedule. I intended to study every nook and cranny of the Louvre, but I haven't progressed far beyond my old friend the Winged Victory of Samothrace, the Sumerians and ancient cultures, Venus da Milo and the paintings of the School of Fontainebleau. Procrastination is begetting panic, and a frantic rush down endless corridors to see the Mona Lisa, impenetrably restrained behind glass. More compelling is Raphael's nearby portrait of Castiglione - I would have liked to meet him, despite what I imagine to be his po-faced book on table manners for would-be Renaissance courtiers. I rush into a spacious gallery to stand entranced before Watteau's Voyage to Cythera, the fabled island of luxuriant foliage and seductive sward, where silent music wafts on a fragrant breeze of gold and blue and mossy green. Equally intriguing but less alluring is the gigantic painting of Napoleon in Notre Dame; he has taken the crown from a diminished pope to place it on Josephine's head, artistry elaborating events. I read somewhere that Napoleon was only five feet plus in height, at least five inches smaller than me.

When not out to discover Paris, I'm finishing the first volume of Proust's *A la Recherche du Temps Perdu* and taking an imaginary journey along winding sentences into a never forgotten childhood of sensory delights. They're the longest ever written, a sheer literary *tour de force*. This book is my companion, already used in self-defence, I remind myself as I warm to its presence in my bag or hand.

My mind is flitting all over the place, chasing ideas, people and places, following different routes in my campaign to conquer Paris, and the need to say my goodbyes. A constant rawness, an unremitting feeling of vulnerability irks me. Good manners decree, (or in other words, my mother), that I should return the philosophy book to Madame Magny, although from my departure note she will think I'm already in Spain. I duck the issue and relegate it firmly to the innermost recess of my mind. It will keep resurfacing, especially when I'm nearing the end of a relentlessly long Proustian sentence.

Restlessly I return to the Place de la Concorde to walk down the Tuileries, to swim into Monet's lily ponds. A walk again, sandals rubbing, to Notre Dame to soar up into the rose window of Mary, the Queen of Heaven, also the Virgin in the rose garden, woven so lovingly in the tapestry I have revisited in the Musée de Cluny. One reason I return to Notre Dame is to search for the memorial to Joan of Arc which I never can find, though Mike insisted it's there.

Joan of Arc. Napoleon. Why do the French make heroes of people who've been defeated? Joan of Arc was caught up in a French civil war with the English meddling across the Channel; a romantic, courageous figure. Perhaps it is the same with Napoleon. He was a great general, though it didn't save him in the end, nor did the prodigious legal and educational reforms he carried out. To me he seems to have betrayed the democratic ideals of the French Revolution by becoming Emperor and leading his country into further decades of confusion. I slot this into my growing list of topics to discuss with Mike on return. It's sad we aren't here together, but then I wouldn't speak any French.

My wandering thoughts lead me into a narrow street lined with galleries. I love to linger looking at the window displays. One in particular catches my eye, dragging me inside. 'A new, young, exciting painter, Bernard Buffet, rejects non-figurative art!' proclaims the poster in the window. I've already noticed it on some of the publicity pillars and half-promised myself to see the exhibition. A very spiky Joan of Arc in armour, hardly an athletic young girl soldier, moves round the series to face varying historic challenges. Her followers alike are whey-faced, skinny and two dimensional. Here and there a warmer colour stands out from the gloom of greys, chilly blues and dull greens, a touch of brownish-red here, burnt gold there, as if the fading afternoon sun has touched them up with a last desperate flick of the brush. The gallery is deserted, except for another figure, like me, deep in scrutiny. I turn on my heel, apprehensive that I might be waylaid by the gallery owner.

This evening as I'm about to go to sleep, the bedroom door handle turns. I freeze. If it's an unknown member of Guy's family, I'll feel embarrassed, an intruder. Or perhaps Guy de Lavallière has invited another person, stranded like myself?

'*Ça va?*' It's Guy. What relief. Busy as usual, he has just come to dump his things and see if I'm managing. I recount what I've been doing, with a tinge of regret at not having had the courage to go into the literary cafés Madame Magny haunts but where she didn't choose to take me. I've now learnt how to drop a hint or two.

'*Pas trop tôt lendemain matin...*' Guy has other plans for early tomorrow morning, but he promises to take me later round the Quartier Latin. He'll be ready by eleven so we can tackle the Musée Rodin first. He hasn't been there for so long, and he remembers I'm keen to see it.

Actually I reminded him of this, but he has the charm to weave the museum into his impromptu plans for his young guest. I shall do what I can with the help of a man who obviously likes me a lot. Or enough to help me out. I'm prepared to give him the slip if he too makes unreasonable demands on me, as might easily happen in his own home. I've put aside the money needed for such an emergency - the convent round the corner takes in young women for a few francs. There are snags: rising at seven in the morning to pray and back before nine with no chance to go out after then. Very restrictive, but safe and cheap.

After fussing around some of the rooms Guy leaves, waving *adieu* with a little giggle and reminding me he'll be here at eleven tomorrow. I don't hear him return.

❧

I have breakfast, slip out to buy a few essentials, and on my return he's ready, freshly shaven and grinning.

'*Allons-y! Rodin!*' We take the metro, though I'm amazed he hasn't a clue how it works. I check my map and find we have to change. We walk along streets of honey-coloured stone buildings and large wrought-iron gates with tempting glimpses into cobbled courtyards. They must be the *hôtels* or private residences of the famous courtesans in the times of Louis XIV. Or was it Louis XV? Guy isn't sure. He's propelling me along the streets at such a high speed that my strides begin to strain my underwear. In abject horror, I fumble at my waist to find that what I fear has happened – the elastic has snapped and my knickers are descending! I grab one side through my dress and look desperately for an open doorway. If only we were in a district with flats. I could cope with a *concierge* or two, but not with the off-putting high railings or walls with firmly closed gates. I pause, wondering whether I can confide in Guy. No, it might be misinterpreted as a 'come-hither' gesture, and I'm disinclined to retreat to a nunnery for the last bit of my stay in Paris. We pass two more gates. By now I can't even push them to see if they'll open to save me – I'm using both hands to stop the descent whilst gripping my bag. At last! Here's an open gateway. In I plunge. Facing the street to try and stop Guy or any stranger seeing me, I hitch up the back of my skirt, seize the offending garment and pull it down to my ankles. Just as I let the skirt go and am bending to pull my underwear from under my feet, comes, '*Bonjour, Mademoiselle!*' I jump, swivel round to trip over my knickers and end in a heap on the ground with the white garment shackling my ankles. Fortunately I put on a clean pair that morning, mindful of one of mother's favourite expressions 'always be dainty'! Instead of coming to my help, the gardener, or whoever he is - definitely not the count who must own this property - leans back against the wall. His weathered face creases in uncontrolled mirth, my discomfort fuelling his hilarity so much that I long for a just revenge: that his old leather belt snap from under his considerable paunch, and that his trousers too fall down! I swiftly disentangle my knickers, push them into my bag, and hurry back to come face to face with Guy on the pavement outside.

'Pardon!' I just wanted to look more closely at the architecture. My instinct for survival warns me to keep everything with Guy on a controlled level of friendly companionship, while accepting his hospitality as well as his offer to show me Paris. Will he take advantage of my circumstances? I'm worried. Is it sufficient for him to be flattered by the company of a young and, I hope, vivacious woman, hardly more than a slip of a girl?

I just cannot trip up, have an accident or in any way or let the wind blow my skirt up until I return to my suitcase. It would be unwise to buy knickers while exploring Paris with Guy!

I glance at him. He is striding out beside me with a hint of a smile on his long, aristocratic face. His mouth curls upwards at the corners under an aquiline nose matching his long fingers, delicate and white as in portraits of people who never do anything but gesture, languidly. His pale green eyes have a perpetual, slightly benign smile. Upon reflection, I realise I have never seen him angry. If a discussion is hotting up, he'll just slip away. Sleekly.

The house Rodin once shared with other artists is set back from the street in a sculpture garden. I have mostly seen his work in illustration: the *penseur*, thinking eternally above the Gates of Paradise and the Burghers of Calais that moved me almost to tears when I first saw them in London near the Houses of Parliament. After my visit to the *Bains Turques*, I'm intrigued by the human body and the way Rodin depicts it, clothed or naked. Where is Guy? I spy him caressing the buttocks of a naked statue on the terrace. Inside the gallery he buzzes from room to room, gaily patting or fondling the anatomy of nude female figures with a boyish look of mischief - catch me if you can! Why don't any of the custodians notice? I would like to stroke the bronzes, I half admit, though not quite so specifically as he does. Perhaps we should leave. He is waiting for me outside the front door, smoking.

'*Au Quartier Latin?*' Maybe his interests are more musical than artistic. I fear he might find all this art stuff rather tedious.

I pick my way gingerly to the metro, worried about tripping on the uneven pavements. The district is too discreetly residential to have cafés and bars at regular intervals like the *Rive Gauche*. Now is the time to ask Guy about '*con*' and the postcard-seller at the Louvre who chased me out of the museum. He giggles and casts a sidelong glance at me. Funny how a young foreigner has learnt the vulgar but trendy slang so soon.

'*Çela ne se dit pas en bonne compagnie!*' Not the correct word to use in polite society, but then I'm hardly in any sort of society when buying postcards. Madame uses it frequently to mean silly, stupid. I was annoyed, and wanted to defend myself by saying the woman in the shawl was being unreasonable. I now recall the scene in *Henry V* when Katherine, the daughter of the king of France, is about to be wooed by Henry. While learning the parts of the body in English she is coyly dismayed at the word 'gown'. In her pronunciation it sounded like '*con*' - a familiar term for the female organ. Where did Shakespeare find his outrageous pamphlets like the *Canard Enchainé* or his Madame Magny? Why do rude words flourish as social outcasts over so many centuries?

'Is *Quincaillerie* a common surname, like *Leblanc* or whatever is your equivalent of Smith, Jones or Brown? I like the sound of it and it looks somehow strange.' Another flash of his green eyes in a sidelong glance.

'*C'est le nom d'un magasin, pas d'une fami.* stupid can you get! It means an ironmonger. I blush, to inspect the paving stones, placing one leg neatly ir other. Guy turns to see what I'm up to as we approach ι

As soon as we emerge in the 'Boul Mich', Guy's h. .d starts swivelling from one side of the road to another.

'*A manger un bout de pain?*' I'm ravenous and dismayed by the offer of a scrap of bread. Fortunately it's more than I think. I try a *croque-monsieur* for the first time, ever curious to know what this 'nibble the gentleman' titbit might turn out to be. No more, it transpires, than the French version of Welsh rarebit. So much for names and culinary expectations. Guy's eating some toasted bread with bits of bacon, or something similar. *Croque-madame?* I didn't dare ask, wary of being tiresome with all my silly questions. This *bistro* is the sort Madame Magny described to me. When things heated up at the Deux Magots - too many literary luminaries wanting to talk to her - she would escape to a small, unfashionable place like this, take over a whole pine 'stall' to write and smoke and think. Our *bistro* is divided into sections by high partitions of light brown wood backing hard benches and a table which, I suppose, are designed to encourage patrons to move on when their shoulders and buttocks have ground too far into the boards. I can imagine Madame taking over her 'stall' and lasting many hours on one coffee, imbibing in a smoky atmosphere supposed to be intellectually impregnated, but which I sniff as more one of drowsy self-esteem. A sort of, 'Look at me, this brain is visibly ticking over great thoughts; observe and pass quietly by'.

Guy nibbles his food leaving the crusts on his plate, and pays the bill.

'*On prendra du café au Deux Magots?*' I shoot up from my hard bench, delighted that he seems to remember all my requests. He isn't a bad type after all. Guy is watching me. I smile at him, half ring my lids in the way I think men like, because it makes them feel wanted.

As he politely stands aside, I sweep out of the *bistro* forgetting my lack of underwear. My skirt's recent lengthening into a semblance of the New Look has left a tiny, weightless hem on a generous width of material. The only gust on this sunny July day meets me and up it flies to billow out like a parachute. I panic, letting my handbag drop as I grab the material, bunching it up on one side. Guy promptly picks up my bag, smiles and puts his arm round my shoulders.

'*Qu'as-tu?*' No, I won't explain what's troubling me. The day darkens. Tears of tension fill my eyes. Worse, I feel a twinge presaging the monthly curse. All I really want to do is to take a taxi back to the flat to repair my misfortune. Guy smiles a bit too much as he hands me the bag and the sultry afternoon settles down unthreateningly.

The famous café is surprisingly empty. It is mid-afternoon by now, siesta time and perhaps not the moment for luminaries to meet in deep discourse. I am, truthfully, a tad disappointed. Guy settles down at a table by the window, asking me which way I'd like to look. Inwards, to absorb the atmosphere. The fittings are, as far as I know, typical of the Thirties, the sort of interior my mother cherishes because it reminds her of the pre-war world when she fell in love. The war had slammed that chapter shut; she deplores the dry lines of the 1950s 'clean' utilitarian styles. Here it is all greens and browns and cane seating. Windows display flower designs in frosted glass. Yes, definitely my mother's world.

Three tables away a youngish man is scribbling intently, occasionally consulting a tome beside him. That reminds me of the recently published book, the latest in philosophical fashion, that Madame Mangy lent me. I'll have to return it unread. There's no time to cope with it, what with exploring Paris, practising French and tackling Proust.

I look around more hopefully as a group comes in and sits at the far end. Guy seems to know them; he nods in their direction but doesn't move. Is that because of me? I recognise the older strong-faced writer from Madame's party, her neighbour Simone, now in deep conversation with a man wearing thick glasses. He too looks vaguely familiar. Near their table are two others occupied by tourists, probably Americans, who spend their time scanning hopefully anyone entering the premises. The coffee is good, cups soon refilled, and Guy for once doesn't seem restless. More people are drifting in. He looks around as if expecting something to happen. The only moment I turn to look out of the window, he is gone. Françoise Sagan's dark-haired literary agent has joined the older writer, and Guy is talking to her. He returns excited.

'*Une bonne nouvelle,*' he beams at me. 'That's Martine. She works mostly for the literary crowd. But my friend, the young composer, is now on her books. I asked her to take him on as a favour. His latest composition - he was showing it to us at Dominique's - has been chosen as one of three to be performed in an important concert. *C'est magnifique!*'

Indeed. But why am I being treated as an outsider? Or worse, as a child? I've long since learnt that sulking gets me nowhere, so I force a smile, keep my eyes calm and, I hope, serious. Guy chirpily babbles on with more details about his friend the composer and about Martine, who has been so successful that her husband has left her. Here we are on two separate tables, all people who know one another, so doesn't it count that I was their hostess's house guest at the reception? I'm not quite sure whether ignoring me would be considered rude behaviour. By whom? Certainly not in their lights.

'They can't be disturbed,' Guy babbles on, 'because it's not easy to get Sartre to agree to anything'. That's it. The great man himself. And the expanse between our two tables is a strategic one created by two women for different reasons, I imagine. Guy is humming to their tune and I'm being kept well out of it all. The adult game is, I observe, either commercial or amorous. I'm only just learning the ground rules and feel more uneasy by the minute.

Guy looks at his watch.

'*Allons-y!*'

'*Où?*' He has promised to take me to a Jean Cocteau film. As we leave, I glance back at the scene inside. It looks like a still from a 1930s movie: tourists drinking tea and nibbling cakes while trying not to observe the young man reading - he is no longer alone - or the table with the Great Man, heads together in conversation round the puffs and wisps of cigarette smoke. Martine looks up and Guy waves at her. She smiles.

The moment we are back on the pavement I place my left hand firmly at my side to keep the skirt decorously under control; my right hand holding the handbag appears to be attached to my other thigh. Guy encircles my shoulders and lightly kisses my cheek. Watch out, Valerie! His behaviour is changing. No one is watching. I'm not too happy about seeing a film with him in an affectionate mood, but it has been agreed and I desperately want to savour the latest Parisian taste in film and theatre. We talked a lot about it at Madame's, and I have, tactfully I hope, reminded Guy of the promises he tossed in my direction at those earlier moments in my destiny.

The cinema is only a few blocks away, and it's the first show in the afternoon, neatly timed to be followed by dinner, the theatre or night club if so inclined. The afternoon is waning into evening, a time deliciously tinged with melancholy. It's quite crowded inside. Though there isn't much dialogue, what's said is so significant that I'm pretty sure I missed the point of the film. Deceptively clear, it didn't, to my mind at least, illuminate the images of a car dashboard that talks to the hairy arms at the wheel, or of long roads with Lombardy poplars like the Hobbema picture, except that has colour, and not the grim texture of black and white war newsreels with troops tramping along similar avenues. Then a young man in a strange dark outfit appears, modern Mercury on a motorcycle; he stands talking, the breeze ruffling his fair hair. I stifle a sob. He reminds me of Ludmilla and Alexandre's Jean, *beau comme un ange*. All the while I'm trying, gently, to keep Guy's exploratory hand off, or at least further down my thigh. At one point, when I'm absorbed deciphering the angelic motorcyclist's words, the hand ascending my anatomy makes a discovery that agitates it considerably, utterly ruining my involvement in the film. I push it away and deliberately burst into tears. This proves an astute reaction. Guy pulls out his handkerchief, and the erring hand moves to offer it to me, his other embracing my left shoulder in an anxious hug.

'*Ça ne va pas?*' I do want to see the end of the film, but without his indiscreet fumbling, so I reassure him.

Ça va très bien, merci.' It's fine, thanks. His fumbling restarts with renewed energy. Oh dear, my phrase is meant to refer to the film, not the groping! I take hold of his wandering hand, squeeze it and firmly replace it where it should be, on his knee or at least on his anatomy, not mine. I lean forward and look intently at the screen, hoping he'll get the message. No, his hand is nothing if not persistent. The film ends leaving me confused. Outside, shadows veil the gentle, dusty July evening in seductive darkness. It might be too late to make my planned getaway to the nuns. I shiver in the warm air and clap my free hand against my skirt, aware that he has made the discovery, but at least hasn't mentioned it.

'*Ecoute, je dois voir quelqu'un... Mes affaires, tu sais...*' I feel liberated. He has some sort of business appointment. Strange at this hour, but anything can happen in Paris, I conclude. I tell him I understand and that I'll return to his flat to do some work. It has been a lovely day, just the things I always dreamed of doing.

'*Après demain, nous irons au théâtre?*' As if to make up for ditching me this evening, he invites me to the theatre the day after tomorrow. Ah, just the Parisian experience I hope to have before I leave! At least I shall be suitably dressed.

'Merci. Au revoir. A après demain.' Rather silly, I thought, to say 'see you the day after tomorrow', when he'll be returning to the same flat this evening. I know my bedroom doesn't have a lock. Should I move to the nuns now, and not risk the next day?

I watch his quick, busy walk down the 'Boul Mich', a would-be youthful figure kept in trim by not eating crusts. Before lost to sight he is joined by a woman in a dark, neat business suit. That's quick. His appointment. Strange that he puts his arm round her shoulders and seems, perhaps, to embrace her, but people are now between them and me. She looks familiar. My imagination is no doubt working overtime.

A forlorn figure stops by the rubbish bin near Guy's flat and surreptitiously discards a piece of offending underwear. Once inside the entrance hall, I feel lonely. I would prefer to go out somewhere. Dancing. Nobody to go with. Paris is rejecting me. Well, I have only a short time to go, then on to Spain. I'm excited but also apprehensive at the prospect. Finishing all the scraps I can find in the kitchen, I retire into the bedroom to decide what to do with the time remaining before my departure.

It is not yet seven o'clock. I can still retreat to the nuns. They are just round the corner, but the idea depresses me. A sort of benign prison, it seems. I can always put a chair against the door in case Guy tries to enter my room, though it seems rather rude, as he's my host. I'm presuming his intentions are dubious judging from his hand's behaviour. Well, there are only three more nights. I'll risk it. I've a busy day tomorrow washing my clothes so they will dry on the line outside the kitchen window before I leave. There are cards to write and places I haven't yet seen. On my last day I must pluck up courage to bid farewell to everyone I've met through Madame Magny, and to Madame herself. Her book must be returned. I pick it up to see whether, in the time I unexpectedly have to myself, I can read enough to speak to her intelligently about it. I prop myself up with pillows to tackle the convoluted thoughts, struggle to page ten, and then stop. Folded pages in new French paperbacks show they are untouched; the purchaser has the task of slitting them open to leave a feathery edge. From page ten the pages are uncut. So Madame herself hasn't read this book! Dear Dominique is practising lifemanship - I was introduced to this in my first year at university. I'll return it with all the pages slit to shame her, though I'm not sure I can read enough to impress. I struggle on, waking up in the morning to find the book on the floor and the chair in front of my bedroom door undisturbed. Not a sound in the house. Where's Guy?

I leave after washing and hanging out my clothes. He doesn't seem to be at home, but I haven't peeped into his bedroom. Anyway, it isn't my business. I'm to meet him at Madame Magny's *bistro* soon after seven tomorrow evening, so there's plenty of time to revisit my haunts around the Sorbonne and the Île de la Cité. I might even meet the student who followed me the first day! This time I'll speak to him. He might have introduced me to people my own age. No good regretting. I shall behave differently, be more open and welcoming for the next part of my voyage. More receptive, I add as an afterthought.

❦

Today is my last in Paris, the day of farewells. After finishing the packing I go out and buy a half-*baguette*, a hunk of *gruyère* cheese and some cherries and eat them sitting on a bench in the Jardin du Luxembourg, waiting for something to happen. It's after midday and the children are on holiday, though by now they have been gathered home for lunch. It's difficult to find something to do at this time of day other than wander, as all museums except the largest are closed over lunch and the siesta. What about the Russian church first? Madame is unlikely to be there at lunchtime.

It is farther than I remembered. One o'clock in the afternoon, and the iron gates are closed, locked. A wave of resentment - suppose I wanted to pray, to speak to God, and I'm locked out of his house? How can Père Eugraph do this to me? It would be impolite to visit Ludmilla and Alexandre at lunchtime, so I walk along the street looking at patches of sunlight on the blotchy bark of plane trees and posters pasted on to the advertisement columns. Better to sip a drink outside a café, and watch the world and his wife go by, as my father would say. But the world's wife is cooking, and the world is at home hanging around for the results. The roads are deserted. In the street where I often went shopping for Madame all the shops are shuttered. Not a soul. This is the sacred hour of the repast. I sit on the only iron bench I can find in the shade near Place Denfert Rochereau and decide to take a nap myself, like the rest of the world.

After five minutes I give up, neck aching and head lolling backwards. I'm afraid I might snore or snort just as someone passes by. There's nothing so embarrassing as looking ridiculous when unconscious. And defenceless.

With some difficulty I manage to spend an hour doing nothing early on a July afternoon in Paris. Past two o'clock. Surely I can call on my Russian friends? Anyway, I need to say goodbye to Jean.

Ludmilla peeps nervously round the door at the end of the cluttered passage.

'Ah, c'est toi, Valérie. Entre.' She looks dazed but pleased to see me. I apologise for having woken her before the end of the siesta, but Ludmilla replies simply that she has been spending a bit of time with Jean. Alexandre is somewhere in the countryside with clients; a whole family wants horoscopes before two proposed marriages take place. A delicate matter.

'Why isn't the church open? I went there first.'

'It always used to be. Père Eugraph insisted it should be, day and night. Then the *clochards* began to return night after night; it became their dormitory, dirty, smelly. So against his will, but after a lot of time praying and asking for inspiration from God, he told us it should only be open when someone is there to check who comes in, and never at night.'

'Didn't he find out what the parishioners all thought?' I judge his behaviour to be rather autocratic.

'Perhaps he did. But God spoke to him, and Maxime asked for volunteers to make up a rota. He couldn't find anyone for meal times, so that's why it was closed.'

While speaking, Ludmilla has been putting out biscuits and made some tea. She does things like this without you even noticing. Always a welcome. We talk of the younger children, the two dark-haired girls who are away spending the day with a family from the church. Pierre is working, though Ludmilla hopes it will only be a holiday job.

'Perhaps he'll continue to study,' she continues wistfully. 'Père Eugraph thinks he is as clever as Jean.' Her eyes mist over. 'Pierre has been attending evening classes, but he gets too tired and wants to stop.' Ludmilla has the habit of pausing to think between sentences. 'We need his money, but we also want him to start with a chance in life.'

She puts her hands round her cup and gazes into space. I've read somewhere that people need to mourn. My mother hasn't grieved enough over Uncle David's death. He is still her daily burden of unresolved sorrow.

'Let's go and talk to Jean.' Ludmilla takes my hand and we enter the tiny bedroom shrine. Ludmilla kneels and prays and weeps, whispering all the time as she clasps a tiny icon that fits into the palm of her hand, while I try to concentrate on one thought. Peace, I choose. I fight off images of men weighed down by muddy uniforms laden with destruction, marching along roads lined by

Lombardy poplars, straight and endless, on and on. But peace flows only in obvious clichés: doves in a blue sky edged with the glow of sunset, or bright sunshine over fields of ripening wheat, cattle grazing, a church spire in the background and the glimpse of a thatched roof behind bushes laden with ripe blackberries. We stay silent a long instant, then,

'Il faut partir.' I look at my watch regretfully. I want to stay with Ludmilla, but there are other visits to make.

I nervously turn the corner into Madame Magny's street and am observed by the *concierge* in the same grey shawl. Still suspicious, hardly an audible *bonsoir* either. I step out of the lift on the third floor as so often before, hesitating which door to knock on first. Pierre and Colette's might be better, so I won't have to give Madame the excuse that I must leave to see them? Perhaps in her strange vocabulary of emotional responses, she will resent this. Or will it be even worse to leave her saying I have an appointment with Guy for supper and the theatre? This was what I really wanted to do with Madame, but she was singularly reluctant to take me anywhere. The proverbial horns of a dilemma. As I dither and my agitation increases, I hear the lift returning. A moment of panic. It's Colette, laden with provisions. The problem is solved, at least temporarily.

'Valérie. Bienvenue!' My smile is travelling round the edge of my face to end at my earlobes, so pleased and relieved I am to help Colette in with the shopping bags. She looks tired, but continues to talk: could I stay for supper? Some friends are coming, very informal, but it would be so nice to see me. You're out this evening and leaving tomorrow? How sad. So soon. They too are about to leave as Pierre's dealer has prepared a touring exhibition of his work, so she has been asking for loans of works already sold. It will open in London, then New York, then perhaps other cities. They will be travelling to so many openings the world over that it will be

84

hard for him to get any more work done. She sighs. It's all so exciting...

'*Et toi?*' How am I getting on? I reply using the familiar form of address as Colette has just done to me for the first time. I'm not sure whether it's correct from a younger to an older woman, but Colette isn't old. I warm to her and ask how she feels about all the organising she has to do. She shrugs her shoulders.

'*Moi? Qu'est-ce que tu veux? Rien. Il est fameux, quoi. Il faut du temps.*' So that was that. Colette is working full time, even overtime, as her husband's support. A valid choice, if it really is a free choice. My thoughts are distracted by sounds on the spiral staircase. It's Pierre and he want to know what I have been up to. I tell him of the strange experience I had of trying unsuccessfully to find a shrine to Jean d'Arc for a friend of mine who insists there is one in Notre Dame, and then wandering by chance into a small gallery exhibiting a series of oils about her life. Does he know this artist?

'*Bien sûr!*' He adds that Bernard Buffet is the talk of Paris, almost like Françoise Sagan in literary circles, and that he has already sold so many paintings that he is, so the rumour goes, about to buy an island.

Encouraged by my questions, Pierre admits he has had a lucky break in winning an international prize, which has led to the travelling exhibition and more people wanting his art. '*Il faut toujours repenser son oeuvre.*' The danger is to go on giving the market what it wants, and already he is beginning to tire of his paintings.

'*Qu'est-ce qu'on va faire?*' I daren't address him with the familiar '*tu*', but I'm keen to know what he'll do next. The only way out of non-figurative art is surely to return in some way to the familiar world we all share.

'*Et la série de Jeanne d'Arc?*' What about that series of paintings featuring Joan of Arc?

'*Ce n'est pas mon art.*' Bernard Buffet's works aren't his sort of art. Nor mine. In fact I dislike those spiky, fish bone figures. So far we agree, but I'm baffled by his reaction to success, and the temptation to prostitute his art in endless repetition of what will sell. He gets up rather abruptly and moves under the balcony to pull out a panel and place it on a bookcase. It's made of bronze and worked in wood-like textures, grainy with the familiar bars criss-crossing one above the other. It's as if he has reduced a huge canvas to three-quarters its usual size, extracted the colour and poured the glistening black bars into bronze. New material, same thoughts. A friend owns a foundry where Pierre experiments in bronze casting, but now he has to stop because of the exhibition and all the touring involved.

My life too has changed out of all recognition in the short time I've known them. I have been thinking seriously about art after his huge canvases travelled across the landing into my life.

I must return Madame Magny's book. It is getting late and I don't want to keep Guy waiting. A tentative knock on the door opposite, hoping she won't be there. Awkward, but I could leave the book and a polite note with the *concierge*. No such luck! I feel uneasy at the sound of irregular footsteps inside, then a pause. I steady myself leaning on the wall. The door opens the width of a plank, and two large eyes peer at me as if under a microscope.

'*Alors?*' I don't know where to look, what to say.

'I've come to thank you, to return your book, to say farewell...'

'*Je sors ce soir,*' announces Madame Magny, 'I'll see you back at college. *Bon voyage.*' She pushes her hand out for the book and closes the door, not at all put out by my abrupt departure. She is just in a hurry, because she is going out this evening, and expects to see me at the end of the long vacation. What's wrong with that?

So my misgivings are misplaced. As far as I can see, things are as before. Almost. It might be illuminating to discuss the whole question with Guy. By the time we have met and are eating noodles with some tasty concoction tossed over them, I have revised my plan. Confessions or requests for advice might be interpreted as invitations to greater confidentiality. And who knows where that could lead? I do not judge myself experienced enough to experiment further, check my impulse and steer the conversation towards other matters.

'Does Madame Magny really write her articles or books in one of these wooden stalls, open on one side for all to view? Isn't it rather cramped, too intimate?' I wish I hadn't mentioned the last adjective. How convenient it would be if only one could pull words back as if on a string, or better, strangle unwise thoughts at birth. I'm not by nature tactful. He titters.

'*Ça dépend...* She certainly does come with paper, pen and books. I've seen her. I don't know whether she actually writes anything.' He looks behind him. Perhaps it would be more prudent to enquire about his family.

'*Tout va très bien. Les enfants, je veux dire. Ma femme... on ne parle pas beaucoup...*' He doesn't want to say much about his children. Just the usual things, their ages, what they're studying. Of his wife, only that they don't talk much to each other. Coffee comes, and then off we go to nab a good place at the theatre. Someone has given him tickets for a small experimental play, and the seats aren't numbered. Nor are there many of them. We slip into a shop tucked away in a narrow street behind the Sorbonne, its window covered in theatre posters and a box office squeezed in behind it. One side of the former shop has been knocked into the storage area behind creating a narrow stage with three benches on it, nothing else, faced by about twenty rows of similar hard benches for the audience. People are already sitting here and there. Guy places himself carefully at the front and motions me to follow. I hesitate. It's too close to the stage.

'*Tu as peur?*' He seems to taunt me.

'*Mais non!*' I retort. Afraid? I'm somewhat irritated. Even before the lights go out and in full view of the audience drifting in,

Guy, aware of being trendy and wanting others to notice it too, has his arm around my shoulder, his mouth on my cheek and his hand travelling up my thigh. I begin to shake, suppressing laughter. The hand stops its exploration.

'Don't say anything,' I caution myself yet again, knowing that he will be disappointed this time, if that's what he's up to! I'm learning. He won't be allowed to travel far enough up my thigh to know one way or another, I assure myself triumphantly.

Soon there is only standing room at the back. Two members of the rather dowdy, intellectual looking audience amble on to the stage and sit down on the front bench. They begin leaning back and forth and making unintelligible noises. Shushes all round indicate the performance has begun. Five more performers standing at the back join the man and woman on stage to sit on the benches behind them. For what seems to me far too long they all join in the grunts and hisses and movements back and forth, with an occasional break in the regular pattern of movement, or an excursion into a sideways swing. Then come constipated phrases. Short. Repetitive, at least those I can understand. More silence than words, I reckon, and silence embarrasses me. Particularly when sitting in full view of the actors on stage. Drat the front row. Drat coming here at all. I'm not really enjoying it. I twig they're on a train, and that the two in the front row are attempting a conversation along the lines of:

'Who are you? Who are _you_? I am a traveller. So am I. Where do you live? I live in Rouen. Where do you live? I live in Rouen too.' (They sound like phrases from an unimaginative book trying to teach French!) 'Have you lived there long? About twenty years. Have you? About twenty years too. How amazing!' (This interjection from someone travelling behind them; the others are impassive.) After a while audience and actors alike seem mesmerised. The two front row actors stare at the audience, not at each other, so all are drawn into their company, aptly called the _Théâtre de Complicité_.

On the way out I try to catch what people are saying to one another. Not much. The two on the front bench are husband and wife, travelling on the same train like strangers. Obviously there are layers and layers of meaning to be peeled away to reveal the profound philosophical message, but I find it hard to strip my mind down to the first level, let alone the rest. Once on the pavement, Guy slips into his usual pattern. His hands return to their educated places, he kisses me chastely and says he will have to find the things he is taking to the château tomorrow, and do I have all I need? Will I keep in touch and leave the key with the *concierge*? Then he disappears into thin air. Or rather, among the passers-by.

Should he leave a young girl like me alone in a crowd like this? I have stressed that I'm independent, so he is treating me as if I am. People are flowing along 'Boul Mich', chattering, intent on one another. Never does one feel more alone than in the midst of a crowd. Rudderless. Caught in the tides of others. I chant 'I am as I am; what more do you want?' a scrap of poetry that sticks in my mind -

> *Je suis comme je suis,*
> *Je suis faite comme ça,*
> *Que voulez-vous de plus?*
> *Que voulez-vous de moi?*

- and direct it towards the space in the crowd, just to the left of the plane tree where I last saw Guy.

❦

'I don't really understand what people think of me. Pierre and Colette treat me as an equal. So does Ludmilla. But the others seem to fit me into their own agenda. So many adults appear to survive on double lives. Madame Magny talks about her café life in the *Quartier Latin*, but keeps me well out of it. I'm too young, too stupid, too awkward - take your pick, Valerie. Then Guy. Does he come here to sleep or not? I'm not going to put a chair in front of the door or think of anything except of him going off to his *château,* which I imagine built in white stone with slender pinnacles and a wall and rose garden around it, just like the ones illustrated in the Hours of the Duc de Berry. I would like to be the maiden in the rich green brocade dress. It's the month of May and she is about, I think, to give a love token to a departing gallant as he turns to her, before galloping off with the hunt.'

At this full stop I place the pen beside my journal, turn off the light and fall into a dream where the huntsmen, to the sound of a horn, start off from my bedroom across a flowery meadow towards the dark and mysterious woods. One turns to wave. It is Guy.

CHAPTER 8

I try to fix in my mind the images of Paris that speed past, punctuated by telegraph poles and framed into stills by the carriage window, to relish them in reverie. Shots of street stalls like ones near Place Denfert Rochereau with the delicacies to delight Dominique's culinary fantasies seem more exotic in retrospect. In another dream sequence, Père Eugraph begins to chant far behind the iconostasis in his rich chocolaty tones while Maxime the deacon slowly opens the gates and my nostrils dilate at the thought of incense. The Amazons have left the *Bains Turques* still gripping their stigils, but I catch them in a long shot running out of the French Orthodox church amazingly into the 'Boul Mich' where, predictably, I glimpse Guy swivelling round to ogle them.

I feel wobbly and look down. My penchant for *croissants* and *baguette* sandwiches has bestowed a slightly convex stomach, bra marks on my shoulders and distinct uneasiness about my shape. I almost lost the train, cutting out breakfast as an opportune start to my slimming. Consequently I'm ravenous already.

Clickety-click, clickety-click. The others in my compartment seem to be swinging in time. A middle-aged couple are sitting at the far end. They look Spanish. Her shiny black hair is tied back with a bright kerchief which ill-suits her matronly face. The squat, swarthy husband settles down a clear six inches away from her - they might even be the estranged couple in the play I had endured with Guy! Except they don't speak at all, just stare out of the window at my end of the compartment. Next to them a young Frenchman carefully avoids looking directly at me, though I notice in the window reflection that he does whenever I turn away. Near the corridor on my side, a young mother with her beribboned little daughter, both swaying in time with the train, observe the Spanish couple opposite. Not a very promising group, all rather sleepy and secretive.

Perhaps I should try to find out more about the people I meet by chance. This is my adventure, so I must be open-minded if I want to depict them in my book. I'm relieved to be spending some weeks in a Spanish family with people more of my own age. Carmen sounds fun in her letters; she has a brother as well as a fiancé.

The mother is asking me the usual questions. 'Where are you going? Where do you live? What are you doing?' The others are watching me. I surprise myself with a high-pitched, nervous giggle like Guy's, rather nasal and silly. I stifle it hastily, considering the sound unsuited to my emerging adult personality.

A dull sense of anxiety underpins my growing unease. The child can't understand why I giggled, nor the young man opposite. Outside, the suburbs have given way to wheat fields with straggling hedges and copses. As the sun soars towards midday and we speed away from Paris, the bonds of familiarity began to snap. I'm leaving behind in Paris, valued friends and haunts for new adventures, heading southwards into the Mediterranean heat. What is home, I wonder. When one has marked out the perimeters of one's existence within a place, annexed a sort of patch, however briefly, it's easier to face whatever the future has in store for one. I'm uncertain how long I can travel on without somewhere familiar to go back to. It's both daunting and thrilling, breeding tension inside. I lean back and close my eyes to imagine space rushing by as if past the luscious, glistening black bars in the painting Pierre left in Dominique's flat into the pearly colours beyond, the swirl of the unknown. It's a delicious sensation.

'*Mademoiselle?*'

The young man is offering me the end of a *baguette* in one hand, and a hunk of cheese in the other. I smile in acceptance, without even a thought of my resolution to slim. This is an experience, the unknown revealing itself appetisingly here and now.

'*Je rentre pour passer les vacances chez ma famille à Tours.*' Unlike me, he is going home. A stab of anguish as my mind floods with images of Mike running towards me, mother tending the flowers, and father mowing the lawn... I look out of the window at the wheat fields about to be harvested. The slim young man opposite looks cool and composed in his white, open-necked shirt and light grey trousers while I feel exactly the opposite: fat, hot and sticky. I panic and try to disengage from the conversation. He persists.

'D' you like *Le Grand Meaulnes* ?'

'I've only just begun it.' He doesn't miss a thing. It's beside me on the seat as I intend to read it as a diversion from Proust. I must make conversation.

'I'm interested in books about young people. Also ones by authors who didn't produce much else. Just one masterpiece. Rather tragic...' My voice trails off. I can't really express both my fascination with and fear of how one copes with success, and then tries to match it. How does that amazingly young novelist Françoise Sagan grapple with this? It's pathetic for me to have such a preoccupation when I haven't accomplished anything comparable.

I enjoy talking to the young man, in spite of my clammy state. When he leaves at Tours the heat is so intense that blinds are pulled down over the open windows. It's oppressive not to be able to range my mind over the shimmering wheat as the train races south to deposit the mother and daughter in Bordeaux. I've been lurching in and out of a heavy slumber, in time with the swaying train. We can't be far from the frontier with Spain.

I read on about the teenager schoolboy Meaulnes whose feelings and reactions I can absorb as my own. When he finds by chance the fairytale castle, our paths diverge. My adventure hasn't yet given me the magical, transforming experience I yearn for. Perhaps I ought to be truly grown-up and stop balancing on the boundary between youth and adulthood. If I plan my adventure too much, then perhaps I'm programming out the element of chance that might bring me a similar magical experience?

The Spanish couple, widening the insulation gap between each other, share some food, but hardly exchange a syllable. I'm surprised to see them overcome by the heat. They should be more accustomed to it! The plump wife sheds a tear from time to time, more frequently as the Pyrenees appear on her side of the train. 'What's her story?' I wonder, and then snap my book shut. I must read and talk Spanish. We'll soon reach the border. Why not start now? I'm alone with this couple after all, and they look like simple peasants. Their Spanish won't be too complicated for me to understand, unless they speak some sort of dialect. Spain is defined for me by the great epic poem, *El Cid*, and phrases swim into my welcoming mind. The Pyrenees, where Roland sounded the horn to awaken Christendom to the threat of the infidels, race towards us on the far side. All those centuries ago El Cid, the leader, left to fight the holy war, yet it was more painful for him to leave his family than to have a nail pulled out of his finger. I shudder, clenching my hand. Which side, infidels or Christians, practised such barbarous torture, I wonder, feeling the pain of parting as acutely as the Spanish hero.

They are called Enrique and Consuelo, and are just travelling to the Spanish frontier. Consuelo wipes another tear and explains that they will stand on the French side waving to their relatives beyond. She was a girl when her parents fled Spain after Franco defeated the republicans, but the ageing leader, *el generalíssimo*, won't allow them to return, or even see their relatives.

'*Estoy muy triste. No puedo olvidar, muchas muertes, mucha crueldad.*' Sadly, she couldn't forget; many deaths and much cruelty. The cruellest of all wars, a civil one. I was leaving the war zone of World War II, the wider stage of my youthful experience, to enter neutral Spain, still reliving its Civil War twenty years ago. Consuelo's pain would be as acute as El Cid's more than eight centuries ago. Enrique is curious to know where I'm going. To a family in Andalucía. He warns me that Andalucians never talk about anything serious. He sighs.

'Our parents fought for nothing. And here we are, perpetual exiles. We all cling too tightly to the hopes or illusions of our parents. We work in Paris, just get by in French, but think, speak and carry on our lives as if we are in the Spain which rejects us.' He adds defiantly, 'I don't want Franco's Spain. He'll have to die soon, or even better, be assassinated!'

I'm enthralled. Again I've misjudged appearances. No peasants these, but children of the revolution. I sit bolt upright, excited at the prospect of understanding a strange country ruled by a dictator. I hadn't thought of Spain in these terms. We embraced as the train reached the frontier station.

'*Adiós y buena suerte!*'

The yellow dust-speckled rays of the setting sun make the customs shed seem drearier. Rows of trestle tables separate customs officials in tired sweaty uniforms from passengers and their luggage. I heave mine up and wait, looking around and wondering where Consuelo and Enrique have gone to wave to their relatives and shed more tears of exile, despairing there will ever be any change. Sensing some unusual presence, I turn back to the concentrated gaze of five customs officers, one pointing his gun uncertainly in my direction. The other travellers have either gone their various ways, or been cleared out of the shed. I am alone.

'*Qué cosa tiene usted dentro?*' They point to the case. What's inside it? I'm bewildered. I tell them: clothes, a few books, papers.

'*Apri, por favor, con velocidad!*' What are they fussing about? Oddly, as I click open the catch that still holds and untie the strap I bought in Paris, they all step warily back.

'Take the contents out one by one.' I look pretty innocent, hardly the type to indulge in drug smuggling or whatever. In any case, why me? They don't have any sniffer dogs, or any reason to suspect me more than anyone else. Or is it that they have seen me with the marked couple, Consuelo and Enrique? Horror of horrors, have the couple planted something on me? But they hadn't been anywhere near my case - it has lain untouched on the rack for the whole journey. The air tightens around me. I untie the string to pull out my rather worn but clean underwear, which has never bothered me before, with the rest of my clothes, shoes, sponge bag and presents until the bottom comes into view and I pick out the Proust volume with one hand, my alarm clock with the other, tipping the empty case on its side for the suspicious officers to see. One edges over to the table, gingerly holds up the alarm clock and puts it to his ear. His slow smile is shattered by the alarm shrilling into his ear. He yells, drops the clock. The armed *guardia civil* drops his gun, the bullet ricocheting across the wooden floor leaving a jagged furrow. You could slice the silence. Then he grins and nudges his neighbour who bursts into loud guffaws of relief, followed by the others. They crowd round me as I try to control a slight tendency to tremble after the gunshot as well as shame at the state of my underwear which they appeared to be contemplating with ever-increasing hilarity. I can't understand a word. They are all waving their arms and speaking at the same time. I want to get out. Back go my clothes, books, papers, in any order, just to escape the pandemonium and find the train for Madrid and some calm.

The sky is speckled with stars. A train stands by a low platform with Madrid written on a wooden plank. I clamber in, fleeing the shouts that seem to be pursuing me accompanied by heavy footsteps.

'*Señorita! Señorita! Ha olvidado...*' A hand comes in the window with my alarm clock, battered but still ticking.

The other travellers are already settled into the compartments, commandeering as much space for the night as they can without being challenged. I bump my luggage along the corridors of two carriages until I find a compartment with a couple and a small child. Safer than most of the others inhabited predominantly by males. Women here don't travel alone, and those that do are invariably with their family, and that means children. Not a calm or comfortable night, but an unthreatening one.

The dismal light is turned off after the polite exchange of greetings and the settling down rituals of all tired travellers. I sleep a bit, swinging to the rhythm of the train as it lurches across the prairies of northern Spain, careering into the future faster than I can bear. Over the dark Ebro, then, after a long stop at Burgos, the train charges relentlessly forward, snorting steam and smoke into its wake. Sunlight awakens me. Hot and sticky, I've arrived in Madrid.

I flop on to the nearest platform seat and rehearse the phrases I'll need. Spanish words stick in my memory like isolated blobs. I try in vain to mould them into cohesive sentences, but slip automatically into French. Elbows on knees, head on hands, I attempt to conjure up some mental and physical energy. It's only eight o'clock and already too clammy. Now Valerie, calm down and solve one problem at a time. First, find the youth hostel. *Donde está el Albergue Juvenil, por favor?*

'*Bastante lejos, señorita.*' I look up, startled. I hadn't meant to practise aloud. This small, swarthy thirtyish man with a red check shirt and twinkling eyes has heard me ask where the youth hostel is. He says it's some distance off. My head droops at the prospect of struggling there in this bathhouse atmosphere. He presses his advantage.

'*Hay una posada aquí a mano. Vamos?*' He reaches for my suitcase, making me jump to my feet, perplexed. He is suggesting a nearby lodging house, but I'm worried about the price. Youth hostels are more predictable. '*Muy poco,*' he assures me, and I capitulate, exhausted.

The *posada* in a nondescript three-storey building is indeed close by. The entrance hall is dark even on a bright Mediterranean day, but the frosted leaf pattern on the windows and the ubiquitous crimson upholstery are not without charm. I thank the swarthy man, give him a tip from my small stock of pesetas, check the cost, reasonable, and approve of the basin in the second floor room I am offered. Alone in it, I try to wash my face in the trickle of brown water which is at least a degree cooler than my skin temperature, lie down on the blue and white striped coverlet, and wonder what to do next.

My plan was to stay with Carmen from mid July. We have built up a rapport in our letters, with me learning to write more idiomatic and less literary Spanish and she postponing her attempts to write in English. When Carmen explained that she had to delay my visit until after the weekend because of visiting relatives, I determined to explore Madrid, Córdoba, Seville and Granada in these unexpected days of freedom. Toledo can be visited in a day from Madrid. El Escorial too, the palace built by Mary Tudor's husband, Philip II. I had read in my guidebook that it was really a monastery dedicated to Saint Lawrence who had been martyred on a grid iron, yet another gruesome execution. As I lie on the bed trying not to fall asleep, this energetic programme seems less appealing.

After nearly an hour of sleepy indecision, I unlock the bedroom door to find the bathroom. An indicative smell leads me to a hole in the ground with two shoeprints in enamel, rather obviously suggesting the required foot position and, under a grubby basin, small newspaper squares next to a bin. I'm less enthusiastic than ever, but remind myself that the room is cheap and I do want to explore Madrid.

The swarthy man in the red check shirt is waiting for me outside. I'm too tired to remonstrate, and set off to find a free tourist map in the station information kiosk. He is following, but I don't care. I have tipped him, and anyway, he is probably returning to his patch. A quick study of the map gives me a good enough grasp of central Madrid; I decide to make for the Puerta del Sol and the heart of the old city. Reviewing my plan for the day, I check I have brought enough pesetas from England, and stride out, feeling better with a clear aim in mind.

Finding a bench in the shade near the Puerta del Sol, I scan the square. Oh heck, there is the same man, and others dotted around with all the time in the world. I'm the focal point of those brown eyes. Bending my head to avoid looking at any of them by chance, I fix on my rather grubby sandals and feet. A nervous twinge in my stomach must be the physical pang of loneliness. I yearn for a fresh Surrey summer's day, my mother's salads and for Mike. I might not have thought enough about him recently, but he's here, sauntering reassuringly into my thoughts. I grasp the edge of the bench as if it were his arm, recalling our conversations and how reliable he is, with his unruly shock of hair always flopping over his left eye in an irritating way. Here I am on this sunny morning in the centre of Madrid, a day full of promise ahead, but the eyes of those men are crawling all over me, inhibiting my movements. A tear of frustration spills over my lower lid, then another and another until I see the ogling men, staring beggars, striped canopies over the cafés, lampposts and all the square's panoply though a quivering curtain. I am alone on an uncertain quest, far from home and friends, pining.

'Stop feeling sorry for yourself!' I say out loud. I'm going to stride across the square in the direction of the Prado, determined to do something positive. The best refuge from indecision is a museum. I've heard Van Gogh's self-portrait is hanging there, and feel sympathy for his anguished self-doubt. Trying out my best Spanish on an attendant, he frowns and mutters something about not understanding me. Is my Spanish that bad? Never mind. I'll wander through the rooms on my own, airless though they are, and stop where my eyes lead me. Predictably to Velasquez's *Las Meninas*, the courtly world of intriguing secrets. The more you look, the more you see. It's uncanny. Here I am standing where the king and queen, reflected in the mirror at the far end of the room in the painting, once paused. They were admiring their daughter in her crinkly, beribboned dress. You can imagine it rustling stiffly and richly as the child fidgets or pirouettes. A painting strangely distant, uncannily close. There's a bench in front of it, inviting contemplation. My eyes wander over to a group of men in white shirts arranged diagonally on the dark ground of a vast painting. It is hung so low that as I approach I shudder to find I am looking from behind a row of executioners at their victims. No seat here; you stand frozen in horror. Goya's *Tres de Mayo*. More atrocities, past, present, and what about the future? My eyes fill with tears, for lost causes, for man's inhumanity to man. And woman.

Refreshed, I move on to the roomfuls of Titians, then down to the basement in search of Van Gogh. I am nothing if not determined and thorough, when it suits me. Here's an unexpected sighting of Mary Tudor in a picture familiar from history books, all stiff and stern in neatly starched ruffles. There's a strange portrait of a furtive man beside a huge sunflower which steals the picture from him. Van Dyck's self-portrait. I must have confused the two 'vans'. How stupid.

I ought to leave while the shops are still open, if they keep the same hours as in France. A bread roll, some cheese and a slice of melon later, I am sitting on a bench in the Retiro park near the Prado and feel those male eyes on me again. Better not to focus on anything but the map. I shall spend the afternoon looking at the Plaza Mayor and the area round the royal palace before returning to the tourist office. I have one day to go to El Escorial and Toledo. Then I shall leave for the south.

All afternoon I walk not sure of what I am doing. Dust browns my feet and etches the creases in my skin. It sinks into the unironed crumples in my dress fresh that morning. Relentless sweat in league with abundant dust progressively dispirit me as the shadows elongate and I trudge along the chosen streets on my map. Back at the station, the tourist information office is about to close.

I'm informed gruffly that there's no way I can go to Toledo and El Escorial on the same day. Too far, and in different directions. The elderly man in the kiosk slams the metal grid down between us. I am on my own again.

The shops are closing, so I buy more bread, ham and cheese, though my mother counsels at least one cooked meal a day. Even if I had been able to afford it, a full meal would be difficult to swallow. I don't know if I'm hungry.

I'd feel better after a wash. No bath. So I use the basin in my room until the tap runs dry leaving my legs soaped and unrinsed. Frustrated yet again, I lie on my bed to consider the options. My journal? A letter to Mike? Both are good ways of using up an unexpected empty evening. I'd prefer to go out, find a tap or fountain to wash off the soap, and then sit in a café, or wander along the streets looking at people, buildings, shops, but dread having to deal with errant males. Spanish girls always go around in packs, never fewer than three or four, before lunch or for the evening *paseo*. By nine in the evening they are safely penned in at home.

Falling asleep instead of going out, I wake near midnight on a bed that shudders, wincing each time the cab doors clang shut. Beams, as if from a lighthouse, sweep across my room through the thin curtains as coaches rev out of the garage directly opposite my window. After each departure, furry-dark silence returns and I fall asleep to reawaken at each repeat performance. The stench of oil and petrol sizzling on the hot engines of the leviathans seeps through my window. I try closing it to ward off smell and sound, only to suffer claustrophobia as if imprisoned in a sauna.

Dawn comes with a trickle of birdsong, soon dispelled by the rising sun and temperature. Would it have been wiser to turn northwards in the month of July? It's too late now. Just after dawn is the coolest time of the day, and my head is already throbbing. All Madrid awaits me, the Escorial, or Toledo, were I to make the slightest effort in either direction. No, I couldn't stay another day by these juddering monsters. I'll pay and leave.

I could have stepped into a coach for Toledo or the Escorial that morning, right below my room. Nothing easier. Tickets on the coach, and away. Instead I worry my way to the station behind the coach depot, change my last francs into pesetas and get my student ticket for the next train to Córdoba. *Vamos!* Going south at last.

My train leaves in half an hour so I've time to choose a compartment without the children that seem to frolic around every Spanish couple, and without young men. Even not so young ones. All might be equally lecherous. I choose a half-empty one with a middle-aged couple and teenage daughter. Things are looking up, more by chance than design.

Ten minutes before we are due to leave, peals of laughter, and a young woman pirouettes into the compartment. She makes a bee-line for the open window treading on toes and casually leaving disquiet in her wake.

'*Adiós! Adiós...*' followed by a torrent of endearments in Spanish in an accent that sounds foreign to me. I'm intrigued by my contemporary in her bright yellow seersucker dress. She's blowing kisses out of the window at a stereotypically handsome Spaniard of thirty something gazing adoringly up at her. Just like a Hollywood star bidding a romantic farewell to Cary Grant or Burt Lancaster, she's balancing excitedly on one foot with the other elegant heel stabbing backwards as if in flight. I'm enthralled.

CHAPTER 9

'*Cómo te llamas?*' The yellow seersucker girl plops down in front of me, opens a bag of sticky sweets and, offering me one, asks my name. The Spanish family is looking on, intrigued. Probably because, so I've heard, no Spanish woman can travel alone until married, and then only with her husband's permission. Their teenage daughter may be scrutinising us more out of envy than curiosity. Smiling back at the newcomer's green slanted eyes, slightly snub nose, red cheeks and curly fair hair, I introduce myself and return the question.

'I'm Renate Hausen. From Hamburg and here to learn Spanish.' She giggles. 'I've a Spanish boy friend!' As if that isn't obvious, I think with just a twinge of resentment. Turning to the window on my side of the compartment I try to find the emotional space to picture Mike adequately, but Renate is chirruping away.

'Carlos had to go and see his family. He wanted me there too, but I have things to do and see in Spain. And Spanish families, you know, are very clinging.' Renate's mother was widowed in the war. Strange that she seems so at ease with me. I'm almost too embarrassed to say I'm English, so from the different, victorious side in the war. I had planned to sidestep this tangle of emotions by avoiding Germany. Renate appears oblivious. I know no German, Renate evidently no English. As I'm uncomfortable speaking imperfect Spanish to another foreigner in front of Spaniards, I try French.

'What luck!' trills Renate, whose French is better than her Spanish and usefully we won't be understood, 'you're going to Córdoba. So am I. Let's travel together!' I set out deliberately to brave the seas on my own, a lone adventurer, albeit mainly on land, but Renate seems interesting and, above all, fun. She smiles, opening her dark red lips to frame gleaming teeth. Those green-slanted eyes, those short ash blond curls... I'm feeling self-conscious about my own straight brown hair almost touching my shoulders.

'We'll reach Córdoba this afternoon, and I know there's a convent that takes in young women like us for less than a youth hostel. Anyway, hostels are usually a long way out, and we don't want to waste time...' Renate seems to have everything sorted out in what I assume is a very Germanic fashion. Perhaps too precise. It might cut out the thrilling possibility of a chance encounter, but I'll go along with it. For now.

South we speed almost free-wheeling over a burnt landscape of harvested plains towards the Sierra Morena, and beyond it, to the great river of Guadalquivir linking Córdoba to Seville and both with the Atlantic. Galleons laden with silver for Ferdinand and Isabella sailed up the Guadalquivir after the discovery of the New World in the late 1400s. I sway into Renate's life story told in rhythm with the train. Another variation on travellers in the play Guy took me to see. I must write Renate's experiences into my journal. Her father was reported missing on the Russian front. Her mother is still waiting for his return. Renate can't bear it all and had to get away, telling her mother she is travelling to learn languages. She really wants to find a boyfriend. There aren't many males in Germany, and the boys her own age, too young to be in the war, are so immature. She prefers older, more experienced men. For no identifiable reason I feel inadequate, yet relieved that Renate doesn't seem too interested in what I'm doing. She assumes I come from London, the amorphous metropolis foreigners imagine sprawling all over England, even after I repeat, 'Surrey, to the south of London'. Let it pass.

It's late afternoon when we reach Córdoba. Within the hour we have checked into the convent, and are out again pausing on the long bridge over the wide river.

The Guadalquivir has dried back, shrinking in the summer heat from its worn banks. Rays from the setting sun hit the river in golden elongated forms. Children are playing around a herd of cattle dallying in the shallows. As the sun succumbs to the greying haze, the sky above fades from green and gold into red under a darkening blue. The boys' shrill voices quicken the twilight, while from the squat whitewashed houses near the banks comes an occasional deep-throated shout. Evening is settling into supper time.

Renate's sturdy figure is bouncing off again.

'Where are you going now?' No reply. I watch her disappearing: short, determined, with firm gait and a decisive, swaying bottom. I lean back over the parapet gazing down the river where the changing light patterns dull into pinks and greys, trying to forget how hungry I am.

'Are you cross?' Renate is back, a cheeky smile on her face, both charming and disarming with two dimples in glowing cheeks. 'Let's find something to eat.'

Streetwise Renate noses out the main thoroughfare where Córdoba *señoritas* are parading arm-in-arm to encounter sporadic knots of youths, arms over shoulders, linked by their raucous camaraderie. We attract no more than a stray glance, the young men wary of being lured away from their stratagems with local girls into dangerous waters, but still tempted by the exotic and, they think, available foreign ones. Not so the married males who proclaim their uninhibited appreciation from pavement cafés, whistling and calling out *piropos* at us. This is so new that I unwisely stare back astonished, provoking even greater outbursts of, '*Muy guapa! Aquí! Te quiero mucho, muchísimo...*' Pretty, beautiful one, I love you... followed by a re-run of the same with variations on *guapa* and *hermosa*. Renate ignores it all. She has perfected a way of striding ahead, swinging her hips but never ever deigning to glance in their direction. Admirable, but when I try wiggling my own bottom it doesn't seem to work. It's too small, and too high above my legs.

All ruminations are cut short by Renate. She summons me to a kiosk where a woman is frying crisp yellow fritter fingers.

'Voilà! Churros, muy saporitos,' she explains in our new linguistic cocktail, a sign of increasing familiarity. The fried *calamares* that Renate finds next remind me of fish and chips, being rubbery squids fried again in batter. Delicious precursors of heartburn.

Whilst I'm consuming the sugary *churros* from my brown paper funnel, Renate unexpectedly makes a bee-line for the most handsome of the *piropo* men in the pavement café. She's laughing, crunching the *calamares* between her white teeth and open red lips and tossing her curls with 'come hither' spun into them. 'You asked for it,' she's laughing at them, 'and now you have it...!' A wave of consternation sweeps round the café tables. Bystanders turned enthralled spectators include tittering girls arm in arm, who swing round to survey Renate and the men at the tables. Groups of youths bob around in the shadows, eyes luminous in anticipation. Renate seems in her element. Safety in numbers? Safety from what? The café clients are confident when chucking seated compliments, but dumbfounded by the foreign girl's up-front response. Those at the back ease themselves up stealthily and slink off home. Those in the front, caught in the full beam of Renate's taunting glance, shuffle uneasily. Not a word now. Eyes concentrate on the bright yellow dress to avoid the challenge in her wide smile, the open red lips, white regular teeth and green slanting eyes. With immaculate timing, she rolls the brown paper containers for the *churros* and *calamares* into tight little balls and tosses them at the nearest bewildered man.

'Allons-y!' she looks round for me, 'we'd better hurry - the convent closes at nine'. Renate holds her hand out to me, ignored by the spectators until then, and her small yellow seersucker bag dangles in my face as she sweeps me away with a grandiloquent film star gesture. Our exit delivers the street from its stunned silence; people slowly begin to whisper, chatter, complain and protest at this unexpected flaunting of age-old customs.

Renate is laughing as we flee from the commotion she has provoked along a dusty unpaved alley to the convent. Everything here is basic: white walls, wood pale blue in the rooms, dark brown in the corridors and chapel crammed with statues of saints, all painted and all male, except for the Virgin Mary, in contrast to the uncluttered cloister, frugal refectory and Spartan dormitory. Ours is where the novices used to sleep, when there were enough of them. Now the curtained cubicles are let out to women in need of a bed for whatever reason. The Carmelite nuns seem kind and unassuming, though the authoritarian Mother Superior is glimpsed in the background, at the end of a corridor or at high table in the refectory, surveying us and insisting on prayers and early bedtime. It's strange that Renate can take to such an environment. I watch fascinated as the German girl loosens the drawstrings of her little yellow seersucker bag. It's unbelievable what she has managed to tuck inside: toothbrush and paste, a tiny child's hairbrush, hankie, small mirror, lipstick, purse and passport. That's it. Renate isn't bothering with the curtains; she just takes off the belt of her sleeveless dress so it hangs like a tent over her arms and shoulders while she slithers bra and knickers down to her ankles. Gathering them up with the soap and towel provided by the nuns, she pads along to the communal bathroom to launder them in a basin together with her one and only handkerchief. Then she washes her body under her dress, brushes her teeth with an energy and relish that fascinates the other three girls in the half-empty washroom and wrings out the wet garments in her towel, drying them over the curtain rails round her bed.

'Are they novices, d'you think?' I whisper to Renate when we're both lying on our beds, wishing the night would pass quickly in anticipation of all the next day would bring.

'Don't know.' She doesn't seem at all interested, turns her back and goes silent.

The three unshaded bulbs strung along the centre of the dormitory emit a dispiriting light. The other girls have settled in at the far end with lots of whispering, their long unfrilled cotton night-dresses thoroughly covering them down to ankles, out to wrists and up to throat on this interminable airless night. Renate has shed her dress and quickly slipped under the sheet, naked. Well, there is hardly room for a nightie in that tiny bag.

I've guiltily completed the card to Mike begun in the train and just finished the first sentence in my journal when a sister comes in and, with 'buena noche', switches the lights out. That is that!

This morning another sister roused us with a morning prayer soon after six. I don't wake easily, but Renate was already sitting naked on the side of her bed, the sheet loosely round her, with her head bent deep in prayerful thought. After the sister left, she surged towards the washroom with the sheet billowing out behind her like a voluminous gown. I followed, fascinated. There are no bath tubs, so perhaps one is supposed to wash oneself in these basins. I found Renate, with two of the narrow ends of the light cotton sheet knotted round her neck and the rest in a half circle around her, washing herself in relative decency.

After prayers at the refectory table, we all sit while nuns - or are they the novices? – serve us in silence with crusty rolls, milk, jam or honey and a choice of fruit. Simple but wholesome fare, I think sleepily. Renate instead is fully alert and planning ahead.

'First to the cathedral, a former mosque, as that's the most important thing to see here. Then we'll buy something to eat and I'll take you on an expedition. There's a corrida de toros this evening and we should get tickets. Have you enough money?'

I'm mildly irritated. Renate is planning everything, assuming that I'm only here to be propelled around by her. She hasn't even bothered to find out my views on bull fights, and already expects me to go to one! Some cheek, so why don't I protest? We set off soon after eight, the light already laden with dust churned up by donkeys plodding produce to street markets. It's already too hot to be bothered, and anyway, I'm not sure what to complain about. I am, after all, out for adventures, and so is Renate, I imagine.

Women are begging outside the convent and near the entrance to the former mosque. I'm uneasy about giving them so little, but I prefer to spread the small amount I can afford so that everyone gets a bit. Renate fixes her glance straight ahead so she doesn't focus on anything at street level. Today the seersucker dress is unbelted, swinging jauntily from her shoulders, dust setting its dimpled texture into relief.

Inside the *Mezquita* it is cool. Endless arches echo in every direction. No nave, no long vista, only innumerable columns and arches creating the most fantastic architectural forest I have ever seen. It becomes the visual equivalent of chanting, of prayers and ceremonies. I half expect carpets and kneeling figures intoning ancient rituals and bending their foreheads to the ground. Instead there are some black-robed widows gathered round small altars The high altar is placed arbitrarily at one end of the middle section, where it doesn't feel right. The building, proclaiming itself architecturally Muslim, though tamed for centuries into Christian worship, portrays a more lasting victory than any of the Crusades ever were. The endless rows of columns create different prospects viewed straight on, or splayed out at an angle. I want to stay all morning, but Renate nudges me outside into the sun and the street markets. A sacristan has told her to cover her bare arms, insisting even while she gazes at him smiling and shakes her head to show she doesn't understand.

'We need to get food for lunch,' she whispers.

Here we are sitting on a bench in the shade in the main square eating cheese, rolls and fruit, with a couple of male beggars eying us. Chance travelling companions, yet I know next to nothing about Renate.

'What did you do during the war?' No reaction. 'It must have been hard. Where were you?'

Renate stares at me.

'In Hamburg. You know what happened there, who did the bombing. And anyway, I told you that my father never came back from the Russian front. I prefer not to think about it all. What's the point? What has happened has happened.' She puts a hand through her light curls and bites into the bread. Hamburg. My knowledge of the war is patchy. It wasn't that my parents were trying to hide things from me, but they tended not to explain them either. I was too young to be told more than they feared a German invasion. Britain had been bombed, so it must be right to bomb the enemy. The idea was to end it all as soon as possible and to build a better world without the Hitlers, Mussolinis, and - what about Franco? Another of the band of dictators still with us here and now. Nothing is ever tidy in human affairs.

'You probably don't know,' Renate's voice is tense as she breaks the silence, 'that there are hardly any men left in Germany for us young women. I just want to have fun and forget. Forget,' she repeats as a way of cutting off this conversation.

She has already spotted a kiosk selling tickets for the *Corrida hoy*, today, in the late afternoon. I know the gladiatorial fights in the Coliseum all took place when the shadows were lengthening, the heat waning and there were more seats in the shade. What does Renate propose to do between now and the bullfight? There seems to be some plan afoot.

There is indeed. A long walk in the heat of the day, and I haven't a hat. Nor has Renate, but she doesn't care. Hopping from one patch of shade to another, if it can be found, I traipse behind her. Across the Guadalquivir bridge again. No cattle in the water which seems to have shrunk back even more. Along a road flanked by eucalyptus trees that crosses fields grazed into dust by the herds, huddled close to the fence in the only shade they can find. And that is precious little, as I painfully discover. Renate stops in front of a door in a high stone wall, and rings a bell.

'It's almost two. Won't the people be eating, or sleeping?' Renate looks at me as if thinking, 'This English girl is pretty inexperienced'.

'Don't you know in Spain they eat after two, and again late in the evening, after the *corrida*? Don't worry. I'll arrange things...' To suit you, I'm thinking crossly, wondering what we are doing by this wall.

The door opens and an elderly woman in black shows us in past vases of sad flowers. Renate is buying a bunch of wilting marigolds that clash with the yellow of her dress.

It is a neat cemetery, cross after cross with little variation. I'm even more irritated at the pointlessness of the long hot walk to the outskirts of town just for a cemetery. Renate strides off in the direction indicated by the elderly woman, without swinging her hips. What shall I do? Partly I'm curious, but I also want to stay in the strip of shade offered by the cemetery wall. Curiosity prevails and I follow in Renate's wake, to find her kneeling in tears by an elaborate tombstone.

'Manolete was my hero...'she's sobbing, 'killed in a *corrida*...' She uses the Spanish term. In English 'bullfight' sounds less romantic. Standing a while behind the shaking seersucker shoulders, I look with increasing horror at the sweat coursing down Renate's face and at the greenish stains under her armpits. She fills the metal container by the tomb from a cemetery watering can. When we leave, the marigolds already look less dejected after their long warm drink.

Leaning against the cemetery wall, Renate uses the last of the water to clean her tear-streaked face before returning the cemetery watering can. Out of her little yellow bag come a mirror and dark red lipstick applied with precise care. Nothing offered to me, no sharing in Renate's organised universe.

A car toots at us on our walk back to Córdoba. Renate's hip swagger has returned to good effect and the result is a lift into town. No hesitation on her part. She assumes I'll take the back seat. Well, anything is preferable to that long trudge, and it is still too early in the afternoon to cool off. Renate is sitting beside a young man with a thick wedding ring who is evidently interested in this foreign girl. They share a passion for Manolete, it seems. The car appears to be taking a long route to the city, but I'm not sure and don't want to show my instinctive distrust.

'He wants to take us to an attractive wood where it'll be less hot,' Renate leans back to explain. 'We've plenty of time before the *corrida*, and anyway, he's going too, so we'll all be there on time.' Whose agenda are we following? I turn this thought over and over in my mind as I wait in the car, the door open, while Renate and the young man go for a walk in the wood. I have no desire to join them, thankful for a moment to write up my journal.

I must be missing Mike as I keep thinking about him. So much is happening even though I'm in a pretty passive situation, trotting around after Renate. Perhaps a fly-on-the-wall sees more, thinks more... I'm worried about going to the bullfight because I strongly disapprove. But the *aficionados* would say I can't criticise without experiencing it. So here I am about to enter Hemingway territory.

It's far too hot to stay in the car, even though they've been in the wood for what seems a long time. I'll sit on the ground and lean against a eucalyptus tree.

I admire Renate. She also irritates me a lot. She is much more worldly-wise, and so I'm a bit in awe, though I wouldn't admit it to Mike. She's out to get the best from life for herself and only seems to relate to me - or to this Spaniard - if it's in her own interest. Is this a cynical approach to life, I wonder? If so, she's young to be cynical, except... but she had a terrible time in the war, and she's trying to cope...

It is so hot I'm falling asleep. I tuck the bag with my valuables under my head and watch the sunlight dappling the leaves above... to wake hearing Renate laughing loudly, the young Spaniard's arm round her waist.

'Hurry, Valerie! *Vas-y!* We'll all be late for the *corrida.'* The afternoon has vanished without accomplishing anything much.

Lengthening shadows now promise respite from the remorseless heat, though our cheap seats face west with the rays of the late afternoon sun stabbing our eyes. Renate appears elated. We're only four rows back. Ideal vantage point. We'll miss nothing. She bobs up and down, restlessly trying to spot where José Maria, her new Spanish friend, can be. I try to repress my apprehension, or prejudice as Renate had called it, amazed there are so many families with small children. Here girls and young women are dressed to kill, Spanish style. It is their festive outing after all! I have never seen such massive tortoiseshell combs, perched high to secure *mantillas* embroidered with a scatter of flowers on a dark ground that cascade over their long black hair. Coral and mother-of-pearl necklaces and earrings are on display, and also, here and there, intricate gold and black inlay jewellery from Toledo. Lighter, musky perfumes mingle with tobacco smoke, the men gesticulating assertively at one another, cigarette in hand, while the women giggle and peep round their fluttering fans. A good idea, just what I need. The sun is setting in a ball of fire; there is such expectation in the air it's hard to breathe. Not even the light caress of a breeze.

A hiccupping brass fanfare announces the event. The musicians stroll into the middle of the arena, while some *banderilleros* enter still wriggling into their breeches and tugging at their red tunics. Their bravado is boosted at each step they take round the edge of the arena brandishing dart-like weapons at the spectators, who yell their approval even before the bull arrives. Renate leaps up and down, waving her arms, predictably catching the eye of all but two of the *banderilleros*. This is only the *hors d'oeuvre!* Twice round the stadium, then in comes the first bull, creases of foam encircling its neck - it must already have been prodded angry in its stall. It snorts, swinging its head. The crowd boos. Not a proud bull, a coward. Boo, boo! The *banderilleros* gather round, dancing from one foot to the other, shouting and waving their weapons. The first darts fly out, stabbing the bull's neck to roars of approval. Others follow. A few men in the highest circle of seats stand shouting to urge them on. Still the bull won't react. It pauses head down, snorting and tossing, darts bristling behind its ears. More and more thrown. Still it doesn't move.

Then the first trickle, curling red below its left ear and slithering slowly down under its neck. Shouts, more stabs and, head raised, the first full bellow. The spectators to a man - and one woman, Renate - leap up, jeering the *banderilleros* to aim even more darts. I hope they'll have none left to add to the quill necklace round the creature's neck. More trickles of blood, and the bull charges at last. The crowd roars. The cowardly creature! Down falls the nearest *banderillero*, a tear in his red tunic masking blood. Louder the cries of *olé!* More and more clamour from the impatient crowd. I let out a half suffocated cheer for the bull now impaling another *banderillero*. The creature stumbles towards us, neck bristling like a porcupine. Renate leaps up to yell in quivering delight, men gathering around her, while the women remain seated in pleasure-flecked fluster behind their trembling fans. The unscathed *banderilleros*, each one more handsome than the other I admit in some disgust, make for the bull who is gazing mournfully, tongue out, head swinging, towards Renate. The *bandilleros* are now more cautious. The bull has mauled two of their company; he has scented blood.

Another brass fanfare, and a resplendent figure runs into the centre of the arena to a shower of applause and more shouts of *olé!* The hero has arrived. No, it can't be true? It's José Maria, the very man who gave us a lift! This is too much of a coincidence for me. I lean back, sickened and alienated.

The *toreador* pauses, arms raised as he swings 360 degrees to command his orbit. His stage or the bull's? The precise spot must be marked in some magical way like the orator's stone in Greek theatres. The bull is still snorting, pawing the sand in front of the entranced Renate, while a *banderillero* tries to prod the animal centre stage towards the pirouetting *toreador,* busy swirling his cloak over one shoulder, then the other, and then back to gyrate round in a crimson haze. The spectators draw in a collective breath like a small tornado imprisoned in the stillness of the fading light. José Maria's tight costume shimmers gold and brownish red, the colour of blood, ominously outlining his figure. His flirtation with death fails to enthuse me. Passions roused, Renate is wildly waving her arms, though unable to attract a single glance from the *toreador* who struts, circles and surges in waves of cloak, waiting irritated for the bull.

To turn the animal to face its destiny, the *banderillero* nearest to us aims behind the ear, misses and skewers a large luminous milky brown eye. Totally nauseated, I turn away and rise to my feet. I can dimly hear Renate calling me 'coward, *cobarde*' as she moves forward with men around her to the ring edge, shouting, arms raised as if bewitched, an incantation to the imminent sacrifice. *Ánima! Ánima!* On, on, and the maddened bull, blood spouting from one eye, sweat foaming over its neck and behind its ears, froth speckled with blood, it thunders at last towards the golden idol, José Maria. *Vamos! Vamos!* The stadium shudders at the sound of its hoofs, stirred by the roars of bull and spectators alike, all spiced by screams of female delight as the *toreador* flings out his red cloak, then swirls it over his head to descend it in line with the bull's charge, hollowing his chest and stomach as it passes. He sinuously turns, whirls his cloak and leaps over it while the enraged animal pauses, raises its bleeding head, and then charges again. *Bravo! Bravo!*

The crowd ecstatic. Another pirouette, swirl of the red cloak, indrawing of breath until, his midriff curled back into a crescent moon, the bull hurtles through it, the *toreador's* heart above, phallic mound below, knees almost brushing the sand.

The bull turns to charge at Renate and the men at the ringside. Elated, young women behind her are losing their head combs as they elbow their way forward blowing kisses to their hero. Venus is sailing into view, though the sun hasn't fully set and there are other bulls to come. This one is toughening up and, pricked back to centre stage by the persistent *banderilleros*, its shoulders rise into a barbed mound. Head down, bellowing, it hurtles towards the resplendent *toreador*, not at his cloak but the gold costume to ram its right horn into José Maria's thigh, pitching him over its neck onto the pincushion of bristling *banderillas*.

'*Bravo! Bravo!*' Standing I yell and clap and even add, '*Bravo, toro hermoso!*' Handsome bull!

The men at the ring edge are turning, eyes and mouths wide, to scorn me. '*Fuera! Fuera!*' Out! Out! they chant, some raising their fists. Others behind, '*Cobarde!*' Coward, this time me, not the bull! The women near me scream in crescendo, on and on, some peering at me from behind their agitated fans, or weeping into their *mantillas*. Drat them, I think, cowards all to torture an animal like that, and I yell the bull on as it turns in its tracks to charge José Maria now limping towards the exit.

Still yelling the animal on, blind with anger, I feel hands on my arm, another over my mouth. I'll bite them, astonished and furious that anyone could do this to me. It's a free country, and...

'*Fuera, señorita...*' Two *guardias civiles* frog-march me out to stand against a wall of the arena by a clutch of curious beggars, and fire a barrage of unintelligible insults at me. Something about disturbing the peace. What peace? Whose?

I'm slumped in a heap against the wall, too angrily exhausted to care where I am. Gaunt faces, young and old, are scanning me closely. Outcasts, the beggars look strangely beautiful, even peaceful in this gentle evening light; their features are sharply etched, the white setting off the brown of their eyes. Slender aquiline noses ennoble them even amid sunken cheeks with dusty wrinkles and lines. Their grubby children have the widest smiles I can remember.

'Where do you come from? What do you do? Why are you here?' Their questions prod me like the darts of the *banderilleros*, but in a friendly way. There must be nearly ten around me now. What are they expecting? Do they really want to hear about my life? They wait, so I start off like a travelling storyteller.

'Nineteen years ago I was born in a distant island, right at the top end of Europe, above France...' I wonder whether they have ever seen a map, or how it would make sense to them. They are surely illiterate. My story in hesitant Spanish is punctuated by yells, roars, moans of frustration or despair or wave after wave of applause from the arena behind. My audience ignores it all.

I finish, and then '*E vosotros?*' They smile and tell me they're not gypsies but itinerant farm labourers. 'Come and eat with us,' and they take me to a shack on the outskirts. We eat *churros* and *calamares fritos* at half the price Renate and I paid the evening before in the main square. I feel bold enough to buy a large portion for everyone to share. The women cut thick slices from a huge loaf and the men pull out a flask of red wine. The idea of drinking from the bottle doesn't appeal to me, but I'm offered it first, as an honour, so I have to start it all off.

It is dark, and for over an hour I've forgotten about Renate, the *corrida*, and my violent reactions. Help! It's nearly nine o'clock. The convent closes at nine. My new friends show me the way back to the town centre and the convent.

'*Adiós! Adiós!*' They stand there in a ragged row, barefoot, clothed in rags and grime, telling me how sorry they are to see me go.

The nun opening the door narrows her eyes, looks disapprovingly at me and states that it has already struck nine.

As I draw the curtains round my cubicle, I think over the evening's events. Angry again, my memories come flooding back as the itinerant workers' world recedes. I'll say nothing about it to Renate.

It is now nearly half past nine and there is no sign of her.

CHAPTER 10

Renate didn't return all night. She couldn't have after nine, anyway. The convent rules are inflexible - strange if you think of its humanitarian calling. I'm lucky to find a train to Seville early on Sunday. So here I am sorting out my reactions by writing up my neglected journal. I won't confide in Mike, who might think I'm getting into bad company. Renate would have gone to find - or meet - José Maria. Why didn't she tell me that he is a *toreador*? Or perhaps she meant to, but couldn't because I'd been turfed out of the arena.

Did I give the bull courage? I hope so. Anyway, I wasn't up to facing Renate after the end of the *corrida* and wouldn't have missed the time with those itinerant workers. She probably didn't want to be bothered with me anyway. I have her address if I want to see her again.

Writing my journal distances me from Renate more than the actual miles devoured by this train. I'm alone in the compartment, with today to spend as I will. No Renate to plot my activities. Carmen expects me tomorrow sometime in the afternoon.

Sparse herds of brown cattle are grazing the rough slopes of the Sierra Morena. Visions of blood, in drops or rivulets mingling with foam from eye, mouth and neck, infiltrate my imagination. I close my eyes and the same scenes appear etched on my eyelids. I stare out of the window at the sun brushing the mountain rocks and the rare rough-hewn hovel tucked into a crease in a meadow. The red of a child's dress turns into José Maria's cloak, a haystack into the dull gold of his *toreador* costume, while a bright flick of broom pitches Renate and her yellow dust-pocked frock into my consciousness. I mustn't get carried away by my imagination. If I curb it, would I have all these adventures?

Writing this down won't blot out the image of the bloodstained bullfighter, Manolete or José Maria or whoever he is, brandishing his sword, cape billowing over his head like a canopy of honour. It oddly reminds me of St. George painted leaping from his steed to slay the dragon!

Renate must have spent the night with José Maria. What did they do? Silly question, but my mind races into vague visions of passionate kisses. Or, as he was wounded, did she assume the centuries-worn female role of nurse and confidante? He flashed a wedding ring yesterday afternoon when they met – what about his wife?

Almost at Seville. Where can I find a room on a Sunday? I might have to rough it. I'll use the train WC to swop my skirt for all-purpose trousers. They were forbidden in the convent. Amid the bustle of arrival, high in anticipation of new encounters in my conquest of Seville, I emerge from my Córdoba chrysalis as the familiar chirpy me, all go and good-humour. I'll deposit my suitcase in left luggage and explore the city. Hurrah, I can go where I want! I'll take the bus to the city centre. There's festive bunting, so something is happening.

Into the morning, head high, sniffing the wind of adventure. To my surprise, eyes turn in my direction. The tide of Sunday merrymakers flows past. I pretend to focus on fascinating architectural features, nose in air with the superior attitude of a mean-eyed camel. Unwelcome Córdoba thoughts return. Why did dumpy, green-eyed Renate, clad in a dress more dust-bedraggled by the minute, command attention, while slender, blue-eyed me was virtually ignored? Blonde versus brown hair? Córdoba has done little for my self-esteem.

I respond in sheer delight to the buzz of a carefree crowd dressed up as if for the *corrida de toros*. Men wear starched shirts escaping from sober suits with a ripple of lace coquetry at neck and cuffs. I like that discrete but telling touch; the peacocks preening.

Women display their usual crown high tortoiseshell combs and *mantillas* to toe-level frills and furbelows, all flounce and flutter.

Some minutes pass before I realise I'm not hearing the anticipated *hermosa!* or *muy guapa!* compliments that had excited Renate on our first evening in Córdoba. Instead there are stifled shrieks and embarrassed giggles from behind hand or fan underscored by the male battle cry, *los hombres llevan los pantalones!* Only men wear trousers! I flinch at a brown glare from beneath thick brows and mascara draped eyelashes, the tip of a fan pointing me out. Refuge is at hand inside the dark, protective walls of Seville Cathedral, but an official bars my way in, indicating my trousers with unconcealed disdain.

I stride purposefully away from the crowds to find refuge in a quieter area of the city. A deserted park bench provides a moment's respite. What are my options? I could take a bus back to the station and pull a skirt out of my luggage, then go in search of a room. Do I have enough money? It's a Sunday; the banks are shut and I only have my ticket and a few coins, barely enough to buy something to eat and to pay for the luggage storage. I might ask Carmen if I can arrive in Ronda a day early; I don't have her telephone number, just her address. It's embarrassing to disturb their careful plans to welcome me. I hardly know this family and my Spanish is too faltering to explain my quandary, even if I can find their number. Nothing for it but to brave the night out in the city. I'm young, and my combat garments are blouse and trousers. So be it.

While sitting on a park bench and planning my next move I notice that, inevitably, two men are looking at me. Their silence is curiously irritating, leaving me mental but not emotional space to think out my next move. They just stand there, scrutinising: my withering stare back, ineffectual. I study the sketchy map in my guide book and strike out towards, I hope, the Moorish citadel.

They trot like obedient poodles behind me, still strangely silent until one calls out,

'*Señorita, señora? Está casada?*' What a strange question to ask me, but yes, I am tired and also hungry.

'*Si, estoy casada y tengo hombre.*' My explanation comes out pat and I'm emboldened, feeling myself safe in a public space with two rival admirers. I am tired and hungry. That's true. Will the strange Spanish customs mean I'll be refused entry to the Alcázar as well as the cathedral? One of my followers pays my entrance ticket before I can sort out the correct change. Quite a relief, but not the best way to save money, however little. The citadel is deserted. A previously unnoticed image of the Madonna in a dark corner of the cathedral has been found weeping tears, real salty tears, on and off for the last two months or so, and today she'll be carried in procession, my followers explain, and venerated at a special mass this evening conducted by the Archbishop of Seville.

Time wanders pleasantly by. The sand-coloured stones, intricate Moorish carving in rooms echoing to our footsteps and bright sun all produce a pleasant stupor, extended by the lunch I'm invited to share with these men at a small restaurant outside the gates. They talk quite a lot and I think I get the gist of what they're saying. The word *casada* appears from time to time, and I do agree that I'm tired. They go on about travel and adventure for young people like me, and I agree with whatever they mean. For some reason I can't fathom they seem involved with South America. Well, that is understandable; most countries there speak Spanish.

It is late afternoon by the time I can free myself. They keep on plying me with coffee and liqueurs that I find too strong and refuse, only to see others appearing in their place. I try to smile and politely sip a drop of each, hoping to keep a clear head. I have a night to get through as best I can. Not a time to be off my guard. I've eaten a lot to sustain me until morning. Smiling at my two companions, I try to thank them politely and get up to leave. They accompany me out. I haven't any clear plan of action so, for want of anything else, I say I have to go to the station to deal with my ticket. They insist on helping me.

This is unnerving. They haven't put a foot wrong; not a *piropo* between them, which is strange, but only polite enquiries about me being tired, or hungry, or wanting to see things, or about travel. All obvious and unobjectionable. No attempt to touch me, or make indecent proposals which I could use as a pretext to send them packing. I'm distinctly uneasy at the smoothness of it all. I've slipped away from Renate's voyage of self-revelation, only to fall into the smooth company of these two nameless men. Come to think of it, they haven't introduced themselves and I don't ask so as not to encourage any advances. It is a curiously anonymous encounter, becoming stranger by the minute.

I'm not sure how to return to the station, so one of the men goes ahead to find the bus stop while the other follows me, as if to protect me from any unwelcome attention. I'm feeling a bit queasy. I'll go into the WC and stay there so they'll be bored and leave. I have to take some books out of my luggage at the station, I explain. They are on holiday, not in a hurry and can wait. I'm scared of invisible tentacles reaching out towards me. The left luggage is nearer than the female WC, so I'll go there first. I could find some pretext to look at my case and knapsack, and then peek out to see if they're still hanging around. If not, then I'll leave the station. If they're still there, I'll snatch a moment they're not looking to slip into the WC

I pull a skirt out and stuff it into my knapsack together with a toothbrush, tooth paste and hairbrush, Renate style. Be prepared to spend the night somewhere outside. I'll leave as early as possible tomorrow for Ronda and Carmen, an oasis of safety and peace.

No sign of them on the platform. Breathing deeply in relief, I turn instead towards the ticket office in the entrance lobby. No luck. There they are standing guard at the only way in or out of the station, smoking, their backs to me. I must find out the earliest train for Ronda tomorrow. Again my luck is out. No train for Ronda before three in the afternoon, one a day. It is a branch line, right out into nowhere. Oh well, nothing for it but to while away the time until tomorrow afternoon. Tenacious they are, still waiting. I dart onto the platform to find the toilet. I don't need it but any delaying tactic might just tire their patience. Change into a skirt? No. Better to spend the night out in trousers.

Ten hot and bothered minutes pass in the WC I must face the danger, real or imagined. Impossible to spend twenty hours or so in the women's WC on Seville station, even if it's open all night! To begin with, the stench... I creep back along the platform and peer into the lobby. No sign of them. 'Oh mother fortune,' I intone silently, 'you haven't deserted me!'

Too soon. As I sail through the main doors they appear on either side and grab my arms.

'Adiós!' I yell, turning more heads with the noise than with my trousers. Shaking myself free, I escape towards the bus, just in time. Others clamber in after me and my pursuers arrive too late. Safety in crowds. I plunge into the heart of swirling humanity in the vicinity of the cathedral, oblivious of protests, shrieks, and jostling to keep me out. Sounds of drums and pipes announce the procession has left the cathedral, just as dusk cools the late afternoon into evening and the candles flicker more brightly around the miraculous image of the Virgin.

Pushing my way in I stand tiptoe behind a tall, fair-haired young man who blocks my view. I can just see the archbishop's crosier and a scarlet clad cardinal, protected on either side by a line of black-robed Klu Klux clan figures peering at the crowd through the slits in their hoods. They carry long candles and, instead of looking straight and seriously ahead, these thrillingly sinister characters are twisting their heads towards the crowd. People call out and eyes behind the slits seem to twinkle, smile or even wink.

Can they be recognised by family or friends? The only sounds are the priests intoning and the choir responding, boys meek in white surplices over red robes. All step forward to the repetitive beats of the drums behind the enthroned Virgin borne on high by six hooded figures, probably the leaders of the confraternity. As the miraculous image passes encircled by a forest of candles set in wreaths of white roses and lilies, I notice that the Virgin isn't weeping. Today of all days she should.

A high note pierces the dusk, hovers, then falls three notes, to pause, repeat, then to sing out again in a cascade of notes dropping down the scale, like a scatter of sparks in the wake of a rocket, blue-white into yellow and gold. The procession pauses to listen; the voice, this time pitched higher still, throws its plaintive notes into the still air, descends, hovers, remounts a few tones, then plunges into a lower cascade of sounds. Another swoop upwards ends in a dying fall. The archbishop raises his eyes to a balcony and intones a prayer to the shadowy figure holding a candle. Around me they are crossing themselves, too tightly packed to notice or care what I'm wearing. I can at last relax.

The procession jolts on, to pause further down the processional route for more haunting invocations. Unlike any melody I have ever heard until the shepherds' plaintive songs on the way to the Córdoba cemetery, these random notes etch the air with their yearning. Strains from the Orient, placing Spain on the edge of Africa, Asia and even Islam, thrilling in sound and sensation.

A prod on my leg, a pull at my trouser hem. I look down to see hands sneaking between the people pressing in around me. Men are bending down to look at my covered legs. How supremely absurd! No peace, not even in a crowd. Desperate, I tap the shoulder of the young man in front of me. Judging by his height and fair hair he might be English, American, or perhaps Scandinavian. And probably English-speaking.

'Can you help me?' He turns, startled.

'Yes. What's the matter?' An Australian accent. What a relief!

'Look, these men won't leave me alone. For some reason they seem to be excited about me wearing trousers. They're lying on the ground to pull them and even poke me! I don't have any money until the banks open tomorrow. I thought I could get by until I leave for Ronda in the afternoon.' Perhaps I've trailed on for too long? He is only a stranger, probably on holiday and not keen to get involved with a woman's problems.

'Take my jacket. Put it over your shoulders while you roll up your trousers.' As he is tall, the jacket reaches my knees, almost disguising the rolled-up trousers.

'Let's find the others and see if you can camp with us tonight.' This Good Samaritan is an Australian student travelling with five more in a large camper vehicle. They plan to spend a couple of days in Seville. I'm welcome to sleep across the front seats.

What a great chance to unwind and swop experiences uninhibited by lack of vocabulary or grammar! They're so friendly, not just because they are decent people, but because their relationships seem to be somewhat strained. Not surprising, as the group met through an advertisement. Two months is a long time to spend in new surroundings with people you hardly know. It's like dipping into a bran tub for a friend, to turn out, if not badly, at least not as brilliantly as hoped. Would any Latin people use this method of finding travelling companions? They don't seem to travel much, and never without the family.

৩৯৫

It's such a relief to have a safe place to sleep. This morning I remembered to change into the skirt to visit the cathedral and see Columbus's monument. Adam Parker, the Australian, insists on meeting me for lunch. Yesterday evening he took me aside to pour out his woes: the tedium of boring companions, the lack of an interesting female companion. So I'm being cast by him in the latter role.

Better safe than sorry, I change money in the bank before heading for the cathedral. A few *piropos* came from the men having early morning coffee at street tables, but they are mostly elderly and just playing at being young again and naughty. Silly and easy to ignore. My confidence has bounced back.

The Cathedral is vast and sombre. I soon find the miraculous Madonna adorned with even more flowers than the High Altar, and numerous candles fluttering in adoration before her. Dark-robed figures, the elderly widows that haunt Spanish churches and are their unsung guardians, tend and add to them. I've come for Columbus's monument. Is Cervantes buried here too? I've read *Don Quixote* in a children's translation, and remember the usual episodes, like the tilting at windmills. I've brought my as yet unopened Spanish copy of his short stories, more suited to my rather jerky rhythm of travelling.

A white-haired woman, tall, gaunt, rather sad-looking, and a fair-haired younger one are sitting close together by the candles whispering over a guide book. On an impulse I go over to them.

'Do you speak English?'

They look relieved.

'How kind of you! We do need help. We don't speak a word of Spanish and it's difficult to read this guide book. Such small print, no plan, and the cathedral is so dark. There don't seem to be any guides.' The older woman speaks in a joyless voice, the other just looks at me.

'This is the first time I've been here,' I confess, 'but I speak a little Spanish. Shall I try to find a guide?'

I approach a sacristan seated in a side chapel behind a small table laden with guidebooks, sacred images and rosaries. He gruffly agrees to take us round, with me interpreting. The tour ended, we sit in the cool darkness. The daughter confides that her mother is slightly happier now they are in Spain where there are no war cemeteries. Her brother's grave in France was the object of their journey from Australia. Now they are on holiday, or trying to be.

I'm reminded of Uncle David who has no grave for my mother to grieve over. The older woman wants to rest a moment, so we sit and she tells me they have been staying with an English friend in Godalming, where my parents are now living.

'The daughter of a family in the ground floor flat had been seriously injured in a riding accident. A brain injury. Our friend was concerned about her.'

'That was me!' I could hardly believe it. Dickens was right; such improbable coincidences can happen! I had been exercising a thoroughbred for a holiday job when an electric milk van ran into it. I fell head first on to the road and spent tedious months in hospital.'

'Really amazing.' They are as astonished as I am. We chat on for a while until I realise it's nearly one.

'I must go. I'm so sorry. I really would like to stay longer but I'm expected for lunch. We'll probably bump into one another again soon.' I'm beginning to believe in some sort of inevitability about these chance encounters.

'Goodbye. Adiós!' As I stand at the cathedral entrance and watch them walk away across the square Adam appears at my side, spot on time.

'You always manage to pick up someone,' he says grudgingly. Does he too want to monopolise me? This fellow is nothing if not tenacious! Well, I'm off to Ronda this afternoon come what may. My small vacation job is assuming the importance of a key career choice.

I'm unfair. Adam and I have a merry lunch together swapping travel and study experiences. We exchange addresses and he rushes with me to the station. I only just catch the three-thirty train which looks as if it has already earned its retirement.

The conductor finds me sitting in a carriage filled with weather-beaten men and women, few below fifty. An assortment of baskets and bundles are piled high on the luggage rack above the wooden slatted seats, its netting bulging beneath them. The engine chugs resolutely away from Seville on a single track over highland criss-crossed by parched ridges. It doesn't take long for the locomotive to puff in protest at the gradient, stopping at halts where still more women with bright red or green kerchiefs over their heads, dark shawls even in this heat and voluminous skirts almost to their ankles, heave on countless baskets with chickens or rabbits peering out in panic. The smell of their droppings vies with the tobacco fumes of men clad in dark shiny jackets and sagging trousers. They are silent for the most part, snoozing even as the sun begins to wane.

At the far end of the carriage two *guardias civiles* lean their regulation headgear against the partition wall. Hats usually progress front to back in a predictable way, varying only in how the brim is turned up or down to indicate the degree of jauntiness. These are unexpectedly flat at the back as if their wearers spend most of the time leaning against walls, eternally on guard. Between them sits a lithe, swarthy individual, alluring in looks and physique. He appears proudly defiant even though he is handcuffed, one hand to each of the policemen. I've never seen criminals in public and am intrigued as well as surprised. I try hard to look elsewhere, but my eyes can't help returning to this latest version of the Laughing Cavalier.

Even so, and in spite of the increasing smell which the open windows and slow pace of the train do little to relieve, I'm nodding off like my neighbours in rhythm with the train. Seconds later it seems, but in reality more than an hour, I open my eyes to shrieks from the two women opposite me who are telling their rosaries with nimble anxiety. Further down some elderly men are standing by an open door. The train has stopped, its engine heaving a sigh of relief; the volume of *Ave Marias* increases by the second. I lean out of the window to observe a trail of men running or stumbling across stubble to the rim of distant hills, the line growing longer and narrower by the minute.

And the *guardias civiles*? Nowhere to be seen. Nor the handsome prisoner. He must be the whole point of the chase across the fields to the horizon. Freed to go and relieve himself, the women tell me between their Ave Marias, he has escaped, presumably through the WC window while the train was moving. It was going so slowly he could easily land on his feet, gaining a crucial lead of some minutes before one of the male travellers notices the prisoner disappearing across the open landscape. The *guardias civiles* leap into action, followed by all the younger men who feel it their duty to capture the fugitive - less boring than snoozing on this long journey. Already we've been chugging along for two hours, and no one mentions Ronda.

The last of the stragglers crosses the horizon. Stranded on the empty landscape stands the train, its engine giving from time to time a half-hearted puff; the squawk and stanch of hens in the still air are more noticeable in the pauses between the prayers. The women opposite scrutinise me with incredulity.

'*Nada rosario? Por qué no dice usted una súplica?*' Why aren't I saying the rosary?

'*No crea en la Madonna?*' Where can I start, and how? I feel a bit embarrassed at having to explain that yes, I am a Christian, but no, I don't have a rosary because I'm not a Catholic but a Christian all the same. All Christians believe in the Madonna.

'*Hereje?*' Oh dear, I'm a heretic to them. As I try to explain, the first man reappears over the horizon and trudges slowly towards the train, followed by the others in dribs and drabs. The prisoner is a violent man. No, not a murderer, but an armed robber. Why did they transfer him on a train, but that is perhaps how things are done in Spain? The glamorous thief, still proud and the least exhausted, is hauled into the carriage and handcuffed again. All return to the places occupied before this escapade, the only change being the tobacco mingling more gruffly with the smell of chicken and rabbit droppings, and a new ingredient, sweat.

In the wake of the men returning over the rim of the hills comes dusk. Still more frequent stops. Women clamber down laden with baskets of hens and eggs, newly-laid out of shock, rabbits and knotted bundles. *Adiós! Adiós! señorita inglesa. Buen viaje!*

It is now after seven. We have been meandering to isolated halts serving hamlets hidden in valleys or tucked behind low ridge hills, frequently pausing to cool the labouring engine whose days are so evidently numbered. When do we reach Ronda? I supposed it to be journey of two hours or so looking at the distances on the map, but that didn't give any indication of the highland terrain or the roundabout route, nor of the age of the train. It's a miracle that the unforeseen stop hasn't caused an accident; a train from the opposite direction, or one behind on the single line might have crashed into us. More likely, there is a train in one direction to Seville in the morning, and another, probably the same one, returning to Ronda in the afternoon. I have patiently asked the question but people don't seem to know. They say something about getting off before the final destination. The conductor appeared once, clipped my ticket, never to return.

Who to ask? The train jolts from one side to the other, revealing the nails fastening the wall panels to the carriage frame, and then hiding them again. It seems very flimsy. Supposing the curve is such that the carriage leans over and pulls out all the nails on one side? When it returns upright, they might miss their holes and the whole contraption fall apart. It's all rather unnerving. I seek comfort in food, though I have nearly finished my snacks. The sultry evening air underscores the major key of tobacco smoke, sweat assuming a minor tone, while animal manure strums still more insistently on the senses.

Not one woman remains. This sudden realisation strikes terror into my unprotected heart. I am the only female on the train! Eyes are poring over me: eyes over the top of the wooden seat the women have vacated, the luggage rack cutting off heads just above eyebrows; still more in the same position, I imagine, behind me, scrutinising the back of my hair and neck. I shudder. They might touch me unexpectedly. A spasm of panic. Four men have moved to the empty seats on the other side of the aisle. Four faces turned in my direction, the white surrounding brown eyes expanding and gleaming in the twilight. Silent, just looking at me. The WC - I could escape there and think what to do.

I summon my dwindling courage to walk purposely, staring straight ahead, to the end where the *guardias civiles* and the handsome thief had sat before they left at a stop not even marked on my map. I push the door expecting to find toilets of a sort on either side. Instead there is an open wagon found, I think, in the Wild West - a caboose, attached to the tail of the train. If it was here that the handsome thief had been freed to relieve himself over the three-foot high wooden barrier around the open carriage, he could easily vault over it to escape. Why didn't they leave him handcuffed at least to one *guardia* so he still had one free to perform, well, what he needed to do? How can women do it here? Luckily I have not drunk much all day, so can restrain myself. For the moment. But how far is Ronda? Where can I go to escape all those eyes? I breathe deeply, concentrate on the fright in the pit of my stomach, and imagine myself rolling it up into a tight little ball to hurl at the sphere sinking into the twilight. A weight lifted. I feel now I can face those eyes.

Ojos azules. Muy guapa. Te quiero mucho... Blue eyes, pretty one, I love you ... are the whispered phrases greeting me on return. Why are these compliments whispered on a train, but called out stentoriously as *piropos* from the pavement cafés? I settle down noting with relief that no one has commandeered the other seats in my section.

I must find out how far we are from Ronda. Which pair of eyes to choose? I turn to a thickset fifty-year old sitting nearest to me across the aisle. He smiles and moves over as if invited to sit opposite me before replying.

'*Entro un'ora.*' Another hour to go before Ronda! We have already spent nearly five hours in the train, with another hour still to go. The lights are too dim for me to make out the faces, still less their expressions. I try again to wrap up my fright into a compact round ball, but the sun has set and where can I project it? I begin to weep. Here I am, surrounded by men and unable to lock myself safely away. Or even to relieve myself, to put it bluntly. And an hour still to go. What will Carmen and her family think of me? It will be after nine, more like ten o'clock when I arrive. Terrible, unimaginable thoughts surge into my mind. Plenty of time for these men to rape me. A serial rape, perhaps, whatever that is.

I contemplate my hands while thinking feverishly, realising that if I look someone full in the face he might interpret it as a come-hither glance. Fifty minutes still to go. I must be careful. When I look up, I see a thin, ferret-like man has squeezed in next to the portly fifty-year old.

'*Inglesa? Americana?*' I force my mouth into a smile and whisper, '*inglesa.*' For some reason they both fish for their wallets and open them to reveal they are stuffed with familiar £1 and £5 bank notes.

'*Gibraltar. Muy bien!*' Furtively approving smiles register all round. Ah, that's it. I had forgotten. We aren't far from Gibraltar, and they are earning sterling in some way. Perhaps smuggling? I'm oddly reassured by this thought. Smugglers seem less violent than robbers. But far less romantic, judging from the two smuggler specimens in front of me. The ferret, who introduces himself as

Rodrigo, has a moustache and plenty of stubble to confirm the animal likeness, while Carlos his corpulent companion has trailing walrus whiskers and greying hair receding to leave a massive brow overshadowing his eyes. His face is expressionless, unlike his companion's quivering mouth and nose, while his podgy hands busily count the Bank of England notes.

If I keep them busy talking, nothing will happen before I can escape on to the platform and find out where Carmen's house is. It will be late, though, and she might think me rude, ill-organised, rightly reproving me for not having contacted her. But how can I phone? She didn't give me her number and I forgot to ask her for it. Anyway, most of these one-horse stations hardly have an electric light, let alone a phone.

My mind is jumping all over the place, but I feel less threatened as the eyes boring into my neck are turning away to follow the conversation. A mouth under the rack opposite me asks where I come from. London? How long have I been in Spain? The usual questions. I stretch my command of Spanish as far as it will go, desperate for talk to substitute action. Once on the platform at Ronda, all will be resolved. I have Carmen's address. It's a small town, hardly more than a village. The minutes tick by at tortoise rate. The darkness outside is oppressive. At each stop I jump up and reach for my suitcase, only to be patted back kindly into my seat. A younger man, his hair cut stiffly into a cock's comb, has snaffled the vacant place beside me. More men are filling up the aisle. I am evidently the evening attraction, for want of something better. As the train chugs on, occasionally whistling into the mountains, never have distances felt so long, glances seemed so threatening, and the proximity of numerous men so distasteful. I can't see if the others around are more appealing than my immediate companions, had it mattered. I think crazily that, if I have to be raped, better by a laughing Cavalier lookalike than this paunchy walrus in front of me, or by Rodrigo the ferret beside him. Desperate thoughts for a desperate mind. I flee to the caboose to get some fresh air, some space away from them, but they follow me, always led by ferret and walrus. They have asserted their right to be my praetorian guard, with the chirpy cockerel sitting beside me as a reserve. Back to my seat, a glance at my watch and its leaden hands. Ten minutes to go if they are telling the truth. Ten minutes like eternity.

I dream Carmen will be on the platform to greet me. I dream all will be pardoned. I dream... I can't believe it! Lights everywhere. Ronda. It actually exists.

Carlos lifts down my suitcase while Rodrigo picks up my bags including the one with all my precious documents and money. I try to take it, but he insists.

'Dónde vas?' They are now using the familiar *tu* and asking where I'm going. No sign of anyone looking for a stranded English girl. At least they are trying to help me. Safer with two of them. I retrieve my bag to rummage around nervously for my address book. When watched, I can never find anything I want quickly. Ah, here it is. I hold it out to ferret and walrus both waiting patiently, and point at *Apartado 21, Ronda*. Carlos looks at the address carefully. Is this all I have? I happily reassure him. I have been writing to this address for over a year now. It is the right one.

'Maybe,' say Carlos and Rodrigo in almost unison, 'but it's a postal address, not a house.'

I bury my face in my hands and burst into tears.

CHAPTER 11

Carlos the walrus takes my arm and propels me with sympathetic sighs to a bench outside the station while muttering to Rodrigo the ferret. Both disappear inside the station repeating my name to make sure they have it right. I've told them my friend is Carmen Fernández. A shower of relief. They can't possibly want to rape me. Whatever they have disappeared to do I don't care. It's a joy to be in the open, contemplating the soft velvet of an unthreatening darkness. People walking across the open area outside the station don't even glance in my direction. No inquisitive eyes, seen or felt; here nonchalance is in the air. I feel lighter, even merry, and smile at walrus and ferret when they reappear, almost standing to attention before me.

'*La familia Fernández...* I'm impressed by their detective work. The Fernández family I know own a sausage factory. It isn't far on the other side of the gorge. They have phoned señora Fernández who is expecting me. Carmen and her brother are already on their way to the station. All is being resolved in the warmth of an evening. I don't know how to thank my unexpected guardians, but they shrug their shoulders and linger, politely keeping me company until Carmen and her brother reach the station square. Then they smile, bow and vanish into the Ronda darkness.

'*Bienvenida, Valeria!*' Slight, not plump as I half expected, with fine light-brown hair and almond-shaped eyes, Carmen looks different from the photo she sent me. Her brother, Juan, resembles her, though he's taller and more tanned. He picks up my suitcase while Carmen explains that their house is at the other end of the main street, but the town is so small that it won't take us much more than ten minutes. We set off into the darkness, relieved only by specks of light in the distance. A parapet and jet softness below. They tell me we are crossing a bridge over a deep gorge. A wide one too, judging from the distance to the lights of the low-roofed

136

houses on the other side. Then up the main street to where the buildings peter away into the open country leaving a tall, isolated three-storey dwelling on our left.

Lights blaze out on the first floor of what my mother would call 'a substantial house'. Two figures are leaning over the balcony.

'*Nuestra madre y Ana.*' There is a bustle of expectation upstairs. Inside, Señora Fernández calls out from the top of solid, marble stairs with spindly iron banisters. They lead on to a wide landing used as a sitting-room which runs the full length of the house with rooms leading off. Eyebrows raised, I'm forcing my eyelids open while Carmen introduces her family and chats excitedly about plans for all these *mañanas* we'll spend together.

Lace curtains are drawn back to let in as much air as possible while moths congregate round the lamp set on a cream brocade tablecloth. Mosquitoes must lurk in its hanging folds, as I find out ruefully scratching myself.

'*Tiene calor en invierno.*' Carmen lifts the brocade to show the small brazier where they put the embers in winter. It seems unbelievable that it could ever be chilly here, but the snowy mountain range, the Sierra de las Nieves, isn't far off. It is often windy, they tell me, and so my mind returns to Don Quixote and the windmills.

'Felipe, my fiancé, will be here on Friday. He has a day off, so we can go on an expedition. There are lots of things to do, and we must practise English. From tomorrow.'

Ana, the elder sister, is watching me closely. She leaves, to return with a servant, primly clad in an ankle-length blue cotton dress and apron trimmed with white lace, carrying a tray with a plate of homemade cakes, china cups and saucers and a steaming pot. A hot drink on such a torrid evening? How strange. It turns out to be the best hot chocolate I've ever tasted: substantial, thick and creamy, perfect for one who has travelled the never-ending distance from Seville on her nerves. Carmen's mother epitomises my idea of a matriarch. Ana is barely introduced. Nearly thirty, she seems firmly consigned to spinsterhood and the care of her parents as they grow old. Not stated, but assumed. She even looks the part in a dress not unlike her mother's, dotted with tiny flowers and buttoned down the front, while Carmen's is all flounces and lace. Their father is conspicuously absent, as now is Juan. Just the women and their guest.

❦

'It was not far off midnight when we finished the hot chocolate conversation and went to bed. I was exhausted, but Carmen wanted to talk and talk - we're sharing a bedroom. She's still asleep, and I'm writing this at a few minutes past nine in the morning. There're noises below, but I don't want to go down to breakfast without her. She is *muy simpatica*, but chatters endlessly in Spanish about her fiancé Felipe, who's keen to marry her quickly, though she's in no hurry. He's a Chemistry graduate and works in Granada. Juan is near the end of his veterinary course at Granada University where he met Felipe. And Ana. Well, she's just Ana. The daughters haven't been encouraged to go to university.

"We read a lot, do embroidery - the usual things." Carmen doesn't seem to mind, but I'm not so sure about Ana. There may be something smouldering there. She keeps on looking at me in an unfathomable way, though that's a hasty comment after only one evening with the family!

I want to ask Juan about 'ferret' and 'walrus', but he slipped away so quickly last night that I had to resort to Carmen. She giggled, and whispered to her mother, who pursed her lips and looked at me curiously, and Ana, who glanced at me too and suppressed a smile. Carmen stated they were dealers in all sorts of things, and doing quite well. I asked what 'things' precisely, but they wanted to change the subject. I'm sure they're smugglers, but can't imagine what they are smuggling. It all remains a mystery. Carmen added they were harmless, to me at least. The señora advised me not to travel on my own, as it isn't the custom for women here. Oh well, I can't change my plans now. This summer is a solo adventure. Carmen is waking up. I must stop.'

Breakfast is a simple affair brought in by another maid, younger than the dark one who served the chocolate late last night at the same table. The brocade is now covered by a beautifully hand-embroidered white tablecloth. Just milk and coffee, with large dry biscuits to dip in the drink. Carmen is chatting away to fill the vocal space she fears her mother might otherwise commandeer. The matriarch soon thwarts her.

'You and Valeria must start English this morning.'

'Mamá, she's only just arrived. She must have a chance to settle in.' Ana frowns at her sister, glances at me, and follows the younger maid into the kitchen.

'*Muy bien!*' I interject to avoid any build-up of tension, 'we can start as soon as you like'.

'*Aquí. Ora!*' pronounces the matriarch, and here and now it is to be. Carmen pouts as the maid clears breakfast away and, anxious to appear professional, I ask Carmen to show me her English text books.

'We learnt French at school,' she declares resolutely in Spanish, but does produce a manual designed to teach elementary English conversation. The older maid delivers the morning post to the Señora still hovering over her visibly irritated daughter, and a letter is placed in front of me. It's from Mike. I use it as a pretext to get Carmen talking, which it does. Boyfriends are good topics, even if Carmen has evidently not studied any English grammar and hasn't a clue about verbs. Nouns jostle, a few colourful adjectives, then a torrent of Spanish to smother her lack of knowledge. Tough going, made worse by the matriarch watching from what seems like her office, whispering instructions to invisible servants within and glancing at her daughter from time to time, to call out, 'No, Carmen, no, no, no!' when her younger daughter takes refuge in Spanish. It isn't an easy situation, and I find it hard to spend two hours with Mike's letter niggling away at my concentration.

A safer and easier topic, I decide, is the house. Carmen does satisfy my curiosity. The ground floor where Juan disappeared is the unmarried male quarter. The main kitchen lies on the other side of the entrance hall and corridor. He has his own room. The other is used by the unmarried deputy manager at the factory. The manager has his own family house. On the main floor are her parents' bedroom, the dining-room and this central sitting area with a sort of kitchen office opening off it by the back stairs.

'The top floor is ours, Valeria. *La nuestra.*' Each floor, Carmen adds, has its own bathroom. The top one is for the unmarried women, with three bedrooms and a large bathroom. The two maids share one room, Carmen and me another, Ana the third.

I expect lunch to end the morning lesson, but Carmen bursts into rapid Spanish once her mother has left for the main kitchen on the ground floor.

'*Andamos! Fuera.*' Down the marble steps past the ground floor quarters of the men and out of the front door where Carmen pauses, swirling round so her wide skirt rises to show her slender, stalk-like legs.

'Let's go and find *papá!*' That would complete the family, but I wish I had pretended to need the bathroom to read Mike's letter, still undisturbed in my skirt pocket,

Papá is at the entrance to a large, hangar-like building with many vents and few windows standing near the factory manager's house. As *mamá* dominates the home, he dominates the factory. Average to small, of spry stature, with light brown curly hair, hazel eyes and moustache, he lacks what I imagine are the typical Spanish looks of his buxom wife, whose plentiful, dusky hair is greying more conspicuously than his. He introduces me to the deputy manager, and vanishes whilst his deputy shows me round the factory, at my polite request. Carmen is easily bored and soon pulls me away.

'*No es muy interesante, Valeria.*' As her guest, I have to obey, though I would like to ask how they make highly-peppered sausages and cure ham. By two in the afternoon I'm famished. I'm placed next to Señor Fernández, of some charm but little talk, amply provided by the female members of his family except Ana. Juan has returned to university in Grenada. I can hear the younger maid clattering up and down the spiral stairs linking the kitchen with the domestic office while the older one serves endless dishes at table: salads, meat hot and cold, fish, melons and peaches and candied fruit that burns my tongue with sweetness. It is all colourfully bewildering, very different from post-war British sobriety.

It is long after three when the matriarch and patriarch retire for their siesta, and I feel free at last to read Mike's letter. I follow Carmen up the marble stairs to our room. Stripped to her lawn petticoat, she eloquently explains what we will do once it is cooler and the siesta has ended. My only escape is to the bathroom.

I noted on a brief visit earlier in the morning that there's no lock. The vast bathroom is fitted with a tub and WC on the opposite side with only the basin near the door. Not even a chair. I wish I could read the letter in a more congenial place than sitting on the WC! Just as I'm starting, the door handle turns and the younger maid makes for the bath tub, turns on both taps and leaves closing the door behind her. I freeze, not sure whether I have been noticed or not. Then Carmen peeps round the door with, 'After you! Hurry up!' Not a chance.

I read the letter sitting on my bed while Carmen is taking her turn on the WC, and it leaves me in ill-defined anxiety. I lie back and dream he is here with me, to be woken at half-past four by Carmen telling me we are going out to visit her friend who has just had a baby. Social visiting it is to be, together with shopping for postcards.

Carmen's school friend has been married only ten months, Carmen enlightens me as we hurry into town. A respectable birth, but only just - she giggles at that. Maria Asunción - they all seem to be called Maria something, even Carmen should be Maria del Carmen - was in a hurry to marry, and tongues had wagged throughout Ronda.

'Everyone knows everyone else, and there's not much to talk about. Marriage, birth, baptism, death, and so on. Jobs, of course. Men are still emigrating to South America, Argentina mainly,' Carmen informs me. Not one mention of the war which has so occupied my life. There is something soft and unfocussed about Carmen, no sense of urgency, no will to get on and do something - not even to marry Felipe! Maria Asunción turns out to be a true Andalucian belle, with a round figure, blooming cheeks and hair to make coal look dusty. She is lively all right, lively and domesticated. Lively about her child, her husband who has returned to the shop he runs in the main street, and her small house with its lacy curtains and heavy brocade-covered chairs. I imagine one draper furnishing all the well-to-do Ronda interiors in a dreary uniform of deep reds and purples. Maria Asunción's creamy crochet handiwork, created during her hours of vigilance over child and husband, provides visual breathing space in the sultry room.

They chatter on about everyone I don't know. It doesn't bother me. I peruse the room and marvel at the way people here wear long skirts in such hot weather. Visiting and shopping continues until well after dusk, probably because most Spaniards expect the siesta to last until after five in the afternoon. It is cooler then, so I suppose it makes sense. But my stomach starts to grumble from about six-thirty, and by nine when the Fernández family, and presumably all Ronda, sit down to a light supper, I'm famished! I must carry sweets in my bag to tackle the pangs of hunger. They may be bad for teeth and waist, but I'll get desperate waiting for their mealtimes.

ᦇᦉ

Today is Thursday and Carmen has an appointment with the local priest. Her mother has indicated she would like to talk to me alone.

'You're like a member of the family,' she begins, somewhat to my consternation as I've only been here three days, 'and I need your help with Carmen. She is getting old,' *mamá* continues, 'twenty-six already, and she refuses to agree on a date for her marriage. Why is she so obstinate? She won't talk to me about it. She has a patient fiancé, but Felipe's getting restless and won't wait forever. You know what men are like. They must have their comfort and satisfaction.' I of all people could hardly be wise in such matters! How old does she think I am? She imagines Carmen will lose Felipe, and how that will make all Ronda gossip. Theirs is quite an important local family, more through wealth than rank, so I suppose gossip could be particularly corrosive.

I find it odd that she chooses to confide in me. At nineteen I'm too young to have experience of what she's worried about; I'm a stranger and a foreigner as well! Or it may be just that. I've come from afar and will soon leave, so I can't spread gossip.

Well, Carmen returns furious. She charges through the house slamming the doors left open to air the place.

'D'you know where my mother sent me, Valeria?' I do, but remain silent. If I am to please the matriarch, it can only be as Carmen's friend and confidante.

'No idea.'

'*Mamá* sent me to our priest, Don José. Not for confession or anything so simple.' It seems he went on and on about her duties to her parents, and to the family of God, and that she should get married and not keep her nice fiancé waiting. She can't make up her

143

mind. Don José has already taken her and Felipe through the rites of marriage and stressed that both have to agree. I try to find out what is holding her back, but all she can say is that she isn't ready. I won't comment until I meet Felipe tomorrow. He'll be coming from Granada with Juan. It should be fun with all of them here. I've spent most of my time in women's quarters and company. Very Spanish When I knew I was coming to Andalucía, I read Garcia Lorca's play *Yerma*. It prepared me pretty well for all this!

❧

Ana sought me out this morning while Carmen was in the bathroom and gave me a handwritten poem. Who would have thought this girl, or woman rather, edited out of the mainstream life of the Fernández family, is an aspiring poet? Good for her. I read it, and others she later put under my pillow - she doesn't want her sister to see them for some reason - and I think they are, well, powerful. Very influenced by Lorca. Heat and passion; imprisoned in hopelessness. Who would have guessed all that lay behind her quiet demeanour? I want to encourage her and talk to her about them, but there is never a space to be alone together.

I'm caught in a web of emotions, though I don't mind. I really am treated as one of the family by all; the only ones I don't know are *papá* and Juan. I sense there is some sort of tension there, but can't fathom what it is.

My own particular problem, besides finding time for an almost daily record of my thoughts and actions plus notes for my novel, is chronic constipation. There is absolutely no way to stop people coming into the bathroom and, as the door is at least three yards from the WC, I can hardly hold it shut. No one pays any attention if I shout, '*occupada!*'. All seem happy to do their ablutions while other members of the family unit - the same sex, of course - airily come and go as they please. I have tried to reason that the Romans did it in rows of loos, almost in public, and the monks too, suspended over a convenient stream, but try as I might, I just can't relax. I'm feeling quite sick and headachy. It is all so embarrassing.

I have attempted various solutions. More fruit and less stodgy food. *Mamá* then worries that I don't eat enough, concerned that I'm not receiving adequate hospitality. I should be concentrating on Spanish, but I'm trying to relax by finishing *Le Grand Meaulnes* on the WC during the siesta, when Carmen stops chattering to snooze and can't distract me in the bathroom - to no avail. All that is needed is a tiny lock. Would Juan or *papá* understand this better? Or should I explain it all to the matriarch? It might be wiser to keep my problem to the women's domain.

Mamá proves strangely elusive when needed. She isn't near either kitchen or pantry though it is six in the evening and the siesta has ended, nor in the sitting room where she is usually to be found. I go out on the balcony where I had first seen the matriarch, and from there survey the road into Ronda, and then the other direction, over the barren hills to the distant saw-like range of mountains. No luck. Wait. A speck grows larger in the far distance, but with a pack animal. That can't be this respectable matron transmogrified into a peasant coming to town. Indeed not. There she is, coming from the other direction, from Ronda. She looks up, sees me and waves before mopping her brow again and disappearing into the house. A moment later she staggers up the marble staircase.

'*Tengo mucho calor...*' She is so hot, and has rushed back from the priest. So many family problems, she confides. Don José gives sound advice, but is too kind to young people. They have to do their duty to Church and family... Her voice drones on as she sinks into her rocking chair near the sofa where I sit close enough to be confidential. I carefully place my legs together, not crossed, sit up rather primly and stroke my hair back in embarrassment.

'I'm having problems...' I hesitate, trying to find the correct expression in Spanish, 'Inside my stomach...' and a horrified expression spreads over the matriarch's face. She turns round to look at me straight in the face, gaping. '*No es posibile! Juan?*' I'm now staring back, equally horrified at the state of her mind.

'No. It's only the bathroom... no lock... I'm,' I scrape around for 'constipation' in Spanish. It's not something one usually has to describe. Then she smiles in relief.

'I have some medicine. I'm so sorry.' She probably finds my woes easy to deal with compared with her troublesome brood, Carmen in particular. And the age-old herbal remedy does work. Rapidly, and fortunately for the lock situation, in the middle of the night when everyone is sleeping.

৵৵

Mike is on my mind. His letter recounted in his jaunty way the main events of his existence, 'mostly work and little play' in his job at the Weymouth hotel. The guests are families with young children or the elderly. He spends his free time wandering on the beach or reading. He misses me greatly and will write again. Nothing much else. He's a mathematician and not given to introspection, but I sense he is unhappy, and not just because I'm away 'enjoying myself' on the Continent. We're much too young to be serious about each other. I'm snatching a moment during the siesta to reply cheerfully but cutting out most of my experiences so we can savour them together in October. That is a long way off, so we'll both have to be patient. I must study Spanish, and I'm also learning to teach. Carmen is absorbing a little English grammar and shows some progress. It is good to be in a family atmosphere for a change, not on the road in constant, tiring stimulation, nor battered by the intense intellectual competition I'd encountered in Paris. Here is an oasis, a backwater where the rest of the world is ignored and has been, I imagine, for centuries, at least since the time of Cervantes when Spain was colonising the New World. The Church and ancestral family morality rule, or try to.

A yell from the ground floor: '*Juan! Dónde estas?*' Juan isn't due back until tomorrow, so why is his father calling out for him? Noises below from the men's quarters; a door slammed to insulate sparring voices.

'*Valeria, viene aquí!*' The matriarch prises me out of the calm afternoon shadows in the living-room on to the balcony. Ana and Carmen are still snoozing.

'Juan has returned earlier than expected and his father saw him coming. They are having another quarrel!' She pulls her black embroidered shawl tightly over her plump shoulders as if to shield herself from the muffled shouts below.

'Neither understands,' she moans. 'Juan wants to be a vegetarian and refuses to follow his father in the family firm. Our livelihood. His father has built this up over more than thirty years, and now his only son refuses to follow him. How can he be so obstinate?'

I'm at a loss to know how to respond.

'There aren't many jobs around, so I don't know what he's going to do with himself...' *Mamá's* voice trails into silence as she leans on to the balcony rail and closes her eyes. I feel trapped into making the only response I can conjure up - a practical one.

'It's sort of inevitable,' I hazard in my best Spanish, 'that a young person nowadays who studies to be a vet would not feel happy about taking over a sausage-making business. Could there be someone else? One of your daughters? Felipe even? One can't force Juan, and I imagine this argument has already been running some time?'

She is silently looking at her hands, inert on her lap.

The argument subsides. A door opens and I sense a figure fleeing under the balcony down towards the town. The grandfather clock marks the silence; the cicadas grind monotonously on and the sun sinks sluggishly into the evening haze. *Mamá* shrugs her shoulders, almost shivering in frustration and despair, and turns into the living-room.

'*Es así. Mañana arriva Felipe. Mañana...*'   That's how things are. Tomorrow Felipe's coming.

CHAPTER 12

Carmen is up uncharacteristically early, and has made it noisily known that she will be having a bath and taking a long time about it. A good chance for me to write my journal, until I feel eyes on me, and look up to see Ana framed in the doorway.

'*Buenos días, Ana!*' She beckons me into her bedroom, and pulls some papers off the only comfortable chair. I look around to see more books on shelves or stacked on the floor than in all the other rooms of this house put together. I sit down, smiling at her:

'This feels like my room at University! Familiar and friendly!'

Ana is tense, as if she wants to struggle out of those dowdy flowered dresses and let down her wavy hair primly tucked back into a bun. Before, I had been at a loss to describe her. Unmemorable would have been the word to use, a gentle character assassination.

'*Tengo che hablar contigo...* I've waited so long to talk to you. I can't in front of the others. They laugh at my writing, so I don't show them any of my poems. I don't have anyone to talk to. You're Carmen's guest, and she controls you, so I have to take second place.'

'I realise that.' I must be careful what I say. 'It's difficult to get away from her. She can't bear to be alone. I'd really like to discuss your poems. You've read Lorca, haven't you?'

Ana picks up a thin worn paperback, and shows me his poems with underlining and comments all over them.

'Why don't you study Spanish literature at Granada University? You could discuss your writing there and meet others with similar interests, like me.' I hesitate. 'I'm trying to write too. A novel, not poetry - I'm too impatient.'

'At least you can discuss what you're doing. My family thinks it a waste of money to send a woman to university. At least, my father does. He's said so many times. I should get married. I even asked him to use my dowry to send me to university. He laughed and said he'd saved it for my marriage, and if I didn't marry, he'd keep it to cover the expense of having me at home. I'm just a parasite, until my parents are old and I become the spinster daughter who cares for them!'

Almost shedding tears of frustration, she looks down at a hand-written sheet hidden in the book she is holding;

'My life is woven in yellow - sand, sun, the silt in the gorge, the bile in my throat, the barren, surly landscape around me: harsh, cruel, unloving ...'

Carmen doesn't come to find me, so Ana and I talk until -

'*Mírame!*' Calling out for attention, Carmen poises in the doorway, one hand on the lintel, the other touching the back of her beribboned hair. A cascade of lace falls over a peacock blue dress finishing just above her calves to reveal still more lace on her petticoats. She drops both hands on to her hips, revolving them slowly as if to set her hands in motion, then thrusts them out, one above the other, palms downwards. Clicking castanets in time with the sharp, dry rhythmic tap of the heels on her shiny black shoes, she advances towards me until our eyes meet, and then flicks her dress round to click and tap herself out of Ana's room and down to the living-room where there are sounds of a new arrival.

Ana and I look at each other and smile. Ana is, in fact, rather attractive in a subtle way. She isn't so much plump as rounded, her tawny eyes and hair unusual with an olive complexion. I hug her, saying, 'We'll talk again,' and hurry out to join Carmen.

Below the whole family, apart from Ana, has assembled in the living-room to welcome Felipe. She is absent and not missed. Juan stands apart, looking more and more gaunt and nervous as his father's jovial off-duty voice soars over the company. Felipe is predictably the centre of attention, with Carmen and her mother suitably fussing over him. I pause on the lowest stair to take in the scene and pluck up courage for the next act I am to enter.

Uncertain which way Carmen's mood might take her, I hope my friend will decide to spend the day alone with Felipe. I need a break from teaching, a chance to catch up on some reading and to escape from the house along the track that leads to the mountains and into raw nature. Later I might be able to talk to Ana in her friendly untidy room.

Felipe is immediately introduced. He fumbles a few words in English and raises my hand to his lips;

'Carmen's friend is mine too. Welcome to Spain.' He is dark, conventionally Spanish in looks, of medium height with a sallow skin, long straight nose and deep-set, kindly eyes; while not exactly handsome, he is certainly personable. I wonder what is holding Carmen back. At this precise moment, nothing appears to be. Her mother, a perplexed frown on her face, observes her daughter who is in a perpetual flutter, touching Felipe's neck, kissing him on the cheek, hugging him, and then snatching his arm to lean on it, just like a newly-wedded bride! I share the matriarch's dilemma. It just doesn't seem to add up.

It is a festive evening. Carmen dances, Felipe claps an accompaniment which the rest of us follow. Not long after midnight Carmen rustles into our bedroom and turns her back to me so I can unhook her dress before sinking into sleep, a smile on her face.

໑ঔ

'*Andamos, Felipe?* Valeria wants to see the Roman ruins.' I raise my head in surprise at Carmen's suggestion. I have been told about the ruins and expressed a strong interest. They've never been mentioned again, so I haven't reminded her, thinking I might go and find them on my own, if I can slip out for half a day. I haven't even been consulted about today's activities! It is Saturday, time for excursions. *Mamá* bustles out to return shortly with a packed lunch for us. Felipe takes the knapsack and we set off, Carmen's mother having fussed me into wearing a wide brimmed straw hat too.

'Don't let them out of your sight!' the matriarch whispers as I'm about to follow the couple outside. Considering I'm the stranger here, younger than both of them and more likely to get lost, what odd advice to give. It's like an official departure! The rest of the family stands on the balcony and waves as Felipe revs up the Fernández car to take us to the nearest parking place to the ruins.

There the three of us set off side by side along a cart track, Felipe politely enquiring after my family and making all the right noises. He is well-mannered. I tick 'manners' on my imaginary list of desirable qualities, but he is not particularly interesting - yet. I feel fragile this morning, for some reason I can't work out. Is it the effect of the sun, becoming hotter with every step? Or my overactive imagination? The hotter it becomes, the more relentlessly the cicadas chirrup. As we amble towards the ruins, Carmen and Felipe move a few steps ahead to walk hand in hand confiding in each other. It isn't really polite to exclude me. I should have insisted on staying home to read a book and talk to Ana. There isn't anything much to see, just boulders, cactus-type scrubs, dried-out tamarisk and other trees I can't identify dotted here and there. Little shade, no water, only a rare scrap of green disguised by dust.

A sensible girl like me should not be reading a novel written in French while walking in Spain and learning Spanish, but I started it in Paris, and must finish. It entices me into a make-believe world, where a young man, 'Le Grand Meaulnes', is dreaming his way through wintry pastures and ancient forests to glimpse a castle. There before his startled eyes is a *fête galante* or *bal masqué*. Fantasy or fancy dress? I trail on behind the couple imagining I am the girl Meaulnes is watching – radiant, vivacious and mysterious.

What makes me look down? Oblivious to the incessant grind of the cicadas, the blinding sun, stultifying heat and calls from

Felipe to observe the eagle soaring above, I am so engrossed in my dream that only an atavistic instinct stops me, foot in air. A viper wriggles away under a rock on my right leaving a sensation of movement, the sickening thrill of fear. I shriek and shriek, body rigid, mind skewered.

'*Qué tienes?*' Felipe looks back at me.

'*Una vípera...*' My voice trails away as I point towards the rock. He prises the stone up with his stick. There it is, a viper coiled up with zigzag stitching down its back. I freeze. The shriek rises again inside me with a rush of nausea. I hold my throat and close my eyes after Felipe deftly hits the snake before it can strike. Danger over, yet nausea is engulfing me again. He taps round a stone in meagre shade, and then insists I should sit, put my head between my legs and breathe deeply while he calls Carmen back. She shudders at the sight of the mangled reptile and begins to weep. Out of pity for the creature or fear for her or her friend's safety? Felipe commands the situation.

'*Es mediodía.* Time to take a break. We could have lunch at the ruins with more shade and better places to sit. It's only twenty minutes away now. Can you manage it, Valeria?' Felipe asks anxiously. Of course I can, as long as he keeps close to me with his stick and his calm confidence.

When we arrive at what was a Roman temple, Carmen has calmed down sufficiently to spread a red and white check tablecloth over one of the flatter stones, but only after Felipe has tapped and searched every nook and cranny.

'I'll try to find a scarab for you, Valeria!' he jokes, 'but they don't seem to have stayed around since the Carthaginians and then Romans left centuries ago.' I feel distinctly cheered. Carmen's face is charmingly animated, her pale brown almond eyes glancing at Felipe as she busies herself with the picnic. In her mother's absence she is remarkably practical. Whilst eating lunch, trying to forget the viper incident and relishing my new role as chaperone and advisor, I continue checking Felipe's suitability for Carmen. Resourceful, unruffled, reassuring, considerate, knowledgeable, sense of humour - I tick all of them. Why then is Carmen postponing their marriage?

Though Felipe has passed muster on most counts, how traditional is he about women and our status? Or perhaps that doesn't bother Carmen. I imagine she will at least want an open-minded husband. This might be a good time to find out about something in the Fernández family that puzzles me.

'Felipe and Carmen, why d'you think Juan refuses to follow his father in the family business?' I hope I have stressed the right words, especially the 'family business'. Carmen shrugs her shoulders.

'He's made like that,' and she crouches down to wipe the dishes and pack them away. I look at Felipe.

'It's not my business...'

'He's your friend, though,' I insist, somewhat tactlessly.

'Families are important. I'm not sure whether children should revolt against parents who have brought them up conscientiously and paid for their education. They see it as a sort of insurance for their old age, and this is understandable.' He looks into the distance, and starts to get to his feet.

'No, wait,' I protest. I want a bit more time in the shade. 'Don't young people also have their rights? If Juan is a vegetarian, feels strongly about animals and doesn't want to enter his father's business, what's wrong with that?'

Again Felipe hesitates - he is trying to marry a daughter of that family after all! I'm too persistent.

'Look, there aren't many jobs around. I've been offered a better one in an Argentinean firm dealing with agricultural fertilisers. Juan would have a more secure future taking over a well-established business, settling down, marrying and having the backing of his family from the outset.'

'So what about his conscience?' Maybe I shouldn't say this, but I can't stop. 'The Church teaches one should follow one's conscience, which is supposed to be inspired by God.' Felipe is silent. The cicadas continue unabated. Afternoon will soon be slipping into evening. Time to move. I throw in my last card.

'Why can't someone else show interest in the business? Señor Fernández and his manager could easily train you, Carmen, or Ana, or even you, Felipe.' Carmen looks at me, startled.

'Valeria, you're mad! I don't know anything about business.'

'You could learn.' Carmen raises her eyebrows at an idea that would never have entered her mind and wipes her brow for the first time today. Felipe gazes at her, trying to understand her feelings. Even I am startled by my assumed position: I'm the youngest, and here I am asking questions, offering advice and even solutions! I'm apprehensive when Felipe takes up my ideas.

'I'd wondered about the factory but Señor Fernández has never suggested it, so I assume he has come to some agreement with his son. Also, I hesitate to suggest anything that might upset either of them.' His is a delicate position: Juan's friend, Carmen's fiancé. 'So I'm following up the other possibility,' he continues faltering as he speaks, 'that position in a chemicals firm in Argentina offering more scope for promotion than the one I'm working for now, which pays so little in any case'.

Carmen looks irritated. We are forgetting the time and I haven't yet explored the ruins. The stones speak more eloquently with blue-grey shadows, than in the stark light of noon. Hannibal passed through southern Spain before his famous crossing of the Alps, some time B.C., though neither Carmen nor Felipe is sure of his dates. Perhaps we're stepping in his very footsteps!

On the homeward journey Felipe and I talk about the Carthaginians and Romans in southern Spain. Carmen contributes little; even the flounces of her dress look dejected.

౿ఞ

155

The following days witnessed more frequent visits from Felipe. He often stayed overnight in the men's quarters. Carmen meanwhile gashed her mouth with bright-red lipstick, spent endless time in the bathroom every morning, became progressively withdrawn, and was even less keen on her English lessons. I'm taking advantage of this to spend some time with Ana, often discussing poetry and literature while the others are having a siesta. I'm glad to borrow more Spanish books to read, though I worry I may be seen as neglecting my duties to Carmen.

I wanted to talk to the matriarch about Ana, but the opportunity never seems to arise. Some days after the picnic expedition, Ana happens to pass through the living-room where the señora is relaxing in her favourite rocking chair with me perched nearby on the sofa chatting politely to her.

'Ana seems much happier,' *mamá* purrs 'and much more attractive. I do wish she'd tried harder when we were introducing her to some really nice young men, like Maria Asunción's husband. Too late now. They're all married, and Ana is too old.' She sighs. I feel so angry I blurt out,

'Why can't Ana study at Granada University, like her brother?' The matriarch smiles gently, pats my hand, looks up at the ceiling and then around the room. There is an unexpected wistfulness in her voice,

'It's not done to send daughters to study away from home.' She pauses, and then looks directly at me. 'If we lived in Granada, then it might just have been possible to persuade her father...' She glances towards the balcony and the sunlight. 'But here, if a young girl lives away from home before she's married, well, how can I put it, tongues wag. Here in Ronda, they wag a lot.' I sense her regrets, and not just for Ana.

'We did try to get her married, and perhaps then she could have studied a little. But,' the matriarch shakes her head and stares at me again, strangely and sorrowfully, 'men here don't find intellectual women attractive. Educated, yes, to about sixteen, or even eighteen, but no more. They must learn how to keep house, and that's quite a full time job as you can see.'

'Señora, did you ever want to study?' This question hovers unanswered, since by then Ana's mother has prised her ample form out of the rocking-chair to advance towards the pantry door where the maids are already clattering dishes in preparation for the main meal of the day. It is nearly two o'clock.

At lunch Carmen, wearing a rather unflattering dark dress, looks wanly round the table to announce that she isn't feeling well and doesn't want any lunch.

'Please stay,' her mother urges, 'take something light.'

In contrast, Ana is clearly happier in a pretty dress she hasn't worn before. However, I worry about both sisters.

Today is the hottest day of my visit. Torpor slumps over the land. Conversation is desultory and forgettable, appetites dejected. Señor Fernández is never at ease without his son or Felipe or other men at table. He often brings in his manager or under-manager, if he has no visiting business friend to jolly along a conversation.

'Put the lights on,' he orders near the end of the meal. It is strangely dark. By siesta time there are rumbles behind the mountains, and the first flashes of lightning.

'At last!' Carmen stands by our bedroom window and pulls her hair down. It floats out around her shoulders, electrified. I can feel mine standing on end. The forked lightning is darting across the sky towards the mountains, followed by thunder booming out over the town to die back into the distant sierra. We stand side by side facing south and watch the jade curtain of rain slowly drawn from east to west over rust red clouds on the horizon. A near forgotten shiver of pleasurable cold slithers down my spine. Carmen pulls the shawl tightly inwards over her shoulders, as if to shelter a secret. A flash of sheet lightning reveals her sobbing. I touch her shoulder lightly, then squeeze it.

'*Que tienes?*'

'*Felipe me deja.* He's leaving me and going to Argentina. Didn't you hear him say it in the ruins? Well, he's serious about it.' She turns away to sit on her bed, lowering her head to weep in despair.

'Why don't you marry him, and try to persuade him to stay?'

'He doesn't think the job he has now holds any future for him. He's restless, like Juan.' Her sobs turn to moans as she rocks backwards and forwards, head cupped in hands. I sit by her and put my arm round her shoulders, trying to understand her fear of getting married.

'Has your mother talked to you?' That is enough to start Carmen off.

'Oh yes. All about men. Their rough habits and all the rest. She says you have to put up with them, breathe deeply and find your own pleasant thoughts to distract you. She herself always thought of lambs, springtime in the mountains, green fields and blossom, and tried to relax. It hurts less then, she says,' and Carmen bursts into renewed crying at the thought. 'I don't want anyone to touch me. I must stay in control of my body, unviolated,' she adds, as if using the word for the first time.

By now I feel totally out of my depth and slightly guilty. My friend might ask me about my own experiences, or lack of them. Fortunately, Carmen's thoughts concentrate on her own virginity, and she has little inclination to be curious about others. She clearly assumes I'm in the same position as herself, but without the trying decision of having to get married or not.

'And Don José only echoes my mother,' Carmen continues balefully, 'though how does a priest know about such matters? He can't marry, so can only learn from what he reads, like me. Little help it is too.' She must have read about passion in all the romantic novels she devours. They are pretty unspecific, but I could approach Carmen through them.

'You've read about the strong emotions young girls feel in novels and plays. What about *Yerma* or *The House of Bernarda Alba* ?' I venture. Carmen doesn't seem to have read García Lorca's poems or to know his most passionate plays. Perhaps I should be more direct.

'Don't you feel thrilled when Felipe touches you...?' Carmen dries her eyes to gaze at me.

'Of course. Don't you see I love him?' she almost retorts, and then catches her breath. 'But he never does anything I don't want him to. He just touches, well, you know, my face, hair, neck, arms. That's fine. But no more.' He doesn't get much of a chance, poor man, I think, seeing they always meet in company.

'Yes, I do like it. But no more.' Carmen repeats, searching for the right expression. 'There's a story by Cervantes of a man who thinks he's made of glass...'

'I know it!' I say quickly.

'Well, I'm easily shattered like glass. If anyone touches me, then I collapse. A sort of breakdown inside, then...' She looks around the room to see if anyone is listening, 'I realise there's nothing there, so I must repair the glass and keep it clear, clean, uncracked between me and the outside. That's where Felipe is, and where he must stay.' I look at her in blank horror. Nothing inside Carmen. I have never imagined anyone could think like this.

It has stopped raining. Outside the sound of water coursing through the gutters, the first bedraggled twitters of the birds and the steam rising from the plain as rays of afternoon sun escape from behind the dispersing clouds. Carmen has stopped weeping, but sits bunched up in her drab shawl.

'I sometimes wish Felipe would come one evening and we could just run away together...' to the never-never land, I add silently.

'You know Felipe is kind,' I say, hopefully. 'I think you should trust him more. He will never hurt you in any way, I'm sure. But he judges it better to marry the way your parents want, to make them, and you, happier. You do have to decide though. You can't keep him waiting forever, can you?' Carmen sighs.

'No, but I don't know what to do!'

✋

The afternoon before I'm to leave, the matriarch summons me into the sitting-room. She regrets I can't stay longer because they all have to leave to visit her sister at the end of July. I sit again on the sofa by the señora's rocking chair and admire the buxom, open-faced lady looking younger than her age, who must have once been a real Andalucian beauty. Strange it is that none of her children resemble her much. I've wanted to find out more about her but have felt too in awe to ask the obvious questions: where was she born, how many brothers and sisters and how she met her husband. Señora Fernández confides more now she knows me better. After all, an English student isn't part of the Ronda tongue-wagging which she both fears and dislikes.

This time she wants to talk. She was born in Granada, the youngest child after two brothers and a sister. If a Spanish family doesn't have at the very least three children, then the couple can't be up to much, and gossip increases as time passes. Her brothers had to finish university first to see if enough money remained to send her too. Her sister was only interested in getting married. The matriarch met her husband because he studied with her brothers at Granada University. Times were difficult. Her husband came from a wealthy family which had good army connections. Hers instead was more modest. So she married young, at eighteen, but that was quite

160

common at the time. Soon Ana was born, then Carmen and Juan. Her own family was on the opposite side from the Fernández during the Civil War in the Thirties. The losing side. Both her brothers were killed. Her sister escaped to the north of Spain with her family, but their parents were caught in the south. They were disgraced because they opposed Franco, and left penniless.

'My husband helped them out, but they were ashamed at having to accept his hospitality, mourned their sons, and died broken-hearted a few years later.' The señora added tearfully that a university education for her was out of the question. She was too old anyway. So she just continued managing the children and household as a wife should, and the Fernández family continued to prosper.

'My husband doesn't see the point of sending Ana to university, though he could afford it. What was good enough for me, should satisfy his daughter. He likes obedience,' she whispers, 'absolute obedience'.

Carmen's mother ends quietly, as if not to disturb the spirits of her past.

'He is generous. He gave a lot of money to my parents. That's why I find it difficult to ask him to send Ana to university. What should I do?' and she twists her hands together, face distorted in recollecting all she had been telling me - a figure out of a Picasso painting.

CHAPTER 13

The coach for Granada stops just after eight outside the house, so the air is buoyant and fresh with expectation. The Fernández family stands in a row waving me off, tearfully in the case of Ana and the señora. They will leave tomorrow to spend August with the matriarch's sister by the sea. For me, Granada will be the last stop in Spain before travelling on to Italy to stay with Flavia. I'm restless - time to move on.

It's a bumpy ride as the only unoccupied seats are in the back of the vehicle. Señor Fernández insisted on buying my ticket, saying it was the best way to get to Granada. I sit by the window to follow the sun lightly brushing and by midday bleaching the mountain ridges. No snowy peaks these, but worn like snagged teeth, with deep purple valleys and a scattering of lean cattle, the 'brave bulls' of the *corrida de toros*. I shudder in recollection. For the first time since arriving in Ronda I'm recalling the hideous savagery of the bull fight, and Renate. Better to travel alone, whatever people might say.

Narrow and pot-holed, the road hairpins its way up the Sierra. That underlying sense of uneasiness is back after a welcome absence. I turn away from the window and meet large, gently imploring spaniel eyes. 'Not again!' I mutter, strangely excited by another version of the Laughing Cavalier. He has sat down by me, squeezing as close as he can, his eyes inquisitive. There is a distinct challenge in his smile.

I am not averse to male admiration, but like Carmen, I have to be in control. Now our eyes have met, involuntarily on my part, we will have to talk, eventually. I resume my contemplation of the mountains, thinking of the psalm that begins, 'I shall raise my eyes unto the mountains from whence cometh my help,' wondering what form my succour will take. It is all strangely thrilling. Odd though, to feel an occasional slither of icicles coursing from tip to toe. There are flutters in my stomach; we are going up, up and up, so when will we reach the watershed, breach the summit to descend in relief and anticipation towards my goal, Granada?

'*Dónde vas? Cóme te llamas?*' The usual questions break out like a torrent of desire. I am called Valerie and am going to Granada. How gallantly he compliments me on my Spanish while surreptitiously measuring my thighs under my light cotton dress. I try not to look at him or talk too much. He appears rather handsome, with sprawling brown hair and the same sallow skin as Felipe, but wider-spaced, less deep-set eyes and a hairy muscled torso, displayed nonchalantly as if he has forgotten to fasten the top three buttons. 'Neat,' I think. The signs are clear. At least he's not devious. He must have got on before me and taken a leisurely look as I made for a corner seat at the back of the coach. The señora has warned me how unwise it is not to wear a petticoat because of the heat. When the light is behind me, men can make out my legs in silhouette, however long and 'decent' the skirt is. Caught between the Scylla of heat and irritating sweatiness or the Charybdis of unwittingly luring male attention, Charybdis it has to be.

Our conversation continues sporadically. He is called Miguel, lives in Granada, attends the university, and is now at a loose end over the summer vacation. He will take me round the city. The coach in first gear is growling at its full load, emitting so much black exhaust that my head and stomach turn in unison. I'm unresponsive, waiting for the vehicle to reach the highest tooth-edge, to descend perhaps into a more fertile valley. Over the ridge we go, leaving me oddly thrilled, my guts suspended for an extraordinary instant. Miguel brushes my breasts in a seemingly innocent attempt to open the window to give us more air. Another shiver of icicles which I ignore. Into second gear with a lurch, the bus roars down towards the city of the Alhambra.

We arrive when the buildings are dusted with a rosy hue in time for an evening aperitif and promenade. Bone-weary passengers dismount into waiting arms and assorted animal-driven vehicles. My new friend, Miguel, takes my arm to show me an inexpensive *alhondiga* where I can stay. It is typically Spanish, he assures me, in a mockingly jocular manner I enjoy. He has summed me up accurately; I'm aware I'm being manipulated but for the moment it suits me.

Miguel leads me along a narrow cobbled lane following a ridge. We have to avoid donkey droppings or poultry messes, for here the town reaches into the countryside. Not far ahead pack mules are standing in front of a half-timbered building.

'*Aquí la alhondiga, tipicamente español.*' Miguel proudly explains that these inns exist unchanged since Cervantes' time, even long before. Always on the edge of built-up areas, they cater for the constantly moving band of traders who arrive with their pack-animals at sunset. The poorer travellers pay for a place in the stables below, using their saddles as pillows and keeping watch over their goods. Others rent a room above and take their belongings and merchandise up with them.

'I'll do that,' I interrupt him, anxious to check my room has a lock, to keep not thieving but amorous hands at bay. Miguel pulls out a cigarette and waits in the yard below, while the wizened innkeeper takes me up slatted hayloft stairs and along the gallery with rickety wooden banisters to a room at the end. Two beds with rough mealy-brown coverlets stand on either side of a dark graffiti garnished table with two rush chairs. There's a small chipped basin in the corner. I try the tap; water flows grudgingly. The innkeeper indicates a solitary WC before shuffling down to the stables. No shower. I shall have to wash in the basin, or find the public baths. I lock the door and sit on the bed to think. No peace. A knock. I ignore it. Why can't I be left along for once? Miguel can wait or leave. Knock, knock, knock.

'*Estoy ocupada,*' I whisper, irritated.

'*Muy bien.* But you must make sure you pay for the two beds,' Miguel whispers back through the gap between the door and jamb.

'Why?' I suppose he wants to occupy it and is slyly getting me to pay. He seems to read my thoughts.

'*Vado a casa. Después a las ocho, andamos a las cuevas de los gitanos, verdad?* But if you don't pay for the other bed, you might find someone else in it. All beds have to be paid for if you want the room to yourself.' It's strange, but logical, and useful advice whether he wants the bed himself or not.

'*Gracias. A las ocho.*' He'll return at eight. I fancy an evening out, and am longing to see the famous gypsy dancing.

Decked out in my favourite mauve and white striped dress flaring out at the hem with a band to mark my non-existent waist, I wait leaning over the rough railings to survey the courtyard below. I'm relieved the frock still fits, after all that food at the Fernández's! Dusk spreads a comforting tranquillity over the merchants and their beasts. Animals without stabling inside are tied to the poles supporting the gallery where I'm standing. They're munching hay that smells of dried spring flowers from the mountain meadows, challenged increasingly by pungent dung and persistent flies.

Miguel hasn't returned. Perhaps he isn't so eager after all - he might even desert me? I can manage, but feel sad about missing the dancing. Could I find my way there alone, without falling into the hands of more unscrupulous escorts? Is he really a student living in Granada? Action is the only way to deal with my qualms. I step firmly along the gallery to the stairs, spring down them to keep up my spirits, pausing for an instant to survey the courtyard where merchants slump in the dusty shadows, eyeballs gleaming at my stage entrance lit by the solitary lantern over the stairs. I smile and swirl on my heels into the nearest stable entrance. Humid heat hits me laced with the acrid evidence of mules and donkeys chewing, occasionally swinging a tired tail or turning their mournful eyes on me. Preferable, less questioning than their owners dossed down beside them, whose eyes assess me, just as happened on the train to Ronda.

I stand mesmerised for what seems an eternity, until a hand clasps my shoulder. I jump in horror and swing round into Miguel's arms.

'I thought you were never coming...' I shouldn't have admitted it. Here I am in an all-male environment. Even the ancient innkeeper doesn't seem to have a wife.

'*Dónde come esta gente?*' Don't they have some sort of meal at the inn? That would provide female employment. Miguel shakes his head. As we stroll along the cobbled street, he explains that *alhondigas* only provide fodder for the animals. Their owners bring food in with them, usually some bread and ham or cheese. We stop at a kiosk, and he buys us *churros* tipped into newspaper funnels for us to eat as we walk.

'*Ahí, las cuevas...*' We pause at the end of a bridge to look across a gorge at the hill opposite speckled with lights between large patches of dark. There lie these mysterious caves. I quicken my step, anxious to see the famed flamenco dancers.

It is warm and close. Pink and white flowers glance out from the oleanders; white summer jasmine perfumes the air, and clusters of deep purple bougainvilleas punctuate our path. 'More, more!' I cry out silently to myself, fearful of losing something intangible. 'I mustn't forget this!'

'*Aquí!*' Miguel shows me an opening into a room.

'*Una cueva?*' I whisper. He is pointing at a low bench on the left of the entrance next to a pair of middle-aged tourists. Two men with white shirts open to the waist above tight breeches, eye us nonchalantly. The space is hollowed out of the cliff, like an afterthought to extend the pavement and narrow street sliced off by the ravine. Compressed space - how can they dance here? My expectations are slipping. It might have been better to leave it all to my imagination, but Miguel seems to know everyone's name. Through another opening to an inner cave, a dark-haired girl, Consuela, in a blue and white spotted dress is half-pouting as if to protest, 'Nobody else coming? We won't perform. It's too hot anyway'.

A cackle of castanets over a slither of notes from the guitarist seated behind Miguel. A stamped heel on the tile floor. Another girl, Rosita, poses, sheathed to below her hips in a red and white spotted dress falling into tier upon tier of crisp flounces, left hand on forehead cupping the castanet, the other resting curled on her right hip. The men leap into attendance, each offering a hand to welcome his partner, bodies taut, muscled, elegantly alluring. Heads pulled in, the women flick their long black locks over their shoulders, point their chins defiantly, then stamp their feet to their castanets as they each circle the floor space to beat out rhythm and territory. A long click on the right castanet, followed by the left one in a rat-a-tat ta ta is echoed by the irregular tapping of their shiny black high-heeled boots as they circle and swirl, so close that eyes meet mine, flounces alighting for a brief moment on my modestly flared dress. The two men withdraw to the far corner, waiting for some sign. The circular dance completed, territory claimed, standing spectators driven back against the walls and into the street, Pilar - or whoever the dancer is - strums her feet centre stage and strikes a new pose, right arm aloft, head back, raven hair flowing loose and eyes scornfully focusing above the heads of the spectators.

Another splutter of castanets, left hand answering right, and the two men spring into action around her. Slowly revolving, they interlace intricate patterns of feet, eyes, castanets. They stalk Consuela, about to pounce. Languidly she revolves, defying the onlookers out of the corner of her eye; then a sudden jerk upwards of the hip in a shower of blue and white cotton, her hand on the other side gathering the innumerable layers over the right arm to display toe and thigh while the castanet chatters in her free hand.

Red and white clad Rosita enters the fray, castanetting in syncopation with Pilar. The four dancers turn, spokes in a slowly revolving wheel, their eyes now unflinchingly bewitching us. I draw my feet back, entranced, ready to leap into action and join them, but the four held-out hands, middle fingers jerking downwards to strike a warning on their castanets, ward me off. I can only watch.

The slowly rotating wheel breaks apart in a violent confrontation of Rosita in red with Consuela in blue, raised hands, layers of flounces flung in proud rivalry, the points of their black lace shawls pulled down to assert their generous bosoms to all assembled. The air enfolds them, as they mould space proudly arching their backs and circling their hands round their hips, castanets patterning the rhythm in harmony with their movements. The men interrupt, slicing the space apart in swift syncopation of hand, toe and heel, casting lecherous looks into the haughty eyes of the two girls. In response they turn heads, flaunt hips and stab the air into splinters of guitar notes to thrill the spectators. A tingle starts in my fingers and toes, spurring me to join in. Prudence and fear of being scorned restrain me. Stamping, lithe and quivering bodies mould curves of voluptuous space. Silence, then syncopation, and the more frequent *olé* from the male dancers, and now taken up by increasingly excited spectators. The sombre, incessant rhythms throb through the blood in a cascade of sensuous sound.

It's overwhelming. I must join in or escape.

'Qué ojos azules! Muy hermosos.' I frown in disbelief and look round at Miguel to find Consuela by him gazing strangely at my eyes. Strangely, blue eyes attract her. After the flamenco, the dancers mingle with the spectators, rapidly dewitching them by offering a gypsy palm. Still dazed in delight and bewilderment, I realise I'm a good four inches taller that the two flamenco dancers, and my columnar body contrasts strangely with the curves of generous bosoms, small waists and large, rounded hips. 'Whew, they can

dance!' I observe, 'my legs would tie themselves in knots.' Lucky I didn't try.

Outside the almost full moon winks at me. Miguel puts his arm round my shoulders, squeezes my upper arm and kisses me under my ear. The disturbing tingle dies away in the humid, sweaty air around people lounging outside. The oleander flowers seem to wilt. The spell is broken. Miguel is short, stocky, too bristly. The moon can wink on to heart's content; I'll ignore the ripples of emotion. One preoccupation now: to find my way back to the *alhondiga* and make sure that no one has taken the other bed. I was too carried away to remember Miguel's warning which I'm now heeding as determinedly as I wish to be rid of him.

'*Vado a la alhondiga. Tengo sueño.*' I'm tired and sleepy, but I don't want to admit I have lost my way, too excited by an evening out with, then, a reasonably attractive young man. Miguel trots along by my side, trying to keep his arm around me as I stride ahead. The street is easy to find, the cobbled lane less so. He makes no objection to showing me the way back to the inn, squeezing and stroking me as far as he can on the way.

The lamp over the stairs to the upper storey lights up the animals snoozing in the yard and the humped outlines of their owners. Hardly a sound, just a muffled snore, a half snort gulped back into a nightmare. Stillness commands the cooling air.

'*Tengo miedo,*' I whisper to him. I had better confide that I have not followed his advice. I might need his help. 'I'm afraid there might be someone in my room. I didn't have time to pay for the second bed as well.'

'Don't worry. I did.' Miguel smiles and all I can see are the bristles rushing out of his nose at me. I scramble as fast as I can up those stairs, beating the boards along the gallery outside the row of bedrooms before mine, slam the door to a curse from the adjacent room, and turn the key in the lock before he calls me to open it. I mustn't remove the key, I warn myself as I feel around for the light switch. Perhaps they have plenty of keys to the room, or one universal key, like one universal WC which I desperately need to use. There still might be someone else, certainly male, in the spare bed. Worse. Two. In mine as well. They might even have double sold it. I've paid, and Miguel has somehow settled for the other bed, but we were absent while the rest of the trading fraternity was settling into sleep.

As the door rattling increases, the cursing spreads into a chorus from one room to others round the gallery. I grope at the wall in growing desperation. Panic engulfs me in anticipation of unknown arms grabbing at me from inside the room, or the would-be assault from Miguel outside which has turned from pleading to sharp jabs at the key hole, to dislodge the one I've providentially left there. I find the switch at last - both beds unoccupied, not a soul besides me. Oh Lord be praised...

'Adiós, Miguel!' I yell for all to hear, seeing the inhabitants are awake and protesting. They will surely come to the help of a poor maiden in distress if need be. My key stops jiggling, the handle rattling ceases, and I imagine Miguel slinking off, defeated. A few minutes later I open the door a crack, to see if the way is clear to the WC. All has settled back into silence. Relief is at hand, however bad the smell!

I turn off the light hoping all the moths lured by the unshaded bulb will fly out into the night. The moon shines in, no longer winking. A short, piercing squeak splits the air above me. I haven't heard that sort of sound before. Perhaps it's my fertile imagination. I'd better close the window to keep the mosquitoes out. It's not yet midnight, not too late for me to sort out my plans. I close the window, turn on the light and rummage in my bag for the now well-scuffed exercise book. That pin-prick of sound again. Ignore it. Stupid imaginings. There are many more important things to do.

I have never felt so pleasurably self-conscious as I did this evening. Totally absorbed in admiration of those flamenco dancers, especially the girls with their supple movements, precision of gesture and beat, I would never have thought I could have won their approval. Also the whole question of blue eyes. I'm a Celt, blue eyes and dark hair, not the Scandinavian type that I thought would fascinate them. Men seem to move me in strange ways, especially those shivers coursing from top to toe, but few actually interest me. I seem to prefer the dark type like the Laughing Cavalier, but he's too groomed to have bristles in odd places, and must have been tall. He couldn't have been Miguel who had to stand on tiptoe to kiss me.

It's a silly old convention, I suppose, that men should bend down protectively and women look up, protected. But I still like men to be taller, slim, wide-shouldered. Miguel has wide shoulders all right, but is stocky to plump. Not my type. And those hairs everywhere.

I should leave before he tries to find me in the morning, if he does. I could phone Flavia in Genoa and ask her if I can arrive the day after tomorrow. I must see the Alhambra in the morning because I need to make notes for the scene where my heroine meets the hero. It may not be right, but I must try it. Anyway, it's the most famous Moorish monument in Spain.

It's now well after midnight. I reckon the travelling merchants will be up at dawn, ready to move on as I am. Time to sleep. It's so sticky in the room I'll have to reopen the window. I'll wash in the morning.

Just as I am about to sink into fitful sleep, that sound pricks again. So acute, thin, sharp, almost supernatural. Another witch-like squeak, and a whirr between the beams. A repetition. In horror I realise there must be at least two bats resting or nesting in the beams above me. Their droppings might fall on my head. They might entangle themselves in my hair. I had better try and chase them out of the window. On goes the light. Two tiny bats are hanging on the beam above my bed. With one end of my knapsack strap I swipe at them, to multiple high-pitched protests and eventual success. Fearful they might return, I'm spending a most unhappy night, window shut, on a sweat-soaked sheet till the establishment awakes at dawn. In daylight the bats will stay outside, but as I open the casement and breathe in the fresh morning air, two black swallow-like souls of witches shoot past my right ear, piercing my eardrum in triumph.

The innkeeper has been brewing coffee since dawn and making an extra *peseta* by selling it to the men as they strap on saddle packs and exchange quips and trading tips. I've bought a mugful too, black and sugared. Bumping my suitcase behind me across the flagstones, I follow a couple of pack animals, one of them lame, being led under the arch into the cobbled lane. Space is offered on one of them. An itinerant salesman hitches my suitcase on to his mule; his clothes and food are in a large check kerchief balanced over his shoulder at the end of a stick. Together we set off.

This muleteer is going out of his way to take me to the station, so I give him a few extra pesetas. He is heading for the mountains to buy more hides to sell on to Granada craftsmen who make belts, wallets and purses for the local markets. He plans to supply a network of cobblers and that's why he has stayed longer in Granada and his mules have less to take back to the mountain villages, just the villagers' needs such as soap and sugar as far as I can see. Lucky for me and my suitcase. We chat about our families, me in more fluent Spanish because relaxed and feeling unthreatened by this friendly, enterprising, illiterate father of five. He has heard of the Alhambra, but is not sure how to get there. The station clerk gives me rough directions and opens the left luggage for my suitcase. A train leaves for France in the early afternoon. From there to Italy. Flavia lives in Genoa, not too far from the French border.

It's a sparkling morning. Here I am, alone and in full control. I take a bus to the hill of the fountains, the magical world of the greatest Muslim palace and garden in the world. The entrance gates are closed, but there are benches near the refreshment kiosk. I sit down, take off my knapsack and plonk it beside me, leaning back to stretch out my arms and legs and close my eyes. It's good just to be alive.

'*Señorita!*' This time a woman's voice, not another would-be laughing Cavalier. I need some hours of peace and quiet to sort out my plans and my priorities. I haven't written to Mike for so long.

'*Señorita!*' I jerk my legs back under the bench, pull my skirt down taut over my knees and, keeping my head low, peep up from under my eyebrows, like the flamenco dancers. A middle-aged woman, tending towards the scrawny, with shoulder-length dyed blond hair, is smiling down at me. With relief, I straighten my back, look up and return the smile. Perhaps she just wants a chat, or advice, or something harmless.

'Can I sit by you?' she continues in Spanish.

'Of course.' Then the usual 'where do you come from?' series of obvious questions. I decide to respond in kind, wondering why this woman wants to talk to me, just like that, out of the blue.

'From Buenos Aires. I'm here with my brother-in-law. We're on holiday in Europe, now on our last lap, and I just wanted to speak to another tourist.'

'I'm studying. Language, and art. Culture, that sort of thing.' I baulk at the thought of being slipped neatly into the tourist category.

'You're travelling alone then?' Elisabeta, as this lady from Buenos Aires is called, seems surprised.

'How can one practise the language otherwise?'

'Well, if you come with us, then you'll get plenty of practice. We know little English. Just a word or two.'

173

It's after nine now, and the gates are open. I want to dream at will through the gardens, untrammelled by others. I turn to the leathery-skinned Elisabeta beside me and hold out my hand.

'So nice to have met you. Perhaps...' Elisabeta jumps up smartly, spruce in her olive green linen dress, only slightly creased under her bottom.

'I'll call Roberto and we'll go in together.' With a scowl of angry frustration I try to extract myself. There is only one way into the Alhambra, by the ticket kiosk. I make for it only to find it blocked by a man of my height and at least twice my girth, hand proffered, smile to his ears splitting his face in two badly-related halves under an implausible shock of tufty black hair.

'*Roberto González. Buenos días, Señorita.*' I am trapped between them, Elisabeta behind me and Roberto in front buying three tickets. I hold mine grudgingly, and start to pull out my purse. Elisabeta takes my arm with, 'No, no, you're our guest today.'

'*Gracias, pero -*' and having doled out the minimum required of my store of politeness, I leap up the slope, over steps, along avenues, dip my hands in the flowing water, run them through the spray under the fountains, stroke the columns, step through ogee-shaped openings cutting sky into azure shapes and skip over bright tiles sparkling in splinters of colour, to pause beneath endless intricate patterns of carved marble, lacy stucco and delicately pierced woodwork. I rush on ahead of my would-be companions, seeking hidden corners, hiding in small side rooms until they pass by into the next hall or courtyard. Then I emerge, imagining the courtyard shimmering with voices of richly apparelled women, demure with arms lightly covered by finely wrought lace shawls echoing the carved canopies, intricate lattice screens, stucco patterns and the brilliant designs of the tiles beneath them. Then I feel the shadows of Roberto and Elisabeta. My web of fantasy torn, I ignore them to flee into the next sequence of spaces, to find a hiding place and give them the slip.

Accomplished. Now I can cast imaginary men, all handsome to a fault and disconcertingly like Jose Maria, into my lively group of women to sip sorbets in their company. Drinks are replenished by servants waiting in the shadows. One of the chimerical girls resembles Renate. I begin to giggle. That is as far as my historical imagination can go!

' *Valeria. Señorita!*' The two shadows are casting their spell. No.

'I need to be alone here.'

'We'll meet you outside, then. For a drink.'

At last I can pause in the central courtyard of the lions and dream about space and colour, the architecture moulding my thoughts, feelings and associations. I yearn for Mike, want to hug him, and resolve to buy a card and send it to him. Amid such beauty, I feel acutely homesick for the first time. Nearly five weeks away. Too long? I have never tried such a long period abroad before. And I must study, practise my languages, write, or at least organise my ideas for the novel. This is so magical a setting that anything could happen.

I trail my hand along the channel of water and turn towards the entrance which is also the exit. It is nearly midday and the heat is too stifling even for me. Only a family buying tickets. The way is clear. I'm probably imagining things, acting like a suspicious child not a confident adult. A lemon drink at the refreshments kiosk? That is appropriate here in Andalucía with its orange and lemon groves. I sit down, close my eyes and, leaning against the back of the bench, slip into a wave of sleepiness.

'I'll buy the *señorita* lemonade.' Elisabeta's voice jolts me awake. 'Come over here and sit with us. You look tired. Why don't you come and take a room in our hotel? I'm sure there is a single room free. Most tourists don't come in the hot season.'

'Thanks, but I'm leaving this afternoon. In fact I should be going now.' More precisely, in two hours' time.

'Have you ever seen real flamenco dancing?' Roberto leans over Elisabeta towards my end of the bench. I nod. 'We'll take you to Seville where the dancing is the best in the world. We can stay in the finest hotel, right in the centre.'

'But I've seen Seville.'

'The dancing there? And the luxury hotel?' Roberto ploughs his line with ponderous single-mindedness. 'Anyway, we can have lunch now, and then discuss what you could do with your looks and brains. You'd be a hit in Buenos Aires, you know. Millionaires there are - '

Even he is daunted by the look in my eyes.

'I'm due back at University in October. I'm not looking for millionaires, or anybody else!' My voice rises to a shrill crescendo - the very thought of me, a brainy girl, I hope, being baited by the prospect of rich millionaires is positively disgusting, the whole proposal lewd and preposterous. What on earth are they hatching?

'I'm a serious person,' I almost shout at him.

'So are we,' he smiles back, 'but we all have to pay our way, and I'm giving you a unique chance to live a good life, earn plenty of money and to see the world without scrounging as you are now -'

'Scrounging?' shrilly, 'I'm not scrounging. I'm paying for everything, and would have paid for the ticket and the lemonade if you hadn't barged in first!' I'm looking from one to the other, this unexceptional middle-aged pair - what on earth are they up to? I search my mind and don't like what I find.

'You're utterly off track. I neither need nor want money. *Adiós!*'

More fast walking down the dusty track to the tarmac in what seems to be the direction of the bus station. Their calls pursue me; I break into a run terrified of a touch on the shoulder, or a tackle from behind. Faster and faster, a hammer beating my heart into my head. No time to stop or gasp for breath, as I wheeze my throat dry. I can't go on any longer. I must look round to see if they are still following. I'll find a doorway and peer out. Here. Just people walking along the street, and a policeman coming towards me. What have I done now? I have to escape, flee, my heels now sore from pounding along pavements. Faster, faster, then a hand catches my shoulder. I scream, a high-pitched note descending in a crescendo of despair as I crash to the ground, my knapsack skidding along the road.

'Señorita, che tiene usted?' Faces are peering down at me, not unkindly. A guardia civil touches my shoulder, wondering why I look so frightened and was running so fast. I'm shaking all over, covered in sweat and dust and indignity. I can't explain it all in Spanish. How stupid they will think I am. I haven't even been assaulted! It's the insistent pursuit of proposals and innuendoes; it's the degrading way I, a respectable young woman, am being picked out for some seedy trade; it is - my sobs become uncontrollable. Two men help me to my feet. A matronly woman with a small child inspects my knees to make sure I haven't grazed them too badly. Another hand from behind is asking me to sniff a small bottle of sal volatile or something to revive me. A cup of coffee and a bun later I'm sitting in the police office trying to explain my fright. That was real enough, even though I suspect they don't quite fathom what it is all about.

The policeman insists on escorting me to the railway station. I'm embarrassed. Do people staring at me in the street think I'm a criminal? Well, do I really care? Not a whit! I'm leaving, and anyway, they can see I'm not handcuffed and a young guardia civil is happily chatting to me. Or perhaps he too harbours lewd thoughts? Help. My mind flees towards Flavia in Genoa - my haven.

The guardia carefully places my luggage in the rack of an empty carriage. 'Adiós! Adiós! Muchas gracias, muchísimas...'

Promptly, at two in the afternoon at boiling point in that cauldron of a day, I slump on to the train going north through Barcelona to the South of France and, with changes and combinations, nosing its way round the northern coast of the Mediterranean to Genoa. I stretch out along the seats and fall asleep, but not before I have cautiously hidden my passport and money inside my jacket which I use as a pillow. Just one more adventure would crack me open into tiny pieces - another woman of glass.

CHAPTER 14

Flavia gives me an enthusiastic welcome. She and her family live in three fourth-floor rooms overlooking the port of Genoa.

'Better a building facing the sea, even if I can't see it from here,' her father Signor Mario Cecconi tells me. Shifting frontiers forced him, his wife, daughter and other Italians to leave Fiume when it became Rijeka in Yugoslavia after World War II. His wife Livia has relatives in Genoa. Flavia told me this when I met her in England, but there was no mention of the cramped quarters.

'At least I don't have to share a bedroom with my parents as some of the Fiume refugees have to,' Flavia is anxious to tell me, 'and there's a spare bed for you.'

Neither had Flavia mentioned that she would be working as a maid in a hotel most days and some nights during the university vacation. It seems a bit odd to invite me to stay, my first time in Italy, in these circumstances. I buy a street map, a copy of Dante and an English-Italian dictionary; the best way to start learning a language is by reading its greatest writer. The grammar and vocabulary will be very similar, I imagine, to Spanish. I want to spend as little time as I politely can in the kitchen where the family cook, eat and even wash themselves behind a makeshift screen. To my amazement, the only WC on the landing outside is shared with three other families.

I'm starting to practise Italian by deciphering the notices down at the port, intrigued by the loading and unloading of crates of peaches and watermelons, with the perky black tugs and majestic liners jostling the unassuming cargo steamers and ferries. Aloof, a destroyer is moored further out in the bay, unwelcome at this display of peacetime activity. Further on behind a breakwater, a few yachts seesaw, waves lazily tracing a rim of foam on the strip of sand; beyond the mountains slide into the sea.

Chapter 14

I decide to frequent the beach in the afternoon taking Signor Cecconi's battered black umbrella, a sandwich, the dictionary and Dante's *Divina Commedia*. Signora Cecconi offered some thin broth the first day, apologising for only having a light lunch while Flavia is out working. She and her mother keep clothes and shoes to slip on when they go out; at home they change into button-up cotton dresses and plastic beach shoes. When we're out together, Flavia will pull her skirt up behind her to avoid sitting on it and creasing it. She didn't do that in England.

These drifting victims of history couldn't have been kinder, but sadness tinges them spreading a soft grey dust over their tiny apartment. Better, I feel, not to be too much of a burden, to be out and independent. So I decide to take off to Milan for a day.

༜

The ticket clerk is half asleep when I arrive early at the station to ask for a return ticket. A pity, but I used up the last kilometres on my student one coming here from Spain.

'Biglietto di ritorno per Milano, per favore.' He looks at me oddly, then gives me a small green cardboard ticket. I check the departures board. *Binario 7*. Easy. I'll reach Milan by mid-morning.

It is a spectacular journey through the Ligurian Alps, when the train isn't burrowing into tunnels, before emerging to steam across the rice fields of the Po plain. I busy myself with the day's ration of new vocabulary to place around the obvious verbs – *avere, essere, andare, venire*, have, be, go, come – and there's the next Canto of Dante's *Inferno* to pore over, before adding to the notes for my novel and updating the entries in my journal.

There isn't much to note down. A long but uneventful journey from Granada to Genoa, and now another to Milan. Strange how full compartments lead to formal exchanges only and little attempt at conversation. I have been told Latin people are garrulous, but this is hardly borne out by my present experience.

180

I'm mildly annoyed at being denied the chance to practise my few Italian phrases. I've bought the *Secolo Decimonono* to read. The gist of the headlines is quite easy, but I have to look up so many words in the feature articles that I idle over the advertisements instead. Why are there so many *massaggiatrici,* I wonder, some with numerous As in front, like AAAAAA *massaggiatrice* and the contact details? Odd. My glance slips down the column to find what seems to be a family looking for someone to care for their children, an occasional, live-in babysitter. That might be a way for me to earn a little money as well as have my living expenses paid. I could, with Flavia's help, try telephoning them this evening.

The day continues just as I planned. I pick up a free street map at the tourist office in Milan station, check the list of places I've marked in my guidebook to Northern Italy and set off along wide 19th-century streets lined with grey blocks of flats. Everyone knows the sooty white cathedral that seems to have decamped over the Alps from the Gothic north into Renaissance Italy. In this vast, dark shrine to centuries of prayer, I can hardly make out the statues and heavily-framed paintings behind all the flickering candles. My eyes adjust uneasily from the searing sunshine outside. Next on the list - the Sforza castle. I remember Leonardo was employed by Ludovico Sforza, Duke of Milan, who was subsequently chased from his city by the French. Leonardo made a trial equestrian statue of a rearing horse bearing the Duke, Ludovico Sforza, in readiness for a full-blown bronze one. The huge plaster model in the main courtyard was shot to pieces by the bored French soldiers billeted there, in the early 1500s, I think. A long time ago. It's nearly midday and I'm hot and hungry. There might just be time to see Leonardo's *Last Supper* near the monastic church of Santa Maria delle Grazie, if I hurry.

That means running the half mile to Leonardo's masterpiece in scorching heat. Flavia's father has been talking of 'dog days', waiting for turbulent storms to clear the heat which increases when the Dog Star Sirius is on the prowl. This August is worse than any he can recall. While scurrying from castle to monastery I am perfecting the technique learnt from Renate in Córdoba: walking briskly with a vague smile on my lips while focusing on something at the far end of the street well above people's heads. In this way I avoid engaging with eyes that might interpret my chance look as an invitation. Calls of *Che bella ragazza!* can be pleasantly ignored, my progress unimpeded.

'It's closed, Valerie! Come and have lunch with us.' I blink to focus on two figures talking in English and blocking my way. Clever of them to realise I'm on my way to Leonardo's painting. The dark-haired one I recognise immediately. Miranda Coldstream is at Cambridge, in the same college and year. Her friend too smiles in recognition.

'We've met, haven't we?' I'm not sure where and when. The face seems familiar. We work it out over lunch; not university, nor school. It must have been that embarrassing dance at a boys' public school, probably Charterhouse as I was living in Godalming. It was a clumsy attempt to introduce us at all-girl schools to young men. She and I had sought refuge in the make-shift women's cloakroom to bemoan the scarcity of attractive males; the current lot were mostly raw, gauche, unable to dance and generally unappetising, we agreed, while frantically rearranging hair and make-up. This self same girl has reappeared in Milan with a mutual friend, both having just contemplated Leonardo's *Last Supper*. Paths seem to cross so easily. To celebrate the deity of coincidences – we can't think of the appropriate saint, if he or she exists – we find a table outside a *trattoria*, and decide to renounce frugality, for the moment at least. *Bistecca alla milanese* it is appropriately to be, although wafer-thin slices of veal coated in egg and breadcrumbs I had always thought of as Viennese *Wiener schnitzel.*

'I suppose,' comments Miranda, 'it's because Milan was part of the Hapsburg Empire, until Italian reunification'. I'm impressed.

I've been rather lazy about reading up the background history of the countries and towns I'm visiting. Never enough time. It's hard even to keep my journal up to date.

'Have you heard from Mike?' Miranda asks.

'Not for ages. I think he has my address in Genoa.' She's right. I should keep in touch with him. So we talk, eat and time slips by unnoticed.

'I'll have to go. Can't miss the Leonardo.'

A sleepy monk is just opening the door of a rather nondescript building at right angles to a church, its dull brick façade enhanced by terra cotta sculpture. He looks me up and down as I pause in the square to take it all in, and then retreats into the shade leaving the door ajar. Inside the monastery it is still as if expecting something to happen. A notice in the refectory reminds me that this oil painting has been restored, the words almost seeming to grumble. There are bits still missing. I slowly approach to where the abbot's table once stood under the painted supper. As if in a negative with random blotches of colour, the apostles lean towards one another, to gesticulate and cry out in grimaces of disbelief while Christ, head serenely framed by shimmering mountains seen through a window behind him, spreads his hands out, palms open towards me, Valerie, alone in the room. I imagine the commotion in the steamy kitchen behind the painted wall, while the abbot in the refectory on this side was berating the artist as the new film of paint was already flaking off. Other visitors wander in, some whispering about the war damage. I sit in peace on a bench to reflect and digest, before spurring myself out to start my sultry return to the station.

I'm taking a different way back through the small alleys behind one of the oldest churches in Milan, Sant'Ambrogio, to the cathedral. The streets curve and turn so often I have to check the map, taking a route through one square into a smaller one with the Ambrosiana Library on one side. It has a fine collection including a

Botticelli, according to my guide book. There's time to spare. The entrance lobby has a friendly feel about it, a place with no need to hurry.

The postcard stand is at the far end of the ticket desk. I follow my usual strategy in art galleries, glancing through the cards to get an idea of the most famous works on display. A page from an illuminated manuscript catches my eye. It comes from Petrarch's copy of Virgil illustrated by Simone Martini. I've seen illustrations of his frescoes in the Town Hall at Siena, secretly preferring him to Giotto. Here he's working on such a tiny scale. How strange. I move over to the elderly man absorbed reading behind the desk.

'*Sono una studentessa,*' with a tentative smile, 'and I'm studying Petrarch at the University of Cambridge. Could I possibly look at his copy of Virgil?' He nods seriously, raising one hand to smooth back locks of fine greying hair while indicating a dark polished bench with the other. I'm alone in the silent entrance hall speckled with the dust of ages. His shoes squeak on the wooden floor boards as he returns with another man in brown overalls. A library assistant?

'*Venga, signorina,*' says the assistant, his parchment face expressionless. I pad after him obediently, uncertain where he is taking me. To sit and wait in a large room on one of a row of seats with high, dark wooden lecterns in front of them. Not a soul stirring. Still the last of the siesta to go, but the library is open, readers strangely absent.

'Am I alone?' I whisper.

'In summer,' the librarian confides, 'scholars go to the mountains or sea with their families, if they can afford it, or stay with relatives if they can't. I'm left here with the treasures'.

He shuffles away to the stacks, a gaunt figure shrouded in a brown overall, sniffing and sneezing to clear the dust in his throat. A moment later he leans over my left shoulder to place a volume on the lectern in front of me. Here it is, Petrarch's copy of Virgil's

Eclogues and *Georgics*. His very own copy! It is worn, the corners slightly scuffed. Gingerly I touch it, to open it just as he would have done. 'Francesco Petrarca,' I remember the professor's precise words in a lecture I went to out of curiosity, 'is the father of Renaissance humanism, the first to speak to ancient writers like Virgil as his living friends'. I pore over another page, wondering how Petrarch, leaning back over thirteen centuries, might have addressed Virgil. 'Enjoyed what I read today, but you might have told me more about... or used different words...' and so on. I imagine him counselling Virgil, though not very convincingly. Would he have been reverential, critical, or fraternally jocular? Virgil seemed a stern type to me when I was struggling through the *Aeneid* at school, hardly the sort to write love poems to a young married woman, like Laura, as Petrarch had done when working for the Pope in Avignon! Stranger still, he'd taken clerical vows of celibacy, but a daughter looked after him in his old age. Streuth! they used to say at school. The human drama behind austere historical fame - very exciting! Turning another page I find my hero has sinned again. Hadn't I been forbidden at school to write in the margins? Here Petrarch is doing it! If you're famous, scribbled comments become 'annotations'! On another page, Simone Martini delineates figures with expressive faces and forthright gestures that look like so many Dantes in tunics and long cloaks - or are they togas – and elsewhere labourers accomplish each season's tasks. Scenes are framed with scrolling stems of flowers and leaves, mythical creatures emerging from horns, buds or chalices, a glorious cornucopia entwining visual fantasy with decoration, all in a breathtaking intensity of blues, greens, and reds.

'*Signorina,* time to return the manuscript.' I look at my watch. It's nearly six. Help! I've been in Francesco and Simone's company for well over an enthralled hour. I smile and '*mille grazie*' the brown overalled man with the parchment face before speeding out towards the cathedral, shimmering less as now partly in shadow, through the Galleria Vittorio Emanuele, heated like a greenhouse at the end of a torrid day (Flavia told me to tread on Taurus's testicles in the mosaic; that brings good fortune in love) and back over a long mile to the Stazione Centrale, thinking of Petrarch and his beloved Laura. If I don't catch the seven o'clock train my ticket won't be valid - I had heard some mumbling about it being a special rate.

I make it, but the train is packed. The Friday rush hour, I suppose. Just my luck to choose the wrong time, but does it matter after such an unexpectedly amazing day? I could never have imagined it in all my wildest dreams. If only I could find a seat, I could settle down to try and read the rest of the newspaper and even dream about Laura or snooze a bit. I'm not used to rising so early. Down the corridor I go, peering into compartments to point at bags or cases, packages or clothes left on unoccupied seats enquiring '*occupato?*' This isn't, it seems, a very Italian way of carrying on, but I have paid for a seat, so will take one if nobody else claims it. A city type grudgingly removes his attaché case from the seat beside him, places it on his lap and opens it pointedly to remove documents. There is plenty of room on the luggage rack, I think in self-justification, but I still sense they resent my uppity handling of the situation.

The train clatters through the suburbs; not a word is uttered by the members of the Latin race seated around me. 'It just shows how pointless all generalisations are!' I comment to myself, 'and who says Italians are small?' The snooty individual who has reluctantly denied his case a seat beside him is hardly small, and opposite is a tall, clumsily proportioned man in his early thirties, I reckon, looking at me curiously - as is everyone else. Still not a word, however, so I pull out my pocket dictionary and set about the newspaper. Shifting my legs, I touch the young man's foot by mistake.

'*Mi dispiace.*' Sorry.

'*Non fa niente, signorina.*' That's all right. Is he shyly - or slyly - waiting for a break to ask my name and what I do? I'll encourage him; a chance to practise a bit of Italian instead of struggling with the boring paper. He is Giacinto, from Genoa, a lawyer who works in Milan returning home for a summer break, and not before time, he stresses for want of anything better to say to the foreigner.

The door to the corridor has been left open to let air in, but irritatingly the ticket conductor still rattles his keys against the glass to accompany his strident '*biglietti*'! I'm the last to show mine as it has caused momentary panic, forgotten in the zipped part of my purse which I have never used before.

'*Ma signorina, non è valido!*' How ridiculous! It must be current. I bought a return ticket this morning because I have used all the miles on my student pass. I tap the ticket.

'*Ecco il biglietto di ritorno.*' Here's my return ticket.

'*No, solamente andata.*'

'*Impossibile!*'

'*Vero, signorina.*' By this time all eyes are on me. It's a one way ticket, Genoa to Milan. I shall have to pay the balance, and a fine too, I fear. I delve into my handbag to grasp my purse. The conductor yawns, resting his shoulder on the door, swinging the keys in his free hand and repeating what seems to me the huge sum I owe. I take out all the notes and coins I have left - not much as I spent more than intended on lunch - and he counts them out in my hands. The other passengers around me, eyebrows raised, are calculating too.

'*Non basta, signorina.*' Insufficient. He pushes the notes and coins down into my palms with the frustration of yet more jobs to do, turns and stomps into the adjoining compartment. I'm left an object of open curiosity: a foreigner allowed to travel on the train at their expense is, I gather, the gist of some murmured comments. I don't know what to do with the money, or where to look, so stuff it willy nilly into my purse, then into my worn imitation leather handbag, staring down at it until my neck aches. A touch on my shoulder. It is now unbearably close and quiet in the crowded compartment. I look up into a pair of wide brown eyes, noting a whiff of wine in the invitation to accompany him. This engaging young man wears a light blue shirt, navy blue trousers and a cap with the words *Polizia Ferroviaria* in gold letters on it. As always, they come in twos, and his companion, a stocky blond, is peering over his shoulder.

'*Venga, signorina.*' Nothing for it but to go. The tall thirty-something-year-old Giacinto who struck up a brief conversation before the conductor interrupted him is gazing, speechless, as the policemen escort me out of the carriage to an unknown destination.

What a name to give a son, I think as I follow the first policeman through one carriage after another, the blond bringing up the rear. Hyacinth! Wouldn't he be teased? The name, his gaping expression, inconsequential questions and comments sum this Hyacinth up: a gormless character if ever there is one. I find myself propelled into a first class carriage with curtains and a blind over the glass on the door. There is a key in the lock. Leaving his companion in the corridor, the dark-haired policeman - medium height, sturdy, not fat, and quite attractive in a predictable sort of way – tells me to sit down and relax. They can't leave me in the compartment without paying, he explains, so I have to be held here on my own until we reach Genoa where they will see what they can do. Presumably I don't have a bank account? I feel relieved. I can't pay, not until I get back to Flavia's room where I have left my store of lira that has to last a month. If this is my temporary prison, at least I can relax in plush comfort and try to read the newspaper undisturbed. I nod at the young man who doesn't seem to have anything pressing to do, and open the newspaper.

'*Signorina...*' The usual questions. No peace for me. I settle back into my seat, place my elbows on the armrests and decide to refine the art of preliminary conversations in Italian, extending my vocabulary by getting him to do the talking. His will be easy to grasp, so limited and hardly likely to suggest many new trophy words to me. I return his smile and lightly try to answer with my limited vocabulary. It is fun, and he is warming to it. With more and more questions, then the story of his life, he grins his way to pushing up the armrest and stroking my hand. Though I have to admit I rather like the caress, I know I should withdraw my hand without causing offence. He persists; his other hand begins stroking my knee. I push that away, but his left hand starts - could he be left-handed? - deftly undoing the buttons on my blouse. Both my hands spring up to deal with the left-handed assault, leaving his right one free to roam still further up my leg. Down both mine dive to deal with the lower challenge, and his left one returns to the upper incursion.

'No!' I shriek in his eardrum, twisting my neck sharply as he tries to kiss my lips. He sinks back, aurally stabbed, his loud breathing and grunts uncannily stifled. I turn my back on him to glower across the plain into the bloodstained sunset. All I hear is a key turning to open the door. Alone. I stand up, stretching in relief, to lock the door behind him, but the key has disappeared. I twist the handle. He has locked me in. What a puny revenge – I can easily attract attention once we arrive in Genoa! Flipping the armrest down again I try to settle back into some degree of calm. The print jumps around in front of my eyes, so I lean back to look out in a desultory fashion. The hamlets and scattered farms appear with the first specks of light from windows and oxen trundling straw-laden carts towards them, the farmhands trudging home behind. It is a calming, hallowed pattern. I don't hear the key turning.

'*Ecco la bella Valeria!*' The blond policeman slips into the seat opposite, grinning at me with untoward confidence. He must have learnt my name from his mate. I scowl back, and swivel to catch the last echoes of sunset on the wide reaches of the Po and a glimpse of the rising moon before the train plunges southwards into the foothills of the Ligurian Apennines. Still some way to go, and this Franco, as he introduces himself, is already leaning confidently towards me, almost leering. I take refuge in the far corner by the closed and covered compartment door. Useless to try it. I have to play for time. We haven't even reached the tunnels yet. The best anti-aphrodisiac, I decide, will be conversation, gushes of it. My limited Italian is desperately pressed into use. Delighted, he shifts to the seat next to me. Alarmed, to keep my distance I lean down on the armrest between us. Encouraged, he tries to catch my face between his two hands and only just misses my lips. Disturbed, I leap into the seat opposite as he laughs and lunges at me, right hand running up the inside of my thigh and the other firmly grasping my neck.

'Per favore!' I whisper, not to startle any passengers in the next carriage. The train is veering into the first tunnel. Many to go, I remember, and how can I fend him off for that long? Talk, talk, talk, I berate myself. It's hard with this man right against me, though he isn't so wily or experienced, perhaps, as his colleague. I'm repelled by the close-up of veins in his cheeks and stubble that rasps my face. Forcing a smile, my hands on each shoulder, I propel him back saying I really want to know more about him, what he does, where he comes from so we can meet sometime in the future - unwise to promise anything, I know only too well, but I have to say something or other. Keep talking.

Voices in the corridor. Franco releases his hold and tries the key. It is still locked. He glances at his watch, annoyed, and stands up to get a stronger hold round my shoulders and lift me up into his arms and over onto the seats his side - he has tactically flipped back all the armrests following my initial retreat to the corner by the door. Before I realise what is happening, I'm sprawling along them with this man fumbling and muttering above me. 'No!' I shout. Swivelling over to the opposite seats I fall on the floor in between. 'No! No! No!' He wisely doesn't try to put his hand over my mouth or I would bite it. Wisely for me too, because an offended Italian, I suspect, is rarely gallant.

'*Su! Su!*' he says, sitting to straighten his open shirt and run his thumbs behind his trouser belt. 'There, there,' as if he has actually succeeded. A knock; a furtive whisper, and the key turns. His mate is holding a tray with three tiny cups of black coffee which he places on the seat beside me pretending, I'm convinced, not to notice the dust over one side of my skirt and legs.

'*Tutto bene?*'

'*Si! Si!*' I lie, choosing not to understand the quick glance exchanged between them.

Genoa at last! Freedom - or a fine. Or what? Both men are reaching for their kit on the racks and tidying up their 'cell' in an oddly merry way after what might have been a long, tedious but hardly tiring day's work. I sit ignored in my corner seat. Crowds are already hurrying along the platform to the exit where there is a long wait as tickets are collected. Hats on, ties restored, jackets donned and buttoned, the two policemen look smartly efficient as they escort me to the barrier, slipping through with me between them. Is it my imagination, but as we jump the queue I feel eyes staring at us? They are only admiring these men in uniform, I convince myself.

'*Addio, Valeria, addio - e, grazie,*' says the dark-haired one. '*Ciao, sei meravigliosa!*' echoes the blond one. Thanks for what? Marvellous? What exaggeration!

I'm lucky to find a seat on the crowded tram that trundles along the sea front, and breathe out in full relief, calm for the first time since the ticket episode. Looking idly at the illuminated shop windows and the people in the street cafés, I catch the reflection of a tall stooping figure strap-hanging. The shape looks vaguely familiar. I turn, and an arm's length away goggling at me is Hyacinth. 'How did you get away without paying the ticket?' his eyes are asking. I look straight at him, solemn-faced - and blow him a kiss. He turns sharply away, but I note his neck is nearly purple.

Chapter 14

Poor Hyacinth. It is all his mother's fault for giving him such a name!

CHAPTER 15

Back in Flavia's flat, I escape into our shared bedroom to check how much money remains. Precious little.

The three Cecconi sit round the table while I eat the meal they have kept for me, anxious to hear what I did in Milan. I recount the usual round of churches and the unexpected meeting with my friends, avoiding my magical encounter with Simone Martini, Petrarch and Laura which is too personal and complicated to explain. Not a word about the events on my return journey.

'I read quite a bit of the *Secolo Decimonono*, but had to keep on looking up words. What does *"niente meridionale"* or *"solo settentrionale"* mean?'

'So you've been looking at the advertisements,' signor Cecconi observes. '*Settentrionale* e *meridionale* mean from the north or from the south of any geographical location, not just Italy.' I feared as much: *'niente meridionale'* or *'solo settentrionale'* meant the same - people from the undeveloped south aren't welcome. How could they print that in a newspaper? How... prejudiced!

'*È possibile?* They're saying they don't want anyone from southern Italy applying? So where does the south begin anyway?'

Mario and Livia Cecconi glance at each other. Flavia is washing the dishes at the sink behind me. The clock on the wall ticks away as her refugee parents decide how much they need to explain.

'Some say the south begins after Rome; others include Rome. Some even believe it starts south of Florence, and so it goes on. Does it matter anyway? They shouldn't put those phrases in, but if one advertiser starts to do it, others copy, and so it catches on.' Livia Cecconi sighs.

∾∾

Flavia complains she is too tired on her mornings or afternoons off to make plans in advance, but one afternoon we could go to a really fashionable beach together. Still, she has to buy a bathing suit first and is saving up. That's why she wants to go window shopping. The steep cobbled alleys up to the main streets are hardly four yards wide, and above them a lively assortment of garments and sheets are pegged to cris-crossing clothes lines like festive streamers. Where rich merchants once lived, washerwomen are bundling bags into courtyards, carpenters planing tables and chests, or taking a frequent break to hail passers-by and smoke leaning against finely carved marble lintels or Doric pilasters. Looking up between the flapping celebrations of cleanliness, I glimpse here and there a coat of arms, a carved St. George identified by the skewered dragon, a stone balcony with broken balusters or a double colonnaded window adrift above this hive of humdrum activity. We emerge into a wider street and begin looking at clothes shops. Few have any bathing wear as by August the selling season is deemed over. Flavia knows this and is hoping for bargains. A few one-piece bathing costumes are dangling above autumn two-piece suits in the smaller, less assertive displays. Nothing very exciting, and Flavia, with such an attractive figure, must be looking for the fashionable bikinis. She is soon flagging on her scant breakfast of a large cup of white coffee and some dry biscuits dipped into it. We find a table at a pavement café to drink coffee and eat cakes paid for with my last Italian coins - the right moment, I hope, to discuss my new plans.

'Flavia, I've almost spent all my money and can't get any more till I return home. I need to find a temporary job. There's an advertisement for a childminder -'

'Shall I ask if there's a job in my hotel?' Flavia butts in, scared of losing her companion so soon. I hesitate. I know I must find a way to give the Cecconi money for my keep which they may be too proud, even offended, to accept. I feel trapped. However, I won't confess to my friend that I have no intention of getting up at dawn to take the long bus ride to her hotel on the fashionable Ligurian Riviera. While child-minding doesn't exactly appeal to me, the terms and times could be more negotiable. Flavia is looking at me almost with a sense of betrayal, so I change the subject.

'What do the As before "*massaggiatrice*" mean exactly, Flavia?'

'Valeria, you're always asking questions!'

'*Domandando s'impara*. It's the only way to learn, and I do want to pick up as much Italian as possible - quickly.' Flavia is eyeing me as oddly as her parents did yesterday evening. Perhaps that is the way the people from Fiume behave, or is it the expression of refugees - though Italians do look you up and down a lot. Then so do Spaniards, from children to grannies. A Latin habit, I suppose.

'When quite a lot of *massaggiatrici* put in advertisements, someone hit upon the idea of coming first by putting A in front. Then the paper's financial experts cottoned on and began charging quite a bit extra for each A. Human nature, isn't it, both to be first and to make money out of it!'

Flavia reveals a tinge of bitterness in place of the usual resignation. She isn't ever particularly lively or enthusiastic, but then she and her parents haven't been in Genoa that long, and times are hard for them. Still, I'm glad she invited me here. Her parents have been so kind, though there is something suffocating about their attention and it upsets me that they can't really afford to have me stay. I'll persuade Flavia to phone the advertisement in yesterday's newspaper before she leaves. Today she's on the evening shift.

෨ඏ

Like so many buildings hastily constructed to repair the scars left by Allied bombing of port installations and stray bomb damage in the old town, the block of flats is grey and nondescript. This small woman opening the door must be the one who told

Chapter 15

Flavia she'd like to see me after the siesta today. Barely thirty years old, she's already the mother of three, the eldest nearly eleven. She stations herself at one end of a room with an imitation marble floor, mock leather sofa and armchairs in front of a balcony overflowing with a heavily laden clothes horse. Standing silently, she's smiling at me with the three children, wide-eyed and curious, a little further behind.

'Rosina!' A male voice from one of the rooms opening off a narrow corridor, 'Rosina, has the girl arrived?' Not very tactful. I hope they don't know I'm a foreigner - that might be as out-of-bounds as the state of being a *meridionale*.

The voice materialises into a lithe, olive-skinned male about my height. He's looking me up and down from the doorway like a filly at the market, before entering his sitting-room to appraise me head on, pausing significantly before pointing to the sofa. He sits down opposite me, while the wife and children remain standing, watching. Will they show me the house, my room? Impossible, as everyone works into the early hours and now it's siesta time. I ask what sort of work they do. Entertainment. His wife dances, though I don't think she looks the dancing sort. She is not exactly plump, but short and unlikely to float around easily on the dance floor. One never knows. My thoughts flash back to the supple Spanish flamenco dancers. Rosina, as the wife is called, is still smiling for no apparent reason. As they don't say anything, just look at me, I ask what they might want me to do. It seems the mornings are important, to give the children breakfast and lunch, and be generally there to help about the flat. Free time? Plenty. Most afternoons and some evenings. That seems suitably flexible to me, so I don't ask who will look after the children while they are out working in the evening. Payment? Signor Mauro Palumbo is evasive. I'll have all meals plus money for shopping and other expenses twice a week, even more often if I wish, but - he is getting up to leave - that would depend on how I settle in. Pausing impatiently at the door,

'*Allora va o non va?*' I'd prefer to go away and think about it, perhaps come back to inspect the room, but signor Palumbo has other things to do and can't wait around.

'Otherwise I'll see someone else,' he adds, 'we're busy people. Tell my wife.'

The two elder children, Luigino aged eleven and Carlotta, just nine - olive skinned with darting eyes like her father - run out of the room as soon as he closes the front door. Four-year-old Giuseppina clutches her mother's skirt, sucking her thumb. Still smiling, still silent, Rosina and her daughter don't move, the sweltering afternoon painting them in stripes through the slats of the half open Venetian blinds. Waiting for me to decide.

I drop my head to contemplate the speckles on the *terrazzo* floor, hoping to find enlightenment. I think I am promised my own room, board and some sort of pocket money for work which leaves me quite a lot of freedom - far more than I'd ever have if working with Flavia in a hotel. But it isn't at all clear what I'll have to do in the morning with the children during their holidays. As stated, it will mean their breakfast and lunch, so can the signora explain?

'Just hot milk and biscuits for breakfast. A snack from the bakery round the corner, and a pizza or pasta for lunch.' It seems easy enough, and I won't depend on the generosity of Flavia's family that has hardly enough for themselves. I'll try it out. At least I can gain confidence by speaking to the children using simple Italian phrases. The signora is asking me to return before six this evening as she has to leave for work after that.

The fine-boned Cecconis, their greying fair hair and grey eyes giving them more a Slav than Italian air, say little, but appear to reproach me for leaving. I insist I have to earn some money and this job leaves me time to work at my Italian. Employment in a hotel would not. I assure them I'll stay all August and drop in to see them. In any case, I haven't said good bye to Flavia.

A transformed signora Palumbo opens the door with the habitual smile, though looking strangely concerned.

'*Finalmente.* I thought you'd decided not to come back.' At close quarters I see her smile comes from the unfortunate gap between her prominent top jaw and the receding bottom one. The signora has either to smile or force her lips to meet. She is wearing a low-cut light green taffeta dress.

'*Vieni!*' She rustles along the corridor to the kitchen to deliver me to my charges, all three sitting at the kitchen table. The floor to ceiling sand-coloured Formica cupboards are crammed with stores; the work-tops are narrow and empty, not even the odd crust or bowl of fruit. The children are chewing slices of pizza out of grease proof paper without any particular relish.

'*Ciao a tutti*! I must be off,' and their mother swirls round to leave in a swish of green taffeta and whiff of lavender. My suitcase is still in the hall so I ask Luigino which is my bedroom. He shrugs his shoulders and turns the radio up louder, while Carlotta takes my hand and leads me to a room with ten chairs drawn up stiffly around a shiny green table and matching galleried sideboard with a glass back, all of brittle-looking synthetic material. Along the far wall, a divan covered by a full-blown flower patterned coverlet. Is that my bed, with nowhere to store or hang my clothes? I look under a faded sprig of anemones to check if there are sheets underneath. Just a mattress as I feared and not even a cushion to serve as a pillow. Carlotta stands staring.

'Sheets?' The child runs into the kitchen to open one of the long Formica cupboard doors to reveal sheets and towels, pillowslips but no pillow. I pick out what I need and remove a cushion from the sitting-room to serve as one, at least until I'm shown where they are stored. Now everyone's out, I'm free to glance into the other two rooms off the passage between the hall and kitchen; one has a huge double bed, and the other, a narrow room the same length as the rest, contains one unmade bed, but not a pillow to be seen.

'*Dove dormi?*' I ask the girl. Carlotta points to the huge bed. I have to think hard to explain to the child that I don't understand where all three of them sleep. Carlotta stands silently uncomprehending.

I soon realise they are well able to look after themselves. No bedtime stories, no washing rituals - they just throw themselves on to the huge bed and fall asleep when they feel like it. They seem able to cope, and can even tell me where to stock up with their favourite food for breakfast and lunch, mostly from the baker below their block and the general store in the next street, open until eight in the evening.

Shopping is a very sociable business. I'm soon talking to shoppers and trades people alike. Two men have already asked me to go out! Less expected and still less to my liking, is the pile of garments heaped by the kitchen sink for me to wash and hang out on the balcony each morning. The sheets and shirts I may take to a laundry three streets away, so it could be worse.

After shopping, my first evening is spent finding ways to arrange my belongings in the dining-room. My clothes have to remain folded in the suitcase which can be pushed under the divan. The journal, notes and writing material are now stored in a shopping bag shoved between suitcase and knapsack. It is too hot to sleep, so I am sitting on the divan to think about my novel and catch up with my journal - nothing written for two days. I've forgotten to buy a postcard for Mike. Actually, I'm more uncomfortable here than with Flavia's family. I've escaped the sad, almost plaintive atmosphere of exile and straitened circumstances blamed on ruthless historical decisions, to what? The Palumbos instead are a strange but fairly prosperous family in comparison, though their living space is still fairly cramped. Tired, I fall asleep and don't hear the parents return.

৩৯৫৫

The Palumbo parents emerged from the family bedroom at different times this morning, well after the children who left the bedroom early, firmly shutting the door behind them. Just after I returned from my first shopping expedition with the two younger children who enjoy helping me, a young woman appeared out of the oblong bedroom. A white sheet she was trailing behind her caught in the bathroom door as she closed it.

'Giosetta! Giosetta!' cried Giuseppina, skipping along the corridor towards the phantom. Too late, she had disappeared.

An uncanny air of expectancy hovers over the seven actually sleeping here. The predictability of the Cecconis is almost preferable, except that signor Palumbo has handed me a wad of lira banknotes 'to keep you going'. I wonder how long he stays in the flat as I only occasionally see him coming in through the front door. All the adults appear involved in the catering and entertainment business, which explains the strange hours they keep. Each to his or her own, but I'm already, to be honest, longing for Flavia and her parents.

৩৯৫৫

I dropped in on them in my free time this afternoon. Flavia's working times are irregular and she wasn't there. After some polite conversation, I left for the beach carrying a wide-brimmed hat - newly acquired with signor Palumbo's pocket money - a writing pad, the *Divina Commedia* and faithful pocket dictionary, for time alone with my thoughts as the day cools into evening. I have slipped a loose cotton dress over my bikini, not intending to create a stir of unusual interest from the other bathers when I take it off.

Another habit I'm perfecting this summer is to concentrate so completely that I am oblivious of all going on around me, whether on a train, in a café or on a beach. I stretch out on the warmly welcoming sand to read and write. Today, however, everything changes. A tickle in the arch of my foot persists even after I scratch it. I look up into five pairs of eyes. Five lithe tanned bodies in their late twenties. Five hands thrust under my nose. A chorus of *buona sera, signorina*. I glance at them, screwing my eyes into an unwelcoming scowl, then slowly and deliberately lower my head to concentrate on Dante's masterpiece. I am a serious student, and not up for chance beach encounters. My antagonists, however, are masters of attrition. The feather tries my instep again. I shake my leg and continue reading. Two minutes later the tingling sensation has moved up to my calf. I shift. Behind my knee now and insistently travelling upwards. Incorrigibly ticklish, I try to control my giggles, dropping my head into my book. *Signorina! Signorina!* - and so opens a new chapter of summer life with a quiverful of male friends. Safety in numbers. I can play one off against the other.

In the evening, the children in bed, I think back over the day's events and the men I met on the beach. One in particular intrigues me. He is taller than the others, light brown hair bleached by the sun, a strong frame and decisive manner with - as far as my Italian reaches - a wry sense of humour. His hazel eyes look steadily at me when he asks what I am reading. He, more than the others, can talk - of literature, art and pronounce on politics too - and when he does, he enthrals me. I can't stop him invading my thoughts. His smile looms up from the pages of my journal, from the open pages of Dante's *Inferno*, even in the clothes I am washing. In short, he is becoming an intruder in my waking life. He soon invades my dreams in the most improbable situations, some so daring they seem part of a film.

A new working day. While busying around my morning chores I am thinking how to cope with my obsession. I'll write it into my novel. The phantom with the white sheet train, Giosetta, emerges mid-morning to commandeer the bathroom for an hour, obliged to unlock the door when the children hammer on it for their needs. I try to slip in too. Now Giosetta, hair still damp and body wrapped toga-like in a white towel, is standing by the cooker blinking and waiting for her coffee to percolate. She has short curly hair, a pert face, slightly mocking expression to all and sundry except me when we talk after shopping or while I'm preparing the children's elevenses or washing their clothes. I'm curious to know why she can hardly enter a shop or walk along the street without some man talking to her and soon asking her out.

'I don't understand you. I'm just an ordinary sort of girl,' I protest, but Giosetta only laughs that off.

'You're tall, have good legs and a jolly face - and you're a foreigner.'

'So what?'

'Haven't you noticed? *Fanciulle* aren't allowed out after dinner.' I'm fascinated by the word *fanciulle*. It is what Francesco, the man I met on the beach, called me: *bella fanciulla*. My dictionary indicates 'maiden, young nubile girl'. It all sounds incredibly odd. So far I haven't been out much after nine in the evening, though no one has asked me to babysit.

Flavia has just phoned triumphantly to say she's off work tomorrow afternoon.

'Valeria, I've been paid and have saved enough to buy a really good dress and swimming costume! Let's go to the beach together tomorrow afternoon. Meet me at two.' By 'beach' she means the exclusive one owned by her hotel.

I still miss Flavia and her kind parents, not sure that living out of a dining-room is much of an improvement. The pocket money helps. It makes me feel independent, and the strange goings-on in the Palumbo household of sorts are a far more fruitful source of ideas for my writing. I've been keeping up with my journal in the evening, and written a few postcards to my parents and friends, and to Mike. He isn't writing to me often, though he knows my movements and addresses. I'm cheered however by the prospect of getting away from the five pairs of male eyes on the public beach.

Flavia looks far happier when stepping out of her buttoned-up house garb into her new dress. She is taking more trouble over her hair and make-up, perhaps because she has a boyfriend. She will tell me if she wants to. After all, I don't feel like confiding in her just now. The long and intimate conversations with Giosetta are fun and reassuring at the time, but indefinable worries remain. It is probably because the confidences aren't balanced, the scales weighted on my side. I've learnt virtually nothing about Giosetta herself, where she comes from, whether she has a boyfriend, and exactly what she does in the bar where she says she works. I imagine her serving, washing glasses, the usual things - why doesn't she say so? Giosetta talks a lot, but actually says little, and now Flavia seems to be treading the same path. I feel lonely sitting on the bus beside her as she fidgets around with her dress, pulling her shoulder length ash blond hair behind her ears, then round her cheeks like a Hollywood star, while the vehicle plies its way, frequently stopping, along the coast.

High on the cliff, the hotel curves forward with balconies thrusting seawards. It is modern and predictable inside, with shiny surfaces relieved by ferns and dwarf palms to provide a discreet touch of the exotic. The tone is hushed to obsequious towards the guests; we are nodded through with a cursory glance from the reception desk.

'I've told them I'm bringing a friend.' Flavia has thought of everything. Outside on the terraces are patches of pink and puce shimmering in the unrelenting glare - bougainvilleas, hibiscus and in much needed contrast, the blue of plumbago and the occasional pure white oleander. Flavia is skipping down the terraces to the changing cabins. Minutes later I emerge into the siesta sun to see her out on the shore in a tight blue and yellow one-piece costume talking to a profoundly tanned young man, both dabbling their feet in the ebbing waves. Not sure how welcome I'll be, I try to walk slowly over the burning sand still furrowed by lunch-time raking. The almost deserted beach is immaculate: no greasy paper bags half buried in the sand; no bottles or newspapers; no blobs of bluey-black engine oil that people pretend to ignore on the public beach. I wade out up to my knees and pause to savour the scene and look at the steamers and an occasional yacht punctuating the flat blue surface of the Mediterranean. A scream. I focus back on the shore and see Flavia with her hand over her mouth and the young man with her frowning. I return hastily, fearful of something untoward.

'Valeria, you can't wear that costume here!' I stop in my tracks.

'What's wrong? I've worn it on the other beach.'

'Not here!' the young man reiterates, 'there are strict rules of decorum'. Decorum, decorum, decorum! A word my mother uses. I ignore them and plunge furiously into the sea, swimming savagely as far away as possible. By the time I've calmed down enough to venture back to the shore my hands are corrugated, my teeth are chattering and the beach is filling up with hotel guests. Their siesta is over. Kneeling in the shallows I check that the top and bottom of my bikini decorously cover me, stand up and march out, scanning the beach for a bright blue and yellow one-piece. Flavia is nowhere to be seen. I retrieve my bag and spread the towel out, deliberately straightening the edges in full sight of the elegant ladies and their groomed escorts in deck chairs. I am clearly only milk to their *crème de la crème*. Defiantly I lie on my stomach and open Dante's *Inferno*. The light bounces off the pages half blinding me. I persist; there is nowhere else to look without having to cope with the stares.

'Valeria!' A man's voice, not Flavia coming to my help. 'Valeria, you have to leave.' I tilt my head to see the bronzed legs of, I suppose, Flavia's new boyfriend.

'Perché?'

'Perché non si può!' The afternoon heat is multiplied many times over by my rage. I turn on my elbow to burn my eyes through him and anyone else who dares tell me what to wear.

'It's not my fault! Hotel guests have already started to complain. The general's wife -' I snort in disgust '- has said she'll leave unless...' I turn back, brow on burning page, silent, motionless. So Flavia is afraid of losing her job. That is the breaking point, as far as my feelings go. I can't let Flavia be sacked. I sit up slowly, gather my book, pen, dictionary, sunglasses, towel and straw hat together deliberately as if acting on a vast stage – I shall probably never ever again have so many eyes concentrated on me - place them carefully into my bag, stand upright and slowly brush imaginary sand off every square inch of my exposed body. So there; they can look at me to their hearts' content! With what I hope is an elegant, stately stride, I stroll across the sand to the travertine steps, up them and along the crazy paving of the terraces pausing to smell the bougainvilleas, to stop at cabin number 47 while I look for the key in my bag. Someone is close behind. Flavia's boyfriend is shadowing me. I raise my eyebrows, hoping he won't be there when I step out fully dressed. He is. I ignore him, appearing haughty which isn't very helpful, and saunter self-consciously into the hotel lobby where a shadow moves. It's Flavia, fully dressed and ready to leave. In fact, she only accompanies me tearfully to the bus stop - to make sure I depart.

'Why didn't you tell me there's a ban on bikinis?'

'How did I know you had one? They're not allowed in Italy.' I stare at her in disbelief. 'Not on fashionable beaches, anyway.'

End of a lovely friendship?

I'm beginning to worry about the effect of my bikini. Is it to blame for those five pairs of eyes on the public beach? Still, even without the lure of the bikini, I've been invited out by various young men - even not so young ones — encountered while shopping or exploring the old town.

'Why don't you go out with them?' Giosetta asks me while putting the final touches to her elaborate make-up, reigning over the bathroom as usual when the Palumbo parents aren't there, which is most of the time. I decide I've had enough of beaches for the time being and am longing for a bath and a quiet evening. I hover at the bathroom door.

'See how many you can go out with in a day!' Giosetta is incorrigible, but the idea is sown. I need time to think and take decisions. I'm shaken, unnerved by the simple fact that my bikini upset a general's wife, Flavia and presumably countless others, all for different and very personal reasons. Is the green serpent uncoiling in their souls?

Giosetta shows no sign of finishing, so there is nothing to do but control my urges and go to my divan in the dining-room. The door is open, though I scrupulously left it closed so the children won't touch my belongings. Signora Palumbo and Carlotta are there laying the table. No sign of my books, journal and various papers that I had left on the table.

'Your things are back under the bed,' the signora says, smiling away as usual. I look at her, eyes glazed. 'We're having people in to dinner,' she continues, adding helpfully, 'you don't have to be here.' My head is throbbing, and I'm beginning to feel distinctly odd. The nape of my neck is poker hot. With all the fuss on the beach I forgot to wear my straw hat. I stretch out on the divan, my bed, saying, 'I'm feeling sick. I have to lie down.'

Six o'clock passes with people coming and going from the shops to the kitchen and from the kitchen to the dining-room, dodging my frequent visits to the bathroom. My head is burning, but

I'm shivering. Giosetta brings me a blanket from the kitchen laundry cupboard as signora Rosina is too busy to do more than make sympathetic noises, interspersing her to-ing and fro-ing with '*Come va Valeria?*' So this is a first, I think: sunstroke, and I deserve it for ignoring the warning to wear a hat. Seven o'clock and signor Palumbo is by my bedside, stroking my bare leg sticking out from under the blanket. The strokes he often delivers unexpectedly in odd areas of my anatomy whenever he slips me a few banknotes are not as pernicious as the sun's. I haven't actually vomited, but the underlying threat remains. I lie still and shiver while my head throbs and my neck burns.

By eight o'clock the smells from the kitchen have increased to a nauseating degree. Loud greetings at the front door are followed by raucous laughter in the adjacent sitting-room, both armchairs and sofa squeaking under weighty bodies. On my way to the bathroom I forget to check if there's a key in the dining-room door. I should have noted that when shown the divan. This is no bedroom but a dining-room with a slice of space for me to sleep in.

Soon after nine o'clock the company transfers their increasing jollity to the dining-room. I dimly note about eight men, and not even a passing glance at my prone body. I should be relieved at the lack of male attention, but instead I'm perversely annoyed. I lie abandoned on one side of a room echoing to male bonhomie; the only females, signora Palumbo and her nine-year-old daughter, are fetching and carrying without even a place for the *signora* to sit down. The liver pâté and hot peppers on toasted bread start them off on piquant tales worth chuckling at. Signor Palumbo heads the table, the conductor of ribald stories recounting male conquests, mainly, I think, sexual and financial, that provoke regular ripples of mirth. Two sorts of pasta, one pale, the other basted with a tomato concoction, lead to more rounds of wine and coarser outbursts. The meat course accompanied by roast potatoes perfumed with garlic nauseates me even more. By the time the dessert appears - *zuppa inglese,* a kind of trifle doused in cream and liqueur – I try to get up for the bathroom, fail and, in pain and distress, lean over the side of the divan to vomit.

Only Rosina notices. She sends little Carlotta to fetch a bucket of water drenched with disinfectant and a floor cloth to dump beside the splatter on the *terrazzo* floor. Not a word; just the assumption 'get on with it. You did it, you clear it up'. Which I do.

Not one man notices anything untoward. Peaches are consumed, the stones pitched on to the floor to join a growing number of cigarette butts. Coffee. Then liqueurs jostle for place on the table, some sickly green in elongated bottles with skeletal twigs or roots of rare plants with occult powers - the mandrake, surely, with its ghostly human form? By this time all are shouting and bellowing in a cacophony of well-fed revelry; it's a strange moment for Mauro Palumbo to stand up and strike his glass with a spoon. Not for a toast. What follows is a heated discussion, difficult to understand except for the repetitive talk of money and *tocca a me* - it's my turn - and endless mention of streets and various locations. I turn to face the wall. I am tired, but my temperature is lower already, and I am more comfortable with an empty stomach.

The company leaves at midnight. Signora Palumbo has cleared the meal away and washed up like any good restaurant chef and bottle-washer. No sign of the children who have presumably fallen asleep willy nilly on the huge bed. I wonder what their parents did when they wanted to sleep. They must push them between their legs, heads at the foot of the bed. That recalls my unhappy experience of air raids and sleeping 'top to tail', as mother neatly put it, with my sister in the broom cupboard under the stairs, the safest place in the house. Alone, the chandelier over the table turned out at last, I snooze off to wake up abruptly at the click of the door handle. Someone is coming into the room! I freeze. A hand rubs the top of the table: a foot catches the leg of a chair -

'*Chi è?*' I scream before a hand muffles me. 'Shush. *Sono Mauro Palumbo.*' What is he doing here in the only bit of the flat that is, temporarily, mine? '*Calmati, Valeria!*' He begins stroking my cheek then my arm. What can I do? Softly he slides off the blanket, finds my hip, then the other, his hand on my mouth as I fill my lungs to yell out. Petrified I stiffen my body. For a few minutes he tries every artifice in his verbal and physical vocabulary. I hear myself growling - it seems as if this is all happening far away and I am watching myself with this silly man writhing around on top of a fully dressed body, limbs clamped together, which I stubbornly consider my own. With a snarl of disgust, the master of the house levers himself upright, turns to crash into the chair he stubbed his foot on before and leaves. The door slams, spinning a key over the shiny floor.

CHAPTER 16

In the light of the morning after, and during the tedious hours of shopping for the children and washing clothes, I see myself for the first time as a simple, naive, easily-bamboozled girl who has a lot to learn about the world. I should have realised far earlier the sort of family I had tumbled into through lack of prudence. My sunstroke is distinctly better, but I am inwardly sick and disgusted at the situation I've got myself into through my thirst for adventure, or money - or a mixture of both. I brood over the way I have been almost polluted by money. What does the Palumbo man mean exactly by the increasing number of banknotes he has been slipping into my hand with a stolen caress, too rapid and seemingly innocuous for me to protest? Will they decrease from now on, or cease altogether? It is a deceitful business, and even Giosetta, who has become something of a friend and companion, is part of their sleazy world. Thinking of Giosetta, I feel rebellious. I shall take up her idea, go out with all the men who have asked me and just see how they'll behave! I can always escape if I keep to the cafés and amusement areas round the free beach.

I start to plan with the list of my contacts in order of preference and availability. Gino at the baker's shop will do initially. I know he's free mid-morning after making bread, and that will suit me fine. I could finish shopping and clothes washing earlier to meet him at eleven, or just after. Giosetta counsels that if you arrive a little late they are that much keener. Careful emotional timing is required. Gino approaches me, his white overall covered in flour which flecks his face and eyelashes.

'*Sì, sì, sì.*' He looks surprised, asking, 'though can't you be free in the evening?'

'*No, mi dispiace*, but I have to work then.' He is quite attractive, the usual average Italian height, just taller than me by a small inch or so, broadly built which doesn't particularly appeal, but all in all he isn't too bad. Fine for the morning slot. Now Agostino is different. He stroked my ankles while I was buying some fashionable light brown sandals with signor Palumbo's second bunch of banknotes. As he knelt down to fit them on I had the urge to fondle his curly, velvety hair and athletic shoulders - he is probably a champion long-distance runner. As he stood up and before he turned to wrap my purchase, I noticed he had long eyelashes falling over slate grey eyes. Rather stunning, I have to admit. He recognises me immediately when I enter the shop and rises to the bait.

'*Domani all'una.*' Tomorrow at one. I hint something about lunch. All is working out perfectly: coffee and a stroll in the old town with Gino; two hours later I shall slip away to meet Agostino to enjoy lunch in a chic restaurant, probably in the main shopping thoroughfare. Shops close from one until at least four in the afternoon. That suits me well, keeping me away from the beach crowd in the morning. After a really good meal I can escape for a siesta and a chance to have a bath and change for the evening. To ensure use of the bathroom for at least half an hour, I shall have to time it carefully while Giosetta and Rosina are still resting. Also I must remember to iron my best dress beforehand, ready for the evening encounter. I am hesitating about the afternoon assignation, torn between one of the others I met on the beach with Francesco or the student working part time in the bookshop where I bought the *Divina Commedia*. He wears spectacles, is earnest and pasty faced - obviously not one of the beach crowd - but he does have a thoughtful, more intellectual air about him. The quiet, bookish, unromantic Carlo might provide an interesting if unexciting couple of hours. As the prime evening slot is reserved for Francesco, it would be better not to select one from his gang for the afternoon to avoid tension - for him as well as me. To crown the day's encounters, I'll ask Francesco to introduce me to Genoa's evening beach life. There it is, all neatly planned, and I'll be back safe and sound, if exhausted, by midnight.

Francesco is lounging on the sand after a long swim with two of his friends, taking turns trying out flippers and a snorkel one of them has bought. It isn't easy to prise him aside. I'm in a hurry. I must see Carlo before he makes other arrangements - though he doesn't seem the type to have a crowded social life. The bookshop is in a road not far from the Cecconis' flat, so I can drop in to see Flavia's parents no later than six; I don't want them to think I'm cadging dinner. Francesco and the others register my presence in the nonchalant manner one assumes towards an established member of the group. Other matters than me are occupying them. I'm a tad irritated to feel myself treated as an appendage to male activities, like their latest silly fixation on underwater swimming. I'll entice Francesco away by asking for some help. Opening the sixth canto of *Purgatorio*, I hold it out to him pointing to a verse,

'*Non capisco.*' All three glance round at me with variations on, 'Wait a moment - we're busy.' I look out to sea trying not to pout, and after what seems like hours I have three simultaneous offers of help with Dante's syntax - and I have always assumed that only Francesco is interested in literature! That accomplished, the three lie back on the sand to relax into desultory comments, a rare anecdote or roll over for yet more bouts of arm wrestling. I am neither included nor excluded, free to enter where I think fit. I pretend to read, but can't concentrate.

'*Prendiamo un gelato!*' Wandering in the direction of the beach café that sells ice-creams should let me casually draw Francesco aside - but no one moves.

'Already had them - get yourself an ice-cream, Valeria!' I try to smile amicably and begin drawing a labyrinth in the sand, zigzagging the lines diagonally away from Francesco. They might draw him magically towards me. He's looking up, interested.

'What's that you're drawing?'

'Come and see,' I coax him. He laughs, without moving. 'Just tell me!' I must rapidly review my tactics while continuing to draw the Minotaur, a spindly Theseus and plump Ariadne to punish myself. Hairy legs move towards me.

'What is it?' It isn't Francesco but small, nervous Bruno, certainly the most sensitive of the three; definitely not the person I'm aiming for. I feel like giving up, but the morning arrangements have worked out perfectly; I must persist. Is Francesco playing a game with me, or aren't the signals clear enough? I explain my labyrinth unenthusiastically to Bruno. Things aren't quite going to plan - perhaps I ought to give up any idea of arranging the evening and let it go to chance. Francesco should, according to form and what I have heard about male behaviour, be eager to repeat the evening we spent together two days ago. A sneaking thought - he might have another girl friend. So I am already casting myself into a role I haven't anticipated or even thought about. Obscurely ashamed, I pick up Dante's *Purgatorio* and pull my handbag over my shoulder. Elbowing himself half up off the sand, Francesco says,

'Going already, Valeria?' He jumps up to follow me. 'What's the matter?'

'I want to see you - alone.' I draw in my breath wishing I could pull those confessional words back with it, but it works. Mission accomplished. We meet in the evening at seven-thirty. I scurry up to the old town, late for my self-imposed appointment to see Carlo at the bookshop and make a beeline for him. He frowns and turns away. Then I realise he is talking to a client. Is he less keen than before? I pretend to look at books but the titles are blurred by worry and haste. My mind is probing the space behind me, feeling and listening for his approach. I start and turn round at,

'I didn't know you bought books on bird-watching, Valeria!' I am almost ready to fall with relief into his arms, except that one hand is holding a pen, the other a piece of paper, probably a boring receipt. He too would prefer to spend the evening with me.

'I have to work,' I lie demurely. He does agree reluctantly to meet me at five o'clock. What a relief! All my men are free and booked for the time I choose. So far so good.

It is now three weeks since my rather hasty departure from Flavia and her family. I am not sure whether I have upset the Cecconis or not, but I feel uneasy and want to spend more time with Flavia's parents, whether their daughter is there or not. It is just after seven, an hour later than I planned. Signora Livia will be preparing dinner and insist on me joining them, which is one of the many reasons why I left to find a job.

The massive faded-green entrance doors to their block are ajar and chickens still pecking around in the courtyard. An array of shirts, dresses, trousers, bed linen and strange flannel shapes, like nappies but much too big hangs from wires stretched precariously below windows. The evening air holds appetising aromas, not the succulent ones of midday olive oil and pasta dishes, but promising more delicate culinary pleasures. Never wise to burden the stomach before retiring to bed, so the signora told me soon after I arrived in Italy. The wide stairs seem less dreary in the evening light, though the WC on the landing still blatantly proclaims its presence, maybe because blocked by newspapers torn into squares that serve as toilet paper almost everywhere I've been this summer. Signor Cecconi opens the door. His face lights up when he sees me.

'*Valeria, che piacere!*' No sign of the signora, or of supper preparations. The only table is covered in photo albums. He pulls out a chair for me and starts to close them.

'Please don't! Can I look at them?' He clearly isn't quite sure how to take this young English student, pleasant and appreciative, but up to what point? I left so soon that he hardly had time to know me. Mario Cecconi moves his chair next to mine and tentatively opens one of the faded blue albums.

'These are of Fiume, mostly of the port where our ships docked, and my family - not very interesting. Our memories.' I ply him with questions, delighted to see Flavia as a small child in their world of quiet, hard-working dignity that war had shattered. The Cecconis are an old family, of modest fortune, which had for generations been associated with the fate of the port.

'My wife will be back soon. She works in a chemist's three days a week.' He tells me he is trying to write the history of the family and it has spread into a history of the Dalmatian coast. It is difficult to do research now his city is part of Yugoslavia. That's why he sometimes unpacks the albums and books he has managed to bring from his library. I noticed when I arrived that a bookcase stands in a corner of the kitchen, but didn't spot the packing cases beside it. I've just seen a photograph from the 1890s of signor Cecconi's grandparents, taken in a library with a grand piano and potted palm trees, the same room where Mario and Livia pose after their engagement. I wonder where that piano is now, and whether, in spite of their reduced circumstances, they are relieved not to live under a communist regime. Signor Cecconi tells me that Flavia won't be back for dinner but he hopes I can stay and eat with them. I've another idea and excuse myself as tactfully as possible to slip out of the front door and across the landing to the WC, not out of need but to check the money I have with me. Just enough, I calculate, to invite them out for a simple meal in an *osteria* Francesco told me about. Meanwhile Signora Cecconi has returned and is clearly pleased to go out to eat, though she protests that she has bought a packet of soup we can all share. I insist, even though it may use up all my reserve money; no more has been forthcoming since the incident after the Palumbo banquet. However, I don't plan to spend anything tomorrow when my four escorts will foot any bill they chose to run up with me - after that, who knows? I have set out on an adventure, and must let it take its course. Here and now I have the chance to do something for Flavia's parents.

The *osteria* isn't far off and I gladly escape from the close atmosphere of the Cecconi's flat. Storms are forecast and the sunset is ominously red. Tables stand in a courtyard behind a low-beamed room with wine barrels and dark grained tables. We choose one under a vine with rather shrivelled grapes. The establishment has an operatic air about it; some inhabitants hang out of the upper floor windows to peer over washing lines at the people eating below, or toss racy comments at one another across the yard. In some *osterie* they only serve wine and snacks. Here we start off with North Italian white wine accompanying crusts of bread dipped into olive oil and peppered or salted to suit one's taste. The Osteria da Emilio serves home-made pasta, thick and dripping with a spicy concoction called appropriately *pesto Genovese,* followed by slices of watermelon, and all for such a modest price that I have money left over, even after a generous tip which signor Mario helps me calculate.

As we leave, I point at the strange shapes of flannel that I'd noticed before on washing lines.

'What are they used for? Babies?' Livia looks at me strangely. 'What do you use, every month?' I never realised...

I return to the Palumbo dwelling soon after ten taking the short cut over the bomb site. Luigino is outside as usual with a gang of boys kicking a football around in lamplight. Carlotta is sitting playing dolls with two other girls. The doorkeeper's children. She's a reassuringly voluminous woman and I imagine that signor Palumbo passes her some *lira* to keep an eye on his children and will deal with any emergency. She has, I've been told, a key to the flat. Giuseppina is there fast asleep in the vast matrimonial bed, all alone.

There are very few cars. In holiday time the children play outside, in the street or on bomb sites where they build dens and improvise games, more or less playful, with bricks, bars and planks, or anything else useful found in the ruins. They eat at home and slumber on their parents' bed when they are tired. It suits their mother and father; it suits them - perhaps because they know nothing else. It suits the pattern of life around them, though it is nothing like the way I was brought up.

I still worry about the Palumbo children after their mother and Giosetta go out to work in the early evening, but have never been asked to watch over them at specific times except in the morning. If I finish my tasks quickly tomorrow, I can hop off after giving the children their elevenses earlier than usual and skip the washing - two loads the day after tomorrow.

In bed early in preparation for the day I've so studiously planned, I'm too restless to sleep. The air is still, my heart pounding and my body tense. 'It's the stifling heat,' I tell myself, drinking glass after glass of water. 'I can't sleep because it's unbearably hot and I stick to the sheets.' Then my fantasies glide into dreams.

∽≪

I was canny enough not to give any of the men my address, though they asked for my phone number. Gino rings at ten to say he has finished work and is free. I'm only just back from shopping, busy preparing the children's elevenses and lunch which will be left for them on the kitchen table. He is fretting, but I have to take my time. It will be eleven o'clock as agreed.

He is waiting outside the shop, but the moment I turn the corner he runs towards me to avoid giving the others working with him any food for gossip. It's tricky for him to go out mid morning when he usually kicks a football around with any young people who happen to have time on their hands. A couple of hours hardly allow him much scope. I welcome him in the Italian that I've learnt from the Palumbo children and Dante, which is all I know.

'*Vieni meco alla città vecchia?*' He'll agree to the old city or anywhere arm in arm with a girl who smiles enticingly.

'*Sì, vengo volontieri,*' of course, he replies, adding with a laugh, '*teco.*' He is cheerful and cuddly with his long fair eyelashes, light brown hair grizzled at the ends by the sun and a freshly

217

laundered look. I immediately tuck my arm under his, surprising him at how easy it is to strut proudly along with me to the most delightful café he knows. We sit outside on the pavement, though I did try to take refuge inside fearing Francesco or my other two dates might pass by, but Gino insists, hoping that some of his friends might see him out with a foreign girl. Such an expansive and promising one too, with a quaint way of speaking.

So we chat over a large coffee pot and a plate of cakes which in other circumstances I would be wary of eating, but now relish. I'll jump lunch if Agostino doesn't provide it, saving money as I am convinced signor Palumbo won't pay me again.

'I can bake better cakes,' Gino boasts, adding another detail to his life history. I had started him off by asking whether he came from Fiume, seeing he is light-haired like Flavia. He returns the interest by gazing at me, more preoccupied by what I am doing this evening and how long I plan to stay in Genoa.

'Don't leave too soon,' he pleads, plying me with more coffee and pastries.

After more than an hour the waiter starts hovering over us till Gino reaches for his wallet and settles the bill, the waiter graciously stationing himself behind me to move my chair back. Gino feels emboldened to encircle my shoulders and draw me into the narrow streets.

'Let's go down to the port,' he suggests. No, never, I reply silently, that's for me this evening. We might run into Francesco or one of his friends - none of them seem to have anything else to do. They are on vacation like me, I assume. Agostino will be safely selling shoes, Carlo books, until one, and I must escape Gino before then.

'No, show me some of the old houses.' Gino stops, looks unblinkingly at me and plunges forward rather awkwardly to pull me close. His bristly chin brushes mine as he tries to find my lips, tingling my cheek as I jerk my head away.

'Why?' Changing his mind rapidly at the thought of deserted courtyards, he agrees, 'Yes, let's do that,' though he is slightly worried, probably having never paid much attention to ancient *palazzi* or churches or the things foreign tourists come to Genoa for. So Gino wanders me into the old town where I delight in the dilapidated buildings, a few boasting an owner's bust or ornamental urn reinstated after the air raids. He trails along without much to say though eloquent with frequent arm squeezes and snatched kisses on my neck, narrowly missing my cheek. We're passing a partially boarded-up mansion when Gino cries out, 'Look, Valeria!' and removes his arm from my shoulder to grab my elbow and propel me into the silent courtyard with *'pericolo'* splashed in red paint over the half-shattered columns of the inner portico.

'It's dangerous!' I protest, but Gino crushes the words into my mouth, passionately pulling my body firmly towards his and bending his knees slightly under me. I slip my right arm in front of his chest, and sling the other round his back, my head leaning over his shoulder to check my wrist watch.

'Gino, I have to go!' No answer. He is too busily involved. I look around, leaning down on his shoulder and pushing outwards with my right arm - an unequal struggle.

'Chi siete?' An old man is leaning over a balcony just above us. Gino propels me against the inner wall out of sight under the portico. *'Andate via!'* the old voice continues angrily. Shuffling steps on the monumental staircase.

'I must leave,' I shout to anyone in earshot. 'I'll be late!'

'Stranieri, tutti stranieri!' The old man stands guard at the half open entrance as I pull myself away and turn towards him. 'All foreigners, and now you come back to mock us. *Inglesi, americani - tutti simili.* Once enemies, now tourists,' and he shrugs his shoulders. He is blocking my way out of his bombed home venting his frustration on me.

Chapter 16

'*Mi dispiace tanto, tanto,*' I blurt, ' but it's not my personal fault,' and touch his shoulder to reassure him as I slip past turning left, and left again to run down narrow streets towards the Cecconis, dodging in and out of alleys so Gino will lose my trail. I can always shelter behind their huge *palazzo* doors. So I do. No sign of Gino.

It has never seemed hotter in this hottest of summers than it does now as I make my slow way to Agostino at the shoe shop. I am more irritated than elated by the first of my four encounters. Gino would intersperse his attempts to seduce me with glancing references to his pals, his morning football, and a recurring grumble that he can't understand why I'm not free in the evenings. If not today, then tomorrow would do. Everything has to be in physical terms; he isn't one for a neat turn of phrase, still less an interesting - or even provocative - comment. I admit he is quite attractive and, though he should have shaved better, the rasping effect was exciting - for a moment anyway. One thing is certain: no return to the bakery unless I reserve an evening for him. Any decision on that account to be postponed until I know the outcome of the three episodes to come.

I am to meet Agostino outside the shoe shop, though he told me he'll be taking the day off. He is there waiting, slender and tall but not so tall as I imagined. At least I look up at him, which is more exciting than looking straight at Gino. New territory, new sensations. Those slate grey eyes are half-smiling with irritating assurance. He holds a rolled-up newspaper in one hand, takes mine in the other, and walks me off without even discussing where we are going.

'*Vado teco, ma dove?*' He turns sharply to look down at me, brow furrowed. What have I said now? I'm apprehensive. This adventure has only just started.

'I'm taking you somewhere special,' smiling assurance at me again. He too must have washed his hair, as it is curlier and bouncier than ever.

'*Per favore,* don't let's go to the port,' I beg, but he smiles down and ignores my request. All is becoming too fraught with possible danger - why is everyone drawn to the sea? Agostino raises his hand at a request bus stop and silently, smilingly escorts me inside the vehicle. We travel along the coast road to a café with a terrace shaded by palm trees and its own beach. I won't swim. I'll tell him I haven't brought my costume, which isn't true.

'*Caffé? Espresso?*' The lean shoe salesman settles down at a table, stretching his legs out so far that I have to step over them to sit down opposite him.

'*Sì, grazie.*' This is a nice enough place, though there doesn't seem to be much food in the offing. It isn't near the port and beach area frequented by Francesco and his friends, nor anywhere near Flavia's hotel. It is discreet. There is even a slight breeze.

'*Temporali,*' says Agostino, not leading from or to anything in particular. Storms he predicts, but there isn't a cloud on the horizon. I'm in a good position to survey him as I sip the strongest *espresso* I've ever tried.

'Glad to see you're wearing my shoes.' Another futile comment, until I see he really is examining the sandals I'm wearing, not to please him, but because they are the best I possess.

'Mine,' he continues, wriggling his toes in front of me, 'are the latest fashion. Moroccan leather - the best.' They are polished to a military shine, beaming out from underneath immaculate fawn trousers and a light white cotton shirt with his initials embroidered on the pocket: A B - Agostino Beretti – I know because the moment my eyes alighted on the pocket he informed me. The shirt is open to the third mother-of-pearl button - a bit fancy - and they don't match the gold chain with a cross and a medallion which, he tells me though I can see it, also has AB. I might have guessed.

'We'll go swimming at four. No earlier because of stomach cramp. They have changing rooms here.' So he is taking it leisurely; he must have already eaten and is measuring out the afternoon and evening before him, or so he thinks. With all my meticulous planning, I have failed to tell my chosen companions that I can only stay with them for a set time. Is it a grave omission? I feel sick at the obvious realisation that with him and Carlo after him, I'll leave a bad taste as I already have done with Gino. I must try to sort out my priorities while chatting nonchalantly to Agostino. We are in the shade but it is still sultry. I find myself forcing my eyes open as he tells me what his mother cooked for him. A grand lunch by all accounts. His father died in the war and he is their only child - that says it all! Everything about Agostino is drawn out, from his sentences ending either in shoes or mother, to his body - more sinew than muscle, well attuned, settled comfortably into itself - and his feet which I imagine long and tapering, impeccably profiled before me in his pride of shoes.

He is tracking my every movement without letting me see it, affecting the languid expression that his eyelashes enhance so well. I must surely be a virgin; a pretty face with a pert sort of nose and blue, almost violet eyes not unlike his favourite film star, Elizabeth Taylor. He prefers taller girls with long legs, and I'm a bit skinny round the hips - as far as he can see. He wants to get me into a swimsuit to decide whether he approves of my figure. He doesn't need to do that for me. He's so proud of his fine cotton shirt which is more see-through than my light chiffon blouse. His trousers are so well cut that little is left to the imagination. Maybe that's a pity.

I'm languishing under a palm tree at half-past two on a sultry afternoon, mightily bored. If he has his way I shall end the evening naked on one of those huge Italian matrimonial beds with him trying sandals with thin silver straps on my feet, bejewelled slippers on my hands, and a cascade of high fashion winter and summer footwear arching over my midriff without somehow weighing down on me. Agostino is an invisible presence in this fantasy, absorbed within his fetish. I sit up suddenly, amazed to see him signal to the waiter.

'A lemonade? Or shall we go for a walk along the sea boulevard to get an ice-cream?' Not so languid as he pretends to be, this Agostino, as he takes my arm in a suave, practised manner and escorts me down the steps from the terrace restaurant.

'Agostino!' I stop, realising it is three already and he has used up his two hour slot. 'Agostino, I have to go to the Ladies.'

How can I find the right bus to get back to the flat and freshen up in time for Carlo? Will I have to miss that assignment? I've no phone number and can imagine the slight, bespectacled, earnest young student pacing up and down in front of the bookshop. How long will he wait? What will he think of me? I could never again pass the shop, let alone buy a book!

The genteel tone of this café doesn't extend to the cramped toilet with the usual pile of torn newspaper squares. I can hardly linger here to ponder my course of action. In fact, the only solution I can think of is as timeworn as can be - female frailty. I despise myself but what else remains for me to do? More time with Agostino talking about shoes and letting shy Carlo down, or -

'Agostino,' I draw my breath in sharply. Then in a sweet little girl voice, 'Agostino, I,' sob, 'I must go back.' He looks at me aghast. What is wrong with this woman? She seems as healthy as could be. Searching desperately for some ailment I blurt out,

'Sunstroke. I feel sick - feverish I mean.' I don't want him to take me to the toilet here and stand outside waiting. He is scrutinising my neck, back and front and right down my low-cut dress, legitimately, to see where the sun has effectively struck.

'I've booked a table at the best restaurant in Genoa ...' but I'm already running along the street to the bus stop.

The only providential event so far in my tightly-packed day is a bus pulling up just as I reach the stop with a good start on Agostino. I board it as it moves off leaving Agostino sprinting after it for a few yards. I turn away, flushed with heat and embarrassment, while the other passengers stare at me.

It's nearly three-thirty; my charges have long finished eating and there's no sign of them. I clear up the mess they always leave, irritated by sympathetic pangs of hunger. This just can't be tolerated. I have eaten enough cakes to last me until after five when Carlo will surely offer me some tea or an ice-cream – I shall have to work out what I want to do with him. The day seems to be stretching even further ahead, rather worryingly when I think of how I might spend time with Carlo. Francesco doesn't bother me. He is too distant a prospect, far into the future at seven-thirty.

Unthinkingly I open the fridge; a half watermelon, huge, luscious, seems to be waiting for me. It is all water, not fattening at all, I reassure myself as I grab each end, cut two generous chunks and return the hardly depleted hulk to the fridge. As I pick out the black seeds and reduce the large portions into neat slices, Giosetta's door opens and the bathroom one closes. My greed has lost me the bathroom for half an hour at least. New plans have to be made. Instead of a shower and hair wash, I'll iron my dress. It's something I should have done in the relative cool of yesterday evening but now there is no choice. I must wear the sort of dress one can go dancing in, with plenty of skirt to swing and show off one's legs - discreetly, of course! Mike found it alluring, and I recall him affectionately as I finish the watermelon. I'll have time now to drop him a note and buy a stamp at the cigarette and sweet shop round the corner, if it is open when I leave for Carlo. I lick the juice off my hands, feel under the divan, pull out the shopping bag used to store away my diary, paper and pens, and search for a postcard. No luck. I'll write instead a humorous letter about some aspects of my morning experience. He likes the ridiculous side of life, and anyway, there isn't much else to tell him, except my suspicions about the Palumbo family. He won't be impressed by the set-up, and somewhat bewildered by my disinclination to leave them. In fact, I don't want to talk about signor Palumbo and his friends to anyone, not until I know exactly what he is up to. It is hot, I am sweaty and dusty and time is stickily ticking onwards. There are stirrings from the main bedroom. The signora will expect to be next in the bathroom if I'm not careful. I stuff my writing bag back under the divan, knock on the bathroom door, slip in after Giosetta and out again in twenty minutes, calling to signora Palumbo as I pass her bedroom. Dressing in a hurry is emphatically not the best way to start off an afternoon of mysterious assignations.

Carlo is thankfully still outside the bookshop though it is after five.

'I thought you'd never come!' Not reproachfully, but in relief.

After Agostino he seems just friendly and companionable, leading me past stalls in a side street selling old clothes, bed linen, all sorts of bags and even bicycle tyres. Carlo seems to fit in here, shambling around in baggy grey trousers, loose shirt and beach sandals. He doesn't try to take my arm or even touch me. He doesn't even look at me, apart from an occasional glance as if to check I'm not bored, but when he does, he winks, which is somewhat out of kilter with his low-key attitude towards me. I am already building a character around him. He'll be from a family like Flavia's; that is, with little money. He has to work to pay for his university books and enrolment fee. Not being the flirting type, he wouldn't be especially popular with either sex.

'*Vieni con me, Valeria.*' He takes me into a still narrower alley and down some steps to a small dark second-hand bookshop. 'Look at these!' He carefully takes out two books in English with red tulips and faded white lilies on a stiff beige cover.

'D'you know anything about them?' They are simple and striking, deeply satisfying, that much is obvious, but I know little about books and design. However, I like these a lot.

'I'm saving up to buy them. They're not expensive, being cloth bound and in English, though they're so beautiful.' I open one. *The Stones of Venice* by John Ruskin, printed in London in 1903 with 'James Osmond' written in thick black ink below *Ex libris* on the book plate.

'They must come from a library. Giovanni found them on a barrow a few weeks ago and bought them for a song. He told me about them.' Carlo pauses to look at me. The wink again. Then, 'I'd really like to buy them. I can't speak much English, but I do read it. A little.'

I never imagined I could have spent nearly an hour looking at the Osmond library with Carlo in a hot little basement bookshop. Giovanni, who can't be much older than Carlo – twenty-six or twenty-sever perhaps - started it after graduating from Genoa University. We sit round his desk at the back of his shop drinking coffee and talking books.

'Who were these Osmonds?' I ask. Giovanni and Carlo are obviously good friends since they keep on interrupting each other as they conjecture. An English family running a shipping agency in the port? Aristocrats living cheaply between the wars? There used to be a large Anglo-American community along the coast round Rapallo. Ezra Pound and his ilk. It makes sense. James would have come from a titled family. 'Osmond' sounds right. They would have had to flee at the start of World War II and left their library. Their *palazzo* might have been bombed, the furniture, Persian rugs, chandeliers and rare pictures looted, the library tossed out as valueless - mostly works in English. James was probably killed in the war, and his grieving parents never returned. No regaining of their paradise, their youth, their wealth, their family life. I shed a tear or two for the imaginary plight of the Osmonds; the two young men look at me curiously.

'These books are so lovely,' my eyes glistening through the teardrops, 'and I think all the Osmonds must have been killed in the war'. Giovanni puts his hand on my shoulder reassuringly.

'There was an English consulate here, because of all the trading connections and sailors. Even an Anglican church; quite a substantial community. I'm sure they were warned and had plenty of time to leave.' Carlo smiles at me, and I realise the wink is just a facial tick.

'I'll try to find out more about them. We could go to the library together,' he suggests, 'Next week perhaps?' I'm not sure I'd like to find out that the Osmond family had a more prosaic fate than I imagine, but I am intrigued all the same. It's too hot to stay in the basement shop, so we take the plywood chairs out to sit amid the bustle of the street. Giovanni disappears without explanation leaving his friend in charge of the shop.

'He likes you,' Carlo says pointedly. 'Could you persuade him to let me have the books from the Osmond library for a bargain price? I've already cleared a corner in my room at home, but will need to save for at least another month.' Giovanni returns with three glasses and a bottle of wine.

'Valeria, one can never do business with friends!' he pronounces gleefully as he pours us each a glass. As I reach out for mine, I glance at my watch. I forget to check the time, and it is rude in any case to inspect one's watch in company. It is gone seven already, and Francesco -

'I have to leave!' Desperate, I gulp down the wine. 'I'll see you tomorrow in the shop. What's this street called? Oh yes, via della Mandorla. I'd like to return here.'

'Pity. We thought you'd like to join us at the local *trattoria*. Another time. Contact Carlo at work. You have his number?'

'Yes. *Ciao, ciao amici!*' I veer right out of the alley into the street with the stalls, then sharp left to jump down steps and short cuts, twice ending up in blind alleys in my haste to reach the harbour.

I've nearly won the bet with myself: out with three men in a day, and that doesn't include my evening tryst! Exhilarated that Francesco and I will be alone with no need to leave at any self-imposed time, blithely confident he is keen on me and with a pressing need to deal with the effects of the watermelon, I arrive at 'our' bench on the sea promenade barely five minutes late. A mother and two toddlers are sitting at one end, a tramp with a beer bottle at the other. No Francesco.

CHAPTER 17

The sun is disappearing behind lumpy grey clouds tingeing them gold and pink. The air is ominously still. Instead of sitting awkwardly between the young children and the tramp, I lean nonchalantly over the railings between the pavement and the beach to curb a surge of anger, leaving embarrassment and fear in its wake; Francesco is the only one of the four men to be late. I arrived just after half-past seven, and it is now nearly seven forty-five. The evening is slipping out of my grasp. I could have accepted any one of the three offers to dine: Gino would have taken me somewhere, but I have lost that chance. By now Agostino will have cancelled the dinner he booked for me - or found another girl. So that leaves Carlo and Giovanni. I am tempted to wander back up to the street market area. It won't be hard to find them as they are going anyway to a nearby *trattoria*. Everyone knows them. If I hurry I might catch Giovanni before he closes shop. I turn to find Francesco standing behind me.

'Where are you off to?' No apology, just the suspicion of a smile.

'*Vado teco,*' and he laughs. 'Valeria, you really can't...' he pauses to shake his head, pushing tufts of hair back from his forehead to reveal the extent of his hilarity. 'You can't go on speaking as if we're in the thirteen hundreds! I'm not Dante, even if I am "*Nel mezzo del cammin di nostra vita*"!'

He's quoting the famous first line of Dante's masterpiece, and I haven't a clue what he's going on about. Worse, he seems to be laughing at me when he should be jolly relieved that I've waited for him and am attempting to speak Italian. He doesn't know one word of English, tries out some so-called French with Italian words made to sound Gallic, and a couple of Spanish swear words. What on earth has he to be proud about, linguistically speaking? I increase my pace, no longer strolling along beside him.

229

This is the assignation I have been looking forward to most, and it's already strained. To begin with, he isn't polite. He still hasn't apologised - let alone explained - why he was late. My mother wouldn't approve of him. Still, as I have lost an evening out with anyone else, I might as well make the best of it.

'*Vieni con me,*' he continues, matching my increased pace, 'not "*meco*", that's old Italian! It sounds quaint. It's delightful to hear you speaking with expressions from Dante, and we do understand. But it's simply not how we speak nowadays!' I slow down, blushing slightly. So I have been speaking Italian like some foreigner starting English through Shakespeare - utterly absurd! Why hasn't someone told me before? Probably because it is too comic. My embarrassment increases, and to counter it I begin swinging my hips in what I imagine is a more alluring, Renate-inspired, way.

'Where am I going "*con te*"?' I stress the modern Italian.

He doesn't answer, taking my elbow to slip me through the bamboo curtain into a dark, cigarette infused interior. 'Not here, please.' I cringe at the thought of spending an evening in this hot, stale atmosphere. Francesco's small, hairy friend Bruno who showed interest in my sand labyrinth is here, and I can feel those eyes again, known or unknown, poring over me. I tug his sleeve.

'It's too claustrophobic here, and I must go to the toilet,' I whisper. He smiles again, that enigmatically irritating smile, and waits for me, chatting meantime to men hanging out at the bar. Then he leads me out at the far end of the tavern, across a street and under an arch with two winged figures sculpted over it holding an inscription. A sober stone town house, detached and slightly forbidding, stands behind a newly-gravelled forecourt. Francesco is following the sound of laughter and voices hidden by a high hedge. He pushes open a wrought iron gate and leads me into a garden of statues, urns and what look like large stone pine cones. Hibiscus bushes and oleanders are flowering in profusion, and lavender lines the paths, its fast-drying spikes of blue flowers still scenting the evening air.

I draw in my breath at the scene unfolding before me: table after table of young people, the women in low-cut dresses of every imaginable hue, while the men wear white jackets even in the heavy air. This surely must be the Osmonds' house! They are celebrating their return. James is the tall young man drinking champagne at the largest table. My eyes are already sparkling at the prospect of talking to him. I can only hear murmured conversation, no clear words, but from the intonation I assume they are speaking English.

'They've returned!' I exclaim to myself, enchanted. Francesco is met by a young waiter in a starched white shirt and dark trousers - almost as handsome as James Osmond - who leads us to a small table on the edge of the banqueting area. This is our starlit night. The magical garden overlooks the coastline that recedes in a flicker of lights on its way to the French Riviera. Bliss, sheer bliss! How could I have ever doubted Francesco? His family must have known the Osmonds. I scrutinise my escort. He looks a little older than James, who is now chatting with an unbearably beautiful young woman on his right - a film star? The waiter returns with two glasses of champagne.

No one notices our arrival, too engrossed in their own conversations. Some are already lining up at a long table clad in a white damask tablecloth. On it an array of huge silver dishes with cold meat, shining tureens of soup, a porcelain dish flaunting a whole open-jawed salmon, and salads galore, from potatoes to peppers via tomatoes and cucumbers, all in nests of salad leaves and then on to every melon imaginable, sliced or diced in wide open dishes. I have never seen the like before.

'Shall we join the queue?' I have long digested the water melon, and my afternoon with Carlo has not provided me with any solid sustenance. I am suddenly ravenous, raring to get at the luscious food, while Francesco is in no hurry, leaning back in his chair and watching me through spirals of smoke.

'Give me a cigarette!' I haven't ever smoked; partly because I have no urge to, but mainly because mother disapproves. Now I want to look calm, worldly - and to control my cravings. He offers me an American one, I note with relief, not a cheap Italian *Nazionale* which emits a strong unpleasant tang. As he strikes a match, leaning forward to shelter the flame, I notice he has a dramatically furrowed forehead under the mass of light brown hair, and smells of sea salt, nicotine and soap.

'We'll eat a bit later. I don't like waiting behind other people. There's no hurry - we've the whole evening in front of us.' I relax, for the first time today without any need to plan. Trying to inhale, I choke as the smoke curls round my throat, and thrust the cigarette as far as possible away from my smarting eyes. Smiling as usual, Francesco pats my arm, plucks the offending object and tosses it into a flower bed.

'Don't try to learn. It's really not worth it.' Then why does he smoke, I think logically, but don't feel that line of enquiry is interesting enough to follow. I'm far more intrigued by the company we are only half keeping.

'Shall we join the others? Or at least you can introduce me to some of your friends.'

'Later,' he replies. 'We have time.' And he lights another cigarette. I feel slightly uncomfortable, as if he is keeping me apart, in reserve for some unknown purpose. Perhaps my dress is too ordinary. Now I'm told there's time, I can look over the other women. They are all, as far as I can see, wearing long dresses, some of them might even be silk. Some have elegant evening gloves like the ones my mother once showed me; open at the wrist so you can shake hands, otherwise buttoned to show off slim arms, sleek right up to the elbow. I gape in awe, followed by a sense of shame — I can't compete, so why has Francesco brought me here? I shake my head in disbelief. But then, nor can he! Completely unabashed, he stands up, accompanies me proudly in his cotton trousers, open neck white shirt and rolled up sleeves, to the end of the buffet table and hands me an ornate china plate and damask napkin, while the young waiter points to the dishes and extols them - as if there were any need to! I could have dived into the nearest one, famished, but am inhibited by my mother's boring insistence on manners.

'Try the cold soup...' I have never known soup other than burning and often tasteless broth, its main virtue being heat. This is served in a small shallow bowl on the centre of the plate so the other delicacies can be piled around it. Francesco finds me cutlery, and we return to our table, last again. The others, I notice, are more than halfway through their first helping. I pick up the spoon, tackle the soup which tastes like ambrosia, and raise my head to look straight at him.

'Why did you quote the first line from Dante when we met this evening?' His eyes don't flinch. Steadfast, I return the look, noticing one pupil isn't at the centre of the hazel green iris

'Because that's just where I am.'

'What, with Dante in the 1300s?' Curiouser and curiouser, as Alice would have said. Here in 1955 I find myself in this wonderland eating a meal from my wildest dreams escorted by a man seeing himself as Dante who lived six centuries ago!

'What's so strange about that? In 1300, when the story recounted in the *Divina Commedia* is supposed to have taken place, Dante was in the middle of his life, aged 35, and so am I.' I gasp. He is that old! He seemed so agile, so lively; I thought he was, yes, quite a lot older than me. About 25 perhaps, 28 at the most. I gape, attempting to chart all his years I hadn't lived.

'What have you been doing all that time? Where did you grow up?'

'I'm from Tuscany, the Mugello area north of Florence. Born in the same valley as the Medici family. Mine wasn't a large family for the times; I was the eldest of four, two brothers and a sister. She died when I was sixteen. We were so poor that as boys we had to wear cut-down trousers, my father's or uncle's cast offs. I had to work from the age of 14.'

'So you left school then?' I'm curious to know how he learnt about Dante, and all the other writers we've been discussing.

'We finished elementary school aged twelve. I did odd jobs as a labourer with my father, until he died. Then my mother went to see the local priest - that was the way one did things then - and he got me into the army. Against my will, but I was fed, clothed and sent money home. That's when I started reading, during the long hours walled up in the barracks. Anything I could get my hands on - Dante, Conan Doyle, Leopardi, Gramsci, Marx - even Shakespeare. Then, just before war broke out, I was sent home on leave. Everyone was talking about the new priest's sister. *La bella Claudia!* I just had to see her, and anyway, I needed to pay my respects to her brother - his predecessor had found me a job of sorts in the army and many of my friends were unemployed.' I listen entranced. A life of real hardship, endurance, excitement - all that I have missed in my post-war progression from school to university, by way of a boyfriend or two.

'What was she like? Claudia, I mean?'

'She and her widowed mother were living next to the church with her brother. She had just left school and was said to have a rich fiancé in Florence. All the young men who hadn't emigrated or left to work in the north were besotted, the local girls furious and frustrated.' That irritating smile again, with mocking eyes, then he looks down to finger the tablecloth. 'The only work they had, apart from helping with the hens and feeding the pigs, or at harvest time, was in the local convent, where they ruined their sight embroidering sheets and pillowslips in gloomy rooms. They were lucky if they earned enough in a week to buy a shirt for their future husband - their dowry. That's all those young women seemed to think about - until Claudia arrived. She would ride through our small town on a smart new dark green bicycle with a huge shopping basket fixed to the handlebars. First she'd disappear into the general store, and immediately men would gather around waiting. Out she'd come, holding her head high, place her purchases in the basket and proudly ride about ten metres to the chemist's, and so on, always cycling the few metres between each shop in the main street. Rumour had it that her perfume, fashionable clothes, fine patent leather shoes and handbag, were all gifts from her invisible fiancé. He never came to visit her. When she went to Florence it was always with her mother or brother, leaving on the morning bus and returning on the one arriving just before seven in the evening. Not the last one, which came through after ten.'

'Did her fiancé exist?'

Francesco shrugs his shoulders. 'No lo so. There was a lot of speculation and rumours about everything to do with her.'

I can't repress my curiosity, 'What did she look like?'

'Dark hair to her shoulders - a bit curly at the ends, grey eyes, long eyelashes and a small, slightly pointed chin. She wore wide skirts, and when she cycled away from her admirers, she went at such a speed that we could see her legs. They were long and slender, and rumour again had it that even her bicycle saddle was perfumed.'

'So what happened to her? Did she leave to get married?'

'I don't know. I started waiting for her when she came shopping, and we agreed to meet.'

'I thought Italian girls weren't supposed to see men on their own? Even now they aren't allowed out alone, and never after nine in the evening. It can't have been easier before the war, can it?'

'No, it wasn't,' Francesco confirmed. 'She told her mother she was going to see a girl friend or someone who was ill, and we'd meet on the way, spending a precious hour together. She was passionate, but there were too many people around the fields and the woodland. So one day she told me her mother was going away to stay with her sister for two nights. So I went at the appointed hour, climbed up the wisteria into the bedroom window to find Claudia sitting up in a double bed - with her mother asleep beside her. She shifted over a bit. There wasn't much space, but enough.' I'm staring agog. He adds, almost as an afterthought, 'and she wasn't a virgin'.

'What happened? Did her mother wake up? Why hadn't she gone to her sister's?'

'That was the problem. Her mother was down with 'flu. Claudia had no way of letting me know. We were very quiet, not even a whisper, but the priest put his head into the bedroom to see how his mother was and saw me. I fled, leapt out of the window, and by morning had packed and left. A few months later war was declared.' I'm spellbound. The James Osmond party and the other guests are crowding the buffet for the pastries and melon. I realise we will be the last to go. In any case, I'm not hungry anymore and prefer to unravel Francesco's past.

'Where did they send you?'

'To Russia, eventually - the worst months of my life. A tragedy for everyone. We Italians were forced into it by the Germans and sent without proper leather boots or clothes to battle through an Arctic winter. The line broke with us. In retreat we had to fight both the Russians and the Germans who blamed us for their withdrawal. My only good memory is of the saunas. Men and women together, but it was so hot one could only look! A bit frustrating, really.' He pauses to laugh at what I imagine are his memories of naked women flitting in and out of wood smoke and steam.

'Then?'

'I'll tell you sometime.' The waiter is whispering to him.

'Let's get some pastries. And melon.' The atmosphere is strangely still, the starless sky so dark above the lamps and candles, all sounds muffled.

We are indeed the last, served by the same waiter. He arranges slices of melon in an abstract pattern around the chocolate éclair I choose. The first raindrop falls right on top of it, followed by thunder growling beyond the mountains. The other guests have moved over to the balustrade and are gazing at the fork lightning lacerating the sky over Rapallo. The thunder and lightning are only a prelude to more raindrops splattering over the damask tablecloths and forlorn scraps from the banquet, abandoned plates, glasses and cutlery.

'It might pass us by,' I whisper while consuming the drier part of my éclair. Francesco is clearing his plate rapidly. 'Not a chance. We must leave. Now.' The candles are guttering as he gropes under the table for the canvas bag he always carries and pulls out an umbrella. 'Quick!' A curtain of rain swirls towards us from the mountains as Francesco puts his arm round my shoulders to propel me out under the arch, though not before I turn to see a bevy of women, so drenched their dresses cling to them like animated statues, fleeing towards the house with James Osmond and his friends pursuing them.

'Francesco, can't we go into the house with them? We're only two - I'm sure there's room for us.'

'No, I've got other plans.'

His grasp tightens on my shoulder as we turn right in the street, my new sandals slipping on the wet paving stones, rivulets of water coursing alongside.

'Take your shoes off,' he shouts above the rush of water. 'You'll have more grip.' He runs ahead, leaping and brandishing the umbrella while I splash in his wake, gambolling down the hill after him. Where is he going?

Chapter 17

'*Alla spiaggia, Valeria!*' To the beach. The warm rain streaks down us. Peeping through gaps in the thunderclouds, the almost full moon tracks him intermittently racing across the sand, stripping and shouting at me to follow. I hesitate, shrinking from the cool-lipped ebb and flow of the breakers. He dives into a vigorous crawl. The moon passes another rent, spotlighting me, an abandoned figure at the luminous edge of a shifting world. In the protective darkness I strip naked, dabble a foot in the water, then plunge. It is soothingly warm. I strike out, the water moulding my body. Thrashing round and round in exhilaration first, I then lie on my back to undulate with the surge shaping my shoulders and hips, swirling around and under my legs and arms. I drift, stargazing. The storm is moving down the coast, clouds thinning, stars washed brighter than ever. Between them sails the unveiled moon, glazing Neptune yellow-green as Francesco comes to carry me off. I veer away, happy as I am, but he ducks under me, swims round behind my head and tows me along by the shoulders. I jiggle my feet pushing back into his grasp, which slips down over my shoulders and round my breasts on the way to my waist. Gently pulling me upright to touch my lips lightly, he whispers,

'It's no fun in water: no lubrication.' I smile that comment away, and we kissed again exploring tastes of salt, seaweed, of adventures, of sirens and long lost loves. We wade hand in hand to the beach, alone under the lamp of the moon. It is a picture postcard setting for a romance - except for our sodden clothes on the beach.

Francesco opens the large umbrella and spreads my dress and his shirt over it. Out of his waterproof bag comes a groundsheet which he flattens out on the sand followed by a huge towel that he wraps round us both. An exciting way to dry oneself, snuggling up to a man. I'm drowsy, stroked and caressed and kissed lying there under the moon, alone on a beach on the edge of the world.

The first squeals from the violin and a loud scamper up and down the scales on the piano while a microphone coughs itself clear, announce that the festivities are starting with a brisk fox-trot. Fifty yards away on a raised platform picked out by multi-coloured bulbs, people are congregating like extras abruptly summoned on stage. The clouds retreat to leave the moon and stars as their backdrop. Some swing into the foxtrot, others order refreshments and sit at the tables drying out under the lights, drinking and looking out to sea, then back over the shore and the solitary figures on the beach. I sit up, as if caught in a random spotlight.

'I really must get dressed.' I grab the bikini I keep in my handbag. Better than wet underwear. Better to be prepared for whatever the occasion offers. Francesco's trousers are slightly damp and his shirt, like my dress, is moist but not clinging.

'They'll soon dry. Let's find some coffee.' This man seems unstoppable. At the bar, he exudes fitness and elusive fascination: the thrall of an adventurer, the allure and manners of a gentleman. Passing me the expresso, he enquires how much sugar I'd like and stirs it, placing the spoon neatly towards me on the right-hand side of the cup.

'A cake or something?' I am too elated to be hungry. Cakes remind me of the buffet supper and James Osmond - has the company moved back into the garden to dance after the storm?

We sit at the only free table. Francesco orders a bottle of Asti Spumante, oblivious of the couples swirling and brushing past on the creaking boards, a face or two turning to gape at us. Francesco's words only just escape the chords and crescendos of waltzes, fox-trots and quicksteps, or the syncopated patter of a Latin American tango. I ask him what is happening now in the middle of his life. Is he, like Dante, in the midst of a wild wood where the way through it is all overgrown? Francesco seems far too assured to be in a similar situation, but I'm fascinated and have to know. The words and phrases come and go: he's been reading

Marx; the Russians impress him; honesty, justice for all workers; human values conquering the grim reality of the misery he experienced as a child. His voice weaves patterns of brightly-charged meaning: universal justice in a workers' democracy; the wealthy have stolen from the poor who work for a pittance to make a few rich beyond anyone's greediest dreams - and on he goes. So, I conclude silently, Francesco is a sort of latter-day Robin Hood. But it's still unclear what he actually does for a living. The more he says, the less clear and more thrillingly bemused I become.

The tide is turning, a breeze transforming ripples into bobbing sea-horses and wafting them off into a fast waltz. Us too. Blurred faces swirl by his shoulder. I'm not too sure how to dance a tango. The floor is clearing; I draw the scene back into focus to pattern my steps on a nearby couple's, raising my head in an attempt to look appropriately haughty as I appraise the female partner, to find her eyes laughing straight at me. Rosina! I push Francesco away, but he continues to dance holding on to me, oblivious. Unmasked - though I'm not quite sure what it is that I have so unwillingly revealed - I grimly survey other couples dancing, realising it is inevitable Giosetta will be here, and so she is. We are locked into a deep trance, waltzing, fox-trotting, Latin Americanising, dancing past midnight, oblivious of everything, the Asti long since drained dry. Two figures spellbound, now alone on the boards over the deepening growl of the surge, sea-horses bouncing closer as the tide races inshore under the café terrace.

We pause and lose the rhythm. I glance up. The moon is watery and the night falling into deep slumber. The violinist is half asleep, the pianist is shuffling his sheet music, the cellist stares hostilely at us, and then deliberately stifles a cavernous yawn with the bow still in his hand.

'We have to play until the last couple stops dancing, damn it!' he mutters loud enough for me to hear. I nudge Francesco,

'*Andiamo?*' I move towards the door at the other end of the café - the musicians stop half-way through a trill and begin packing up - to find I am toppling forward and my head is throbbing. Francesco pulls me upright, and I continue less rapidly, concentrating on placing one foot firmly in front of the other, a task never attempted before. Strange world, strange ways.

Out on the marine boulevard the breeze is more insistent.

'The aftermath of the storm,' Francesco explains, his arm round me as I'm shivering, my dress still slightly damp.

'Could the storm turn back on us?' It is disquietening enough to return to the Palumbo flat in the early hours of the morning, still more under an inconstant moon and the threat of another downpour. He shakes his head, hurrying me into an alley tucked between two shop fronts, turns right then left to unlock a heavy door in an unlit back street. He takes out a torch and lights the way for me to step carefully over cracked paving stones to an internal staircase. Another door to unlock, a narrow entrance passage with a couple of coats hanging on pegs and heavy winter shoes, leading to a bedroom and lavatory - hardly a bathroom - with a shower almost over the WC, no curtain, and a small hand basin. I sit on the huge Italian bed, head throbbing. It is late; I'm tired and need to sleep. Why had I let him bring me into this high-ceilinged room with an unmade bed, piles of books and newspapers, smudged mugs and a plate or two on a pine table? Francesco clicks on the lamp at one side of the bed and turns off the shadeless bulb in the centre. Less harsh a light, more reassuring. He sits beside me to feel my dress.

'Still damp,' he judges disapprovingly. 'It's easy to catch a chill, especially in August when the storms start, hot and sultry, followed by the treacherous night sea breeze.' I think back to the jaunty sea-horses, rising and bobbing more and more as the gusts increase. One arm reaches over to grasp the hem of my dress on the far side, both hands gently easing it over my head and shaking it out as he takes it to a wooden clothes horse in the corner. I lie back and watch him arranging my best dress over the bars, stripping his shirt and trousers to do the same, meticulously. My headache is lifting to leave me strangely merry, giggling at the prospect of the two of us, clad in our dry swimsuits with our damp garments airing before us. I'm giggling even more as I think I should let my damp bra and knickers accompany the rest, to give a fuller display - but can't be bothered to dig them out of my bag.

The sheets smell of lavender and are crisply pressed. My eyes follow Francesco as he pads naked round the edge of the bed, in and out of the minute bathroom, sometimes close to me, at other moments as if at the end of a vast hall performing some sort of ancient ritual, lighting a candle at a shrine to celebrate our athletic endeavours. They wander round his profile watching the candlelight flickering over it, down the arm muscles, and curve over the pale silhouette of his swimming trunks to the tanned thighs and calf muscles as if tracing a figure on a Greek vase. I breathe in; deeply, drowsily sated, my lids slowly close. A distant awareness of almost tickling strokes along my legs burst into tremors of sparks in my head. Half opening my eyes, peering through my lashes, the room appears empty, the candle flame glowing and undulating upwards, brighter now I am surveying it from darkness. The lamp on the table has gone out, the bed tips to my left; I am enfolded, lifted, embraced, as my mind rolls back to the breeze whipping the sea-horses higher, surging them shorewards till they shatter, followed by more and still more, and so I rock with them, a drowsy numbness dissolving into a dream. I am following a child escaping into the bluebell wood on a warm spring evening, the light slanting through the white-barked silver birches. The child turns with a shriek that spirals through my body, piercing me to the quick.

CHAPTER 18

Rain has washed a pearl grey dawn into pale yellow then pink when Francesco leaves me at the Palumbo block of flats. Giosetta is in the bathroom; Rosina and Mauro Palumbo arrive a few minutes after me.

'Come to see me at midday.' Signor Palumbo looks at me longer than usual, and disappears into the master bedroom to find his sleeping place among his scattered children. His wife follows, head bowed either out of obedience or to avoid meeting my eyes. I slump on to my divan and sleep heavily, to be woken by the children clamouring for their elevenses.

It is a rush to do the shopping and the clothes washing, not to mention their lunch. I've no time to attend to myself so I can't understand why, when I return to check my money and review the situation in the dining-room bedroom, my journal lies open on the floor. The children must have gone over my things while I was washing clothes. They have never done that before. I put the journal back in its place in the shopping bag, sit on my bed, head in hands, and sift through the morning. The children have taken their hunk of bread and chocolate to play outside on the bomb site, and only come back for lunch. It can't have been them. Horrible associations are forming in my mind: someone - who? - is looking through my possessions. What for? I am hardly in the mood to play the detective. It is bad enough without one's own room, but I assumed the suitcase under the divan and the various bags where I keep my books, letters and papers would be sacrosanct. Even if living in another family's house, my privacy should be respected.

Signor Palumbo has quietly slipped into the dining-room and drawn a chair away from the table to sit down in front of me. He's drumming my shoulder to make me look at him.

'Valeria. Look at me.' Why don't I? What have I to be ashamed of? Assertively, 'Valeria! We all have to be open and work

243

together in my household. I can't have people carrying on behind my back. I know everyone who matters in Genoa, remember that'. No answer. Then the sound of notes rustling out of his wallet.

'You're short of money. Here's some, but you could earn more, far more, if you'd -' I twist away, half turning my back to him. *'Valeria! Valeria! Non hai niente da perdere - ora!'* How dare he! I have nothing to lose. Why does he add, emphatically, 'now'? I hesitate. He's thrown the notes down on the table and risen to push the chair back in its place, insisting, 'Think about it. I'll be here at six this evening. *Valeria, non hai niente da perdere.'* Nothing to lose! I search for my handbag under the bed, wondering whether that has been rifled as well. It hasn't.

Nothing to lose! I prepare the children's lunch, try to talk to them as usual, wash and tidy the kitchen before fleeing down the stairs past Giuseppina playing with dolls and the doorkeeper's daughters, along a short cut over the bombed site where Luigino and his friends are building a den with planks and bricks, to the beach - his beach.

I drop myself down at the edge of the ruffled sand which the high tide never smoothes, knees apart to rest my arms on them, head drooping. Where is he? Nearly lunchtime, and only scattered individuals on the beach. Once the storms start, the air clears and cools. Time, Italian convention decrees, to wind down the beach season. Only a day to go to September when the sun, I am informed, no longer tans. A few heads are bobbing out to sea, but the sun is against me dappling the water. He must be there somewhere. I drop my head again, close my eyes and breathe slowly and deeply to expel the irritating phrase from my mind: nothing to lose, Valerie, nothing to lose!

'Valeria!' There he is, emerging from the sea like a Greek god silhouetted on a vase, pausing, left hand on hip, the right raised towards me. He begins running, shoulders pulled back, knees and arms flailing as he rushes towards me. *Valeria! Valeria!* Everyone is

calling me. He throws himself down beside me thumping sand into my eyes, to growl,

'Close your knees!' I snap them tight. 'Your feet too!' I draw them together, lean forward and wrap my arms round my legs, chin on knees to hide my embarrassment. 'Everyone can see you, even from the sea.' So that is the way his mind is pursuing me.

His gang are following in a more leisurely fashion, sprawling casually beside me, finding some excuse to touch me, tap my shoulder, tickle my calf, and run their fingers down my spine. I am, it seems, their property, courtesy of Francesco.

'Coming for a swim, Valeria?' No way. 'I've forgotten my swimsuit.' True or not true, it is all the same. Their rough familiarity irritates me. Something has changed. Francesco has been talking. I stare at each in turn, unresponsively serious.

'I found you all much more fun when I first met you.' Francesco is relaxed, smiling in his usual impenetrable way out to sea, as if scanning the warship and coastal vessels with the knowledge of a weathered seafarer. He looks older in daylight, wiser, remote.

'I'm tired.' I continue to fill in time, while complicit smiles are rippling round me; small, hairy Bruno is nudging his neighbour. Me, a caged creature, trapped partly through my own ineptitude; scrutinised, scorned, slandered. Their mockery disquiets me; I get up to leave, dragging my feet

through the sand, imagining Francesco bombarded that morning by, 'Did you ...? How was she ...?' No idea of how he reacted, whether any sensitivity towards me would counteract that nonchalant gloating which so enhances the male ego before its peers. Or so I imagine. Francesco is calling me back; I continue ignoring him, not running or anything emotional, just coolly retracing my steps to the flat.

Mauro Palumbo is waiting for me in the bedroom dining-room. He doesn't mince his words.

'You're not choosing the right people,' he warns, 'and there could be violence.' I haven't a clue what he is talking about.

'I'm not interested at all in whatever you're suggesting.' I don't know exactly what I meant, only wanting to end the conversation by adding,

'It's time for me to leave.' Signor Palumbo studies me for the best line to take. Cajolingly,

'You'll have fun working with Giosetta. Rosina does my particular patch on the street, but Giosetta keeps to the bars and dancing. Your scene. I've heard you enjoy it, and there's a lot of money in it. Ask Giosetta.' I start rummaging in my bags under the bed, pulling out books to repack, then my journal, banging it on to the shiny floor to ring out my disapproval. Palumbo persists.

'You don't have any connections. I can find you the right clients.' I push the books back in the knap sack, retrieve the journal and draw myself up in front of the man, a little closer than strictly comfortable and, stressing each syllable, announce,

'I am leaving tomorrow.' If he turns nasty, I am sure I can spend tonight at Flavia's before taking a train to Venice on my rather roundabout way home. I still have September before university begins in October, but I have to be seriously careful about money. Signor Palumbo's child-minding money will last me through Venice. Then I'll see how the tide takes me.

His offer spurned, Palumbo struts angrily out of his dining-room, muttering, '*Non hai niente da perdere!*' to tempt me to change my mind. I need to plan my time. I have only today left, and I'd really like to see Carlo and Giovanni again. It isn't hard to find my way back to the bookshop where Carlo works. No luck. It's his afternoon off. I try the street market with stalls for second-hand clothes, bed linen, books and everything else that can be sold, but Giovanni's basement bookstore in via della Mandorla is closed. They'll be at their favourite hostelry. The bar tender hasn't seen them today, but thinks they might come in later. I'm in no mood to sit around on my own, so I slip a disappointed note under the bookstore door, lingering to look over objects on the stands outside in the hope one of my friends at least will turn up. After more than half an hour I am expected to buy something, so I smile and leave, running and leaping down the cobbled streets to Flavia's house showing, though no one is watching, that I don't really mind. The flat is in darkness. Two old women sitting on chairs in the street stare inquisitively, the unappointed custodians of the block.

'The Cecconis have gone away to visit relatives.' Trying not to feel let down, I leave a note and comfort myself by strolling through familiar haunts in the old town before turning reluctantly towards the Palumbos. I've neglected my novel but have tried to continue my journal. Too much excitement, too little time or, to be more honest, inclination. Now that someone, probably Signor Palumbo, has scrutinised each page, it is strangely tainted, even if he can't have understood much of it ... Except - I gasp - his name, the people in his flat, and Francesco's. I must leave, but I need to round my stay off. To create my epilogue.

I return for a lonely meal listening to inane dance music on the radio; Giosetta has it stuck on that station and I can't be bothered to search for anything else. I'm pleased to see the children, to give myself to their chatter, to appreciate how much Italian I have learnt from looking after these three engaging, streetwise personalities, all the more amazing for their rather neglected upbringing. Are they loved? Perhaps. Signora Palumbo has given them supper. Cherished? Less so, but I'm not sure they miss what they don't know. The persistent, stabbing phrases – *Valeria, you have nothing to lose! Now. Did you...? Was she...?* - become blurred, more infrequent while I'm playing with Luigino, Carlotta or Giuseppina, but once they've fallen asleep on the giant matrimonial bed, my subconscious drums the words out as clearly as before. I shall have to exorcise them through my journal. It is no use kidding myself I am too tired, though I feel weary at the prospect.

Otherwise the niggling phrases will invade my dreams, awake or asleep.

'31 August, 1955. Date established, a new page - where can I start? Not day by day – I'll never finish. The most important events during my post-Cecconi time in Genoa are meeting Francesco, finding this odd Palumbo household and being able to stay in a dining-room bedroom without becoming unstuck. At least, in my own regard. If I really think about everything that's happened over the past three weeks, I'm struck by the way I've coped, and even enjoyed dealing with strange situations. People might say I can count my lucky stars. Who has lived in the 'underworld' without being physically attacked? Propositioned, yes, but to be honest, I've never felt in physical danger.

Voices, accusing phrases, eyes mocking, fingers pointing - and I don't know how far I'm imagining them - do unnerve me. It's the way people are constructing a totally false picture of me, my emotions and thoughts; an utterly distorted image. I don't mind what people say and think about me on one level, but I'm indignant at people seeing a distorted mask as the real Valerie.

I can't even say my initiation was as emotional or critical as others - particularly men, and I suspect Francesco above all - would like to think. I'm his trophy. This morning he tried to hug me and, as a sort of consolation prize, 'Valerie, you're a woman!' What rubbish! He hasn't a clue about my state of mind, nor is he really interested. Conventional generalisations are so false. I'm not particularly bothered, one way or the other, though convention says I should be. Life will sweep me on to Venice, this episode subsiding into the seed-bed of experience. I need to say good-bye to Francesco - even Gino and Agostino.'

What about Mike? I've hardly thought about him, and I suppose the same goes for him and me. I'll send him a card from Venice.

୬୧

Uncertain whether the Palumbo parents expect me to continue as before on my last morning, though I suspect they don't believe I really am leaving, I put on my autumn outfit – black polo neck jumper and red corduroy trousers – and return to the baker's shop. Gino is surly at first, but smiling when I leave him with a kiss and loaves and pastries for the Palumbo children. As I feared, it is more difficult with Agostino, but I smother him in praise for the sandals I bought and promise I shall buy more on my return, next year perhaps. His mouth smiles acknowledgement; his eyes retain the aloof detachment of a bruised male ego.

Francesco might be tricky. The gang sees me coming. A young man standing by them starts to walk briskly towards me. He takes me familiarly by the arm and turns me round to walk away from the others.

'Francesco isn't here.' I recognise the handsome waiter at James Osmond's dinner party.

'D'you know James Osmond?' He looks bewildered. I insist, 'Giacomo Osmond? His family own the house where we had dinner two days ago.' I didn't realise the waiter knew Francesco's gang.

'Giacomo who? D'you mean Francesco?' We are speaking at cross purposes. He wins.

'What about Francesco?'

'Do you want to see him?' I smile, I hope, indifferently. It won't be wise to show any keenness, knowing how these men talk. What a blatant lie it is that only women gossip - the so-called harem syndrome - while men simply 'discuss'.

'Well, I do want to say good-bye to everyone.' He looks surprised.

'You're leaving already?' I shrug my shoulders. The less said the better, although I'm not sure what there is to reveal anyway. I dislike my habitual defensive attitude, too subservient to what others are thinking, or what I imagine they are.

'I'll tell him.' The others are turning round and calling me.

'I'll say goodbye to them,' I hesitate, 'but what about Francesco?' The young man looks out to sea, then lowers his voice, though nobody is near enough to hear.

'I shouldn't be telling you this, but the best thing to do would be to call the hospital or prison.' A long shocked pause. We stop by the boulevard railings. 'Try the prison.' I screw up my eyes at him, puzzled, confused. 'Nothing much,' he whispers, 'just a question of sheets, towels ...'

❧

'A question of sheets, a question of towels,' the train rattles on towards Venice. At least the rhythm has rejected 'You've nothing to lose' and the short raps of 'Did you? Was she?' That young waiter is crazy to think I can phone a prison. A hospital, yes. But a prison? Why didn't he look more upset? I reel through the events again. 'A question of sheets,' says the train. Bed linen, Robin Hood - got it! He steals - no, takes, the sheets off clothes lines to give to the poor. Or to sell in the flea market near Giovanni's bookstore and live sparingly off the proceeds. There isn't much excess about his life - or is there? An appetite for women? Foreign women? Available foreign women? 'A question of sheets, a question of towels, hospital, prison, a question of sheets,' patters the train.

The regular movement of the gondolas, the slurping and lapping of water and the chug of the *vaporetto* that I take to the youth hostel don't sluice out the recurring phrases running through my mind. The *palazzi* along the canal, the stalls huddling round the Rialto Bridge - all over-familiar from books and postcards - do distract me. I find the Youth Hostel in an old gothic palace by the Ca' d'Oro ferry stop on the Grand Canal. It's evening, just in time to secure a bed.

They are laid out as in boarding-school dormitories, without the cubicles and curtains, along two sides of an echoing hall with a porphyry-coloured *terrazzo* floor. I am tired and hungry, like the others eating in the hostel that evening: Ron the tall Oxford graduate with a hawk profile and judgmental attitude, a journalist starting at Reuters next month; Miklos from Dubrovnik who's left his group to join us and practise English and Maria Pia, called 'Pia' for short. Her father was a priest who let her study chemistry and now she's restoring old Italian masters; she talks in a jumble of vivacious Italian and broken English. Gustav from Frankfurt sits forlorn until we beckon him to join us over the meal. We pool our available money, agreeing to uncover this old seductress of a city until means are exhausted – my gang this time, not Francesco's.

Strange and wonderful strands weave more ideas into my mental fabric: Ron, notebook in hand, obsessive about finding the right stone colour - amethyst, sapphire, emerald or opal - for the sky and the sea and the canals; Gustav meeting me in the barnlike Frari church, clicking his heels to send the searing echo of metal clad toes and heels into the remotest recesses, and raise the spectre of mass military marches. This same Gustav quaintly talks of 'hand-shoes', anxious to please me by speaking English. Pia, older than the rest of us and comfortably knowledgeable about all the religious paintings, is hilarious when recounting her father's previous life in a Dominican monastery or parodying Mussolini with 'and the trains are always on time!' I look anxiously at Gustav, too quiet, someone who only asks questions, never comments, or Miklos, hands always clasped behind his back, high cheekbones, pale skin lightly brushed by the sun, slender, almost frail. Young Europeans drifting together past Istrian stone, bleached by the sun, dirt nestling in the hollows. One lunchtime Pia bargains a cut-price gondola ride and we glide along the outer waterways of the city, where only an occasional gondola slips silently out of a side canal rippling the images of *palazzi* bordering ours.

Summer is ending, not yet finished. All of us except Miklos take the *vaporetto* to the long Adriatic beach of the Lido. Lanky Ron dares Gustav to jump over a deck chair, from the back. Challenged, he runs at it in a surge of anxious energy, leaps high and lands heavily on the occupant. We all beat a hasty retreat (stifling a severe attack of hysteria) to the grubby public beach alongside. No deckchairs, but another challenge: who is the first to reach a raft enticingly moored about twenty metres off shore? More games, more challenges, and a competition on the raft to do the crab walk. Pia laughs her refusal at the others. Ron's too tall to heave his shoulders up effectively, Gustav scores with ease, and I manage three moves before my bikini top pings up to my throat and, furiously embarrassed, their hilarity plunges me back under the waves. All winners, all losers, we relax back on the *vaporetto* to find Miklos.

He's waiting for us outside the hostel leaning against the *palazzo*, smoking. There's a concert in the Doge's Palace, he tells us, but our communal money is running out. Just enough to eat in the Youth Hostel - tomorrow will take care of itself. We wander, Ron running ahead, disappearing into an alley to hide in a door way. Before he can jump we wait, watching his shadow projected by the lamp over the door. We swing arm in arm across Marco Polo's courtyard before he leaps out and scatters us laughing through the archway to dodge in and out of small squares, streets and tight passages between the Rialto and Saint Mark's until we burst into the glorious moonlit square.

The orchestra is tuning up in the courtyard of the Doge's Palace - out of money, out of bounds. I insist we can hear it sitting by the entrance gate. Instead we're all smuggled in as destitute wandering students, to spend a Venetian evening with Vivaldi. The moon passes over, and I think of Francesco lighting the candle, of his silhouette, of the sea and the waves. Back comes the nagging, 'You've nothing to lose,' the staccato 'Did you? Was she?' and that young waiter with, 'A question of sheets'. I want the music to wash them out of my mind while I lean on a friendly shoulder - Miklos's.

He smiles down and pats my arm. I've only just noticed he's left-handed.

Our last evening, a free concert; one more night paid for, and then we'll have to fend for ourselves. The Venetian chapter is ending. I linger to photograph Saint Mark's square onto my memory, fearing I might never return. The precarious uniqueness of each and every experience in my series of adventures quivers into yearning. Exquisite sadness brings a sob to my throat as I slowly abandon the moonlit square, to walk alone under the arch with the clock and the figures that strike the bell at the hour into the brittle light of the huddled shop windows. Unthinkingly I seek darkness, plunging under yet another arch and across a tiny courtyard into a tangle of alleys. A crunch of grit on a paving stone; someone is following me. Ears pricked; neck, hand, thigh muscles clenched, I continue deliberately at the same speed, poised to leap into flight. A hand grasps my shoulder; I gasp, turn fist raised to - Miklos's face.

Just fun between friends, and we continue arm in arm inside the labyrinth of Venice, he pausing under a portico to trace my nose and cheek in the darkness, finding my lips and kissing them gently, dryly. The lamplight cuts past us, contouring the low wall of the canal. The slight slapping of water and two thirds of a gondolier enter right from under a bridge to pass rhythmically off left, leaving a three-column *palazzo* window glowing under double arches at us. His fingers are stroking my neck so lightly they ruffle my senses, setting ripples off through me, and other sharp thrills chasing through them. The lamp in the arch swings, grinding on the edge of a hook. Moonlight muffles the patrician's palace in a creamy light; I don't care about the two silhouetted figures leaning against the columns of the *palazzo* window as I'm floating into myself until - my ears prick again, my body stiffens just slightly. There's an alien sound of wood straining beneath weight, of leather creaking or rubbing. I run my hands gently down Miklos's arms below the shirt sleeves;

while his left arm pulls me closer, mine runs down his right one. I breathe in sharply, feeling a leather glove, hard, inert.

'It was a landmine on the beach near home. Just a game...' My hand covers his mouth.

CHAPTER 19

I pack my regrets into my suitcase, meticulously adding the contact details of my new friends and checking I have Francesco's in my address book. I can't stop worrying whether he has returned from wherever he went, was taken - or captured. I've the time to nip back to Genoa, but not the money. Besides, I have nowhere to stay with the Cecconis away visiting relatives. My gut need is to find out what has happened, but the current is pulling me northwards. Time to move on.

I feel nervous leaving my language zones, though the only way to absorb some German is to speak it. Renate lives in Hamburg and has asked me to stay. We did part company a bit abruptly, but the invitation, I imagine, still stands. Salzburg first; I can just afford a night at a youth hostel and will spend a morning exploring the small city where Mozart was born. Time, space, money - all become inextricable in my anxious calculations to eke them all out.

వింల

Accepting a lift is out of the question, especially after my experience with Renate in Spain. However, when one is offered by a bespectacled journalist in front of the Prince Bishop's Residence in Salzburg, I judge it safe, and vow that I shall try to speak German to him. Gustav had encouraged me in Venice and I did learn a few words. I'm wary of any male who strikes up a conversation, but he has helped me find the funicular to the castle, is respectable looking, even dull. He must be about thirty, but looks older. It is rare for someone of his age to earn enough to run a car. He needs it for his work, of course, being a peddler of words and impressions, like Ron. Things are shaping up well. There is a certain astringency about Salzburg which I savour after the voluptuousness of Venice.

We introduce ourselves. Günter comes from Munich, but reports mainly Austrian affairs. Leaving Salzburg we hum the more obvious Mozart arias together as he knows little English and I've learnt even less German. I seem only to pick up nouns and a few adjectives, no verbs to combine them into action. The verbs are so complicated; someone, probably Gustav, told me they split up and migrate to the end of the sentence leaving one in suspense about the meaning until the end. Most odd. We drive through wide valleys with mountains as backdrop to my thoughts. I fill the silences with images of Francesco. They nag at me. If freed from wherever he is, I figure him on the beach to the bitter end of the sunny season, his friends drifting back to whatever is their normal life for the rest of the year. His seems to leave him a free spirit. His quarters are frugal, stark even, but clean and, yes, even fragrant. I close my eyes to sink into the lavender scented sheets. I might even have dozed off a bit, for when I open them we are driving into Munich and Günter is asking me where the hostel is. It's strange that he, born and bred in the city and not that old, has no idea where it is.

Like Salzburg, Munich is another city of church towers topped by onion domes, many gaping but most under repair. I already feel excited by the prospect of a couple of days here. It won't be much fun, though, trailed by Günter. Journalists do work irregular hours, but he seems to have plenty of free time and money. I'm quickly learning the notes of yet another currency and their equivalent value in sterling. His manner is understated, but he is evidently doing well for himself. Even so, I have absolutely no intention of getting involved with anyone. He isn't the sort to tempt me anyway. A safe type, I'm sure.

'See if bed available,' Günter suggests. 'If full, I find another,' adding considerately, 'I wait'.

I hesitate. My instinct is to take my belongings with me and fend for myself, but that would be rude. He'll think I don't trust him. He might even turn nasty. Surely not! He's been harmless up to now - insignificant to boring, if I admit the truth. However, he has given me a long lift, and it will only take me a second to hop out and run up the steps to the office to find out. The entrance hall is deserted, so I follow the sound of voices to the far end of a corridor. A group of hostellers is washing dishes. The warden has slipped out, but they are sure the hostel isn't full. I don't exactly hurry back to Günter. I've hardly been away five minutes, and he doesn't seem an impatient type.

Whatever his feelings, he has driven off. I've no suitcase, no knapsack, no handbag - no money, address book, journal or passport. Absolutely nothing. Only the black polo neck jumper and red corduroy trousers I travel in. Too stunned even to weep, I collapse on the steps.

❦

Hit rock bottom, bounce back. I am paying for my stay at the hostel peeling vegetables and scrubbing floors. The British consulate will take three days to get me a new passport, lending me money for photos and a ticket home on condition it will be repaid. There is no time for me to do anything except menial jobs in the hostel. They keep me fed and rested and better able to face the tedious dance round offices to get a replacement passport and shops for the cheapest underwear - to wash one set while wearing the other. In spite of all these setbacks, I don't want to be cheated out of the last weeks of my summer vacation.

Worst of all is the loss of my journal and the first draft chapters for my book. I could easily buy another copy of the *Divina Commedia*, though the one stolen had sentimental value as well as important annotations.

'I was learning Italian from it,' I tell Louise Anderson, a woman in her early thirties who is an under-secretary at the consulate, 'though they teased me about my quaint use of words'. Louise has even invited me to her home for dinner. I confide that I have been thinking of a diplomatic career. She nods, but doesn't respond.

'I trusted that journalist,' I admit over my first taste of sauerkraut and peppery Bavarian sausages, 'stupidly thinking my belongings are worthless - except to me'.

Louise smiles. She seems to like me, even in my scruffy state.

'Your passport could be traded for quite a bit of money, you know. There are many stateless people about. He could be a dealer in stolen documents.'

'No. He told me he was a journalist...'

'Oh Valerie! That's what they often say. You can't easily prove it's true, can you?' I stare at her. How could I have been so blind? All those notes he pulled out when paying for anything. The car, the... now it all falls so neatly into place.

'One can't trust anyone then?' I feel like moaning at the iniquities of the world, of people I meet, and of men in particular. Unscrupulous, cruel men.

'What use is my novel to him, my journal, my Dante? I know I can't rethink what I've written. I could try,' I hesitate, not to sound defeatist as well as naive, ' to rewrite them, but they would sound sort of second-hand. And the whole idea for my journal was for the experiences to be freshly scintillating. That man has deadened everything, and all for my footling old passport!' I snort in frustration.

'You shouldn't say that to me! My job prompts me to spell out how strongly I disapprove of your attitude. Here and now, off duty with you... well, I know how you feel.' I wish I could learn to bite my tongue.

'Of course I hate the idea of someone else going round as me,' I screw up my nose, 'and think how awkward it would be if we met!'

'Unlikely,' Louise comments drily, 'in any case, with all the refugees in Europe - not to mention the rest of the world - whoever is now your passport twin will be so pleased to have your legal document. More relieved, in fact, than either you or I could imagine. Think what it'd feel like to be stateless, not to have a legal name or place to belong to, officially not to exist, even though you obviously do'.

A non-person. I feel humbled when I fetch my temporary passport. It has been a tedious business, and I'm only too aware of the consular atmosphere of disapproval. However, I can put up with it all to have my public identity reinstated, and that in itself seems a privilege.

I regret not being able to stay longer in Munich and see more of Louise. She has already warned me that the city has been badly bombed and some of the great buildings, like the exquisite rococo Amalienburg Pavilion, almost totally destroyed. I tell her I shall travel back north without being too specific, since I'm not intending to head straight home as I am supposed to. Penniless, except for the money from the Consulate for my return ticket, with a store of food I am allowed to take with me from the hostel kitchen, I'll hitch my way to Renate in Hamburg. Just less than three precious weeks of my life have to be lived before returning. The theft has left me in the doldrums. Somehow I will catch up with myself in a new journal and continue writing my novel. I am learning the hard way not to trust anyone, except for Louise and people like her, who is who she says she is, a consular official. Not a pseudo journalist. Was Francesco a pseudo something or other? At least he hasn't told lies, but it was what he didn't divulge, the gaps within the experiences he vividly recounted, that worry me more. I must fill them in, but have now lost contact with everyone. My address book, of course, was stolen with all the rest.

I write down the few addresses and fewer telephone numbers I can remember in the blue exercise book - Louise has bought me two - and feel slightly less lonely. A cascade of grief pours through me for all the friends, contacts and opportunities forever lost. I try to snap my memory shut, but every time I open the red exercise book to restart my journal at one end and novel at the other, the grief begins flowing again. Staunch it NOW, I tell myself, fearful it will engulf me. I'm not after all a stateless person, even if I may have lost all my new friends. The person with my passport will now be reconstructing a self, rebuilding the fabric of a lost life. I feel I am drifting away from my recent past as I walk along the main highway that leaves Munich for the north. There are few vehicles, lorries mostly, but none are stopping. I probably look like a gypsy, wearing the same black pullover and red trousers for nearly a week, because I'm worried about washing them at night in case they aren't dry by morning. I must find work quickly to buy a change of clothes. I plant myself apprehensively on the grass verge with just one canvas bag to hold my few possessions.

There is something unfair about the way a girl steps out of a lorry further up the road so she can signal to the cars before they reach me. A cheat. I'm here first. The girl spends some minutes rearranging a huge knap-sack, before she heaves it on to her back and walks slowly towards me, holding out her hand under a barrage of German. The words I picked up from Gustav and the journalist flee from my head, leaving me with three pathetic ones,

'Nicht Deutsch, bitte!'

The girl hesitates, then cautiously in English, 'Where from come you?'

Equally cautiously, 'Surrey, south of London.' I don't have a clue what this is leading to.

'Where go you?' This small girl with dark curly hair and wide brown eyes continues. 'Hamburg.'

'So me! It is good chance. I want to help you because to show Germans not all bad.' Who had thought that? All the hating at home was reserved for Hitler and his henchmen. The Führer's guttural tirades rasping out from our black Bakelite radio in the kitchen had shrouded my heart in undiluted terror. Other Germans were vaguely bundled into the same category as similar populations elsewhere - unwilling victims of an unwanted war. It shows, I think ruefully, how many ways one can lose one's direction, perspective or sanity. All ways of becoming emotionally stateless. Nowhere to belong. One shouldn't have adventures, go anywhere, without a place to leave and return to.

'I help you,' continues the German girl, 'to Hamburg'. Like Renate, she's practical. 'If you nowhere to go, I have extra bed and little stove for heat and cook. I called Heide. And you?' She even knows of a job doing the night shift in a newspaper building. Things are looking up. I admit to my new friend that I hope to be able to earn enough to buy a new skirt and blouse, even perhaps a cardigan as the evenings will be cooler in the north.

'Valerie, easy hitchhike. Always lorry drivers, and safe with two. Good to travel in two.' She has been to see her boyfriend in Bavaria, but is studying in Hamburg. She is two years older than me and very streetwise. The journey is slow, the lorries judder and throb me into a daze; it is a relief to let Heide deal with the drivers. She is right. We are safer together, and three lifts take us right into the centre of bomb-scarred Hamburg. Munich had been heavily bombed too, but the vertical emphasis of this northern city leaves it with a scarred skyline of walls jutting up windowless, roofless; jagged silhouettes like maimed limbs plead to the pale blue evening sky.

'Our bombers did it all,' I whisper to myself, 'But remember London, Coventry cathedral ... All equally useless destruction,' adding, to assuage my misery, 'at least we didn't start it all off'.

Heide tells me she is a war orphan living near the town centre in a nineteenth-century building, officially uninhabitable but which students use nevertheless. The police have far more important things to do than bother young people who are working, often on night jobs, to pay for their studies. There is a student job centre and that's where she has heard about the night shifts at the *Hamburger Abendblatt.*

It is dusk when the lorry driver drops us off at a garage not far from the docks. The streets are deserted; a light here and there behind dingy curtains and windowpanes cracked by the air raids years earlier.

'Repairs come little by little,' Heide explains, 'because all not agreeing - to repair, or demolish. So much bombed - perhaps new city better, no?' There seems to be no reproach in her question. I don't feel I can respond. My words might become weighted in some way or other, open to misinterpretation. I'd better keep quiet, watch, learn and earn something to pay my way. I'm not picking up much German with Heide insisting on English. It is a strange sort of journey and introduction to Hamburg: uneventful but not unexciting, with so much to think about. History nudges in to circumscribe every reaction.

The sun has set by the time Heide turns off into a street with half-guttered blocks. She takes a passage leading to a small inner courtyard and climbs the outside stairs to the second floor, calling over her shoulder, 'not hold railing, it fall out.' Strange the iron balustrade wasn't used for the war effort; in my town all railings around churchyards and front gardens like ours were shorn off to be melted down for armaments. On second thoughts, these were probably left for the inhabitants' safety. Outside staircases with railings are rare in Britain as far as I know. They are usually inside with wooden banisters - no use for the war effort.

There is something clammy about the room. The only window doesn't open properly, the frame buckled by bomb blast. A rough curtain divides the washing and cooking area, more precisely a two-burner stove on a packing crate with a couple of pans, plates, cups and cutlery shoved below willy nilly. It stands beside a cracked basin and a wooden clothes horse with towels flung over it.

'Take one, and here your bed.' Heide points to a divan with two rumpled rugs and a pillow with a hollow in it, like the negative of the last occupant. By now shops are closed, but she finds some biscuits and makes a mug of tea with sugar. No milk, no fridge. I'm determined to help out in every way I can, but am uneasy about laying my face on a pillow that smells of previous occupants.

'Is there another pillowslip?' Heide doesn't quite understand, and then shakes her head.

'It quite clean, I think.' Pillows in Germany are large and square, and I have no spare clothing to lay over it. I'll buy a square pillowslip with my first pay packet. I have to sleep in my underwear, the rugs scratching my bare legs. Having served its double function for so long, the divan has assumed a weary grey texture.

'Heinrich sleeps here nighttimes, but he see mother for tonight. So you use tonight, and sleep there daytime when work night shift.' So organised is Heide that she seems to have the bed vouched for both day and night. My experience of the world is perceptibly widening. For now I'm so exhausted that even traces of Heinrich on pillow, couch and rugs can't stop me falling asleep, though fitfully. I'm too tired to contact Renate. I know her surname and can remember the street has Lübeck in it, so it will be easy to find her tomorrow in the telephone directory. I resolve to spend some time each day trying to resurrect my address book, novel and journal, but can't be bothered with them for now. First of all, I must get that job. I need money desperately for the pillowcase, blouse, cardigan and skirt or another pair of trousers. No one has made any comment about my crumpled garments. Everyone seems too busy finding ways to survive.

৵৶

I am bewildered by the potential proximity of people: present physically like Heide who is taking me to sign on at the *Abendblatt* building this evening and meet the unknown Fritz, who will look after me on the job; unseen Heinrich, who shares the divan bed; Renate somewhere in the same city. Not fully aware of what is happening around me, my mind slips back uncomfortably to Francesco, unable to imagine him in any context. I sit down at the small trestle table by the window and open the red exercise book.

The page stares at me blankly, reminding me of the times I panicked half an hour before going to school without the weekly essay. White lined paper ready for my ideas. The obvious start - date: 9 September, 1955. Pen raised, I stare out of the window, but my eyes stick on the cracked pane and the speckles of light caught in the dust.

'It's approximately ten in the morning and I'm near the port area of Hamburg which we bombed to smithereens not that long ago, and I don't know where I'm going from here. My journal and draft chapters have been stolen. I'll recall what I can and carry on. I might have had time, but no money, to find out Francesco's fate. I'm adrift without my address book.' Distance adds frustration, not thrill to my curiosity, more a nagging need to know than the excitement of pure speculation. The letter x becomes fixed in my mind; 'proximity', 'approximately', place and time, like two bodyless pairs of legs meeting, spokes in a wheel I imagine turning. We are joined in some sort of strange pattern, merging unknowingly.

Here I am, with my new passport stamping out my person, place and where I belong for all the world to know, to pass frontiers according to a clear set of rules, part of the international travelling circus; but for all that I'm not at all sure where the tide is taking me emotionally or practically.

'Fritz come take you to *Hamburger Abendblatt* six in evening.' Heide obviously enjoys planning. 'Now I see ill friend Wolfgang. I show you little of Hamburg.' It's a good excuse to close my exercise book and follow Heide down the stairs, careful to hug the wall and not touch the railings. Practical as ever, Heide has offered to lend me some money, which I can refund from my pay packet. That suits me fine. We relish the appropriate hamburgers on slices of soft bread with a dollop of mustard, all bought from one of the many kiosks in the city centre.

'He has bad time,' Heide says as we scuttle across the square devouring our lunch. 'He join SS. They not believe he only sixteen, because big, how say, big bones?'

Down in the dark basement he inhabits in another grey bomb-scarred building, Wolfgang looks like a Bernard Buffet skeletal figure, eyes settled suspiciously deep into the sockets, the heavy bones edging out from under his tight, greyish skin.

'Here's food, Wolfgang,' Heide announces in a matter-of-fact way. 'Eat, then we take you to Baths. Here is Valerie.' All of twenty-seven perhaps, he looks ten years older, a ghostly clockmaker surrounded by shelf after shelf of hundreds of moon-faced alarm clocks, gleaming in the basement half light like his sunken eyes.

'Nein!' he grunts, 'not the Baths,' grabbing the greasy brown paper round the hamburgers and asking who I am.

I lift some newspapers from a rough wooden chair to sit at his level.

'They're tasty. I've had some.' I speak English because it is all I can do and in any case, it is a less formal way of introducing myself. He gazes at me balefully while biting into the hamburger and moving his jaws with grim determination, as if this were his last meal.

'You'll come too.' It is a statement, in German, drawing me into his world.

Without warning Heide stands, pulling Wolfgang up with her. Propelling him through the door and up the steps to the pavement, she looks back at me.

'Please use key in door to lock, and come.' A strange but not unusual group forms: Heide on the outside and me inside, with a gaunt figure in patched khaki trousers and jacket stooping on the arms of two young women.

'He sometime not undress for shower, 'Heide explains as we sit waiting in the entrance hall where she has paid for him and pushed him through the turnstile into the bathing area. 'Men today, but wait here. I tell people at desk that if not washed, he go again for no more pay,' adding without lowering her rather strained tone, 'but you smell difference'. It is not one of Wolfgang's good days, evidently, as while she is speaking he reappears in the hall.

'No, Wolfgang. Back.' And leaning over to me, 'he not had shower. Just push him through again entrance,' and she hurries out into the street.

So that's how I begin to help Heide with Wolfgang. As she is helping me, this is an obvious extension to the web woven out of necessity. He is happier after his shower, but takes some persuading to have one. Even by just holding his arm, I sense how taut he is beneath the deceptively shambling exterior. His nerves are in disarray, his reactions unpredictable. I try out simple questions in German. Yes, he loves clocks. They give orders, mark out the day, command with alarms. Time, Wolfgang knows, has to be marshalled. The more the better. They also collectively reflect light into the dark room, so he doesn't need electricity. He only reads in the daytime. He sometimes stoops over me, too close for comfort, and rants about the bombing. 'You lot, you ruined my city, my life.' I see no point in responding, except to whisper back into the gloom, 'not only us'. He says that he never wants to go out to contemplate the ruin of his city, his hopes, his youth, but to live in a burrow, where he can fiddle around with time.

༄ஐ༄

Over the days that follow Heide gradually edges me into a daily pattern while I settle into the night shift, placing newspapers I can't read on the conveyor belt with Fritz for sporadic company.

Mornings are spent sleeping on the divan that Heinrich has just vacated – I have bought my own bed linen - and from midday onwards, still sleepy, I get food for Wolfgang and me, convince him to go to the public baths every other day, clean his room and try to reach into his mind to soothe its contorted fears. It drains me emotionally and tries my command of German to its limits. Meeting uncomplicated little Fritz for a meal cooked in his tiny flat or preparing one with Heide in her room become treasured moments of relief before going off to the night shift just as Heinrich is claiming the divan. I am trying to save, though my new clothes cost more than I expected. The evenings are cool and I need a woollen cardigan as well as a light raincoat.

After my time with Wolfgang and before the evening shift I attempt to see more of the scarred city. Gangs of young people are busy. Some of the buildings in Heide's district are beginning to have the panes repaired, even a new window and frame inserted; some inner courtyards have been cleared and the contorted iron railings straightened or repaired. Shattered tiles and glass beside the skeletons of abandoned prams, cane chairs, bicycle carcasses, dead sparrows and assorted rubble are gradually removed, the paving stones below scrubbed in hope of better times. The grim regularity of this late summer episode reminds me of wartime. I'm only writing short entries in my journal:

'It's like war again, all those people in armaments regimented into shifts, and the others, like my mother, looking after their children or cooking their meals in canteens, all active for one third of the day. Another third for sleeping, and the rest for eating and whatever relaxation can be found, usually in the absence of family and friends one really wants to see because they are away or on a different shift. All this accompanied by a pervasive, corroding sense of foreboding.'

Most often during these hours of freedom in the afternoon and early evening, I feel groggy, dragging the weight of sleepiness and uncertainty around with me. My brief journal entry:

'I should be catching up on all the reading I haven't done over the summer vac, but can't do it without the books; even if I had the money and time to get on with it here, I'd hardly find the volumes I need. I should go back to England as Louise said, but then I'll be caught up in all the untried strands of life in a new home, with hardly more time than I have now. I've managed to rewrite much of my stolen journal, but the novel is more difficult. I couldn't do this if I return to find my parents uneasily settled into their rented flat. Here at least I'm sort of independent and in theory doing what I want. Or think I am. There's so much I would like to get done...'

⤳⤲

Heide seems to have moved on with her good deeds and left Wolfgang to me. My free time is mostly taken up with him, now he is venturing out beyond the public baths and is even coming to a tavern with us, or as she puts it, 'When you to take him'. I am picking up some rudimentary German. We have to avoid the sound of boots on gravel. If I don't accompany him to his digs, he can become fretful, even violent. I must allow a good hour for that. Back there he wants me to make coffee, and tries to draw me into arguments. Then he begs me to sit by him so he can persuade me, but then clutches at me passionately, or resentfully - he's totally unpredictable. Occasionally he pounces on me like a tiger, then falls away weeping, as gentle as a kitten. He's handsome in a wild sort of way, and looks healthier now he's eating regularly, so I feel there is some sort of progress. He's not long on explanations, probably because he thinks I won't understand him, but it frustrates him even more when I must leave. I have to watch carefully for the right moment to slip away. My night shift begins at ten. The more I try with him, the more he seems to want.

I need Renate, someone outside Heide's circle, to talk to. The newspaper job has to pay off small debts as well as day to day expenses, with barely two weeks to go before the university term begins. I have been careful not to spend the money from the Consulate for my return fare to England. Renate's surname is Hausen and I remember she lives in a street with Lübeck in it. That's a start. I decide it would be good for Wolfgang to help me, so I borrow Heide's old street map of Hamburg and ask him to look up Street and Lübeck. All he can find is Lübecker Strasse, a road too long for me just to go and ask if anyone knows a Frau Hausen, especially as that is hardly an unusual German surname. He is offering to accompany me, saying that one or two of those areas would certainly have been bombed, as this is a pre-war map, adding something like, 'You British didn't do things by half-measures!' I mutter under my breath that I wasn't involved, remaining outwardly silent, inwardly distraught. Instead, back at Heide's I find a more up-to-date telephone directory and a number for Hausen which has a Lübecker Strasse address. I can just manage to ask in German whether the female answering has a daughter called Renate. A short gasp, then, 'You must be Valerie!'

Frau Hausen is immediately recognisable as a wider, smaller version of her daughter, with a flatter face, her brow ploughed by increasingly unbearable anxieties. She speaks quite slowly, so I understand but struggle to respond adequately in German.

'As if I didn't have enough worries, waiting for my husband to return,' she willingly confides. 'Now Renate is always off somewhere. Never at home.' Frau Hausen plops potatoes, *sauerkraut* and a thick fatty sausage on to my plate. 'He's only missing. Some have returned after ten years, you know.' Another unmarked grave, like Uncle David's. After the meal she takes me out on a bossy little ferry to look at the shipyards. Her suggestion.

'My husband used to work here. There were jobs in the shipyards.' On and on she talks of the good old days, after the inflation in the Twenties when a wheelbarrow of banknotes bought just one loaf of bread. In the Thirties things got better. She doesn't mention Hitler, just the reality of coping with the basic human currency of survival. The Nazi regime had helped, so that was all right by her. The vast Blohm & Voss shipyards for her meant survival, for me they embody evil and destruction. I ponder the image of the 'wheelbarrow loaf', and the absurdity of it all. Bread and water. A roof. Food and protection for her family. This woman, along with so many others, was asking for her rights in exchange for work, not begging. Any work would do. Any work? My mind snaps back to Wolfgang. I haven't seen him for two days, and am beginning to dread his emotional demands on me.

'Renate doesn't write,' Frau Hausen complains, 'though she did tell me you were her chaperone in Spain. And now you are here.' That's the first I've heard about being Renate's chaperone. Now I realise why her mother has been looking strangely at me. 'It's expensive to call me by telephone, but she knows I'm alone.' Frau Hausen blows her nose. 'And to make matters worse, it seems my daughter wants to stay in Paris. She has a job of sorts, but is going out with someone called Simon.' She blows her nose again to try and dry the tears without me noticing. I'm confused.

'Renate's young, and needs a boyfriend.' To try and please Renate's lonely mother, I add,
'With young people it probably won't continue'.

'I hope not!' I suspect there is more to it than just a boyfriend keeping her daughter in Paris, but can't fathom what it is. Frau Hausen is perpetually sitting down and then standing up to do something, perhaps to ensure her body is usefully occupied, her thoughts less intrusive. Perhaps not, as she says half out loud,

'I don't like the sound of Simon. It's not a name we give over here. That is, unless... '

Could it be the Jewish question? Names, names, names, they have so many associations. Peter the apostle was really Simon

270

Peter, and most Christian names have Hebrew origins. This is pure prejudice, I think as I get up to leave, telling her that I'm working on the night shift. Talking of Renate's boyfriend in Paris made me think of Mike. I'm stung by sadness. He must have forgotten me. For some, time passing brings oblivion. Or the simple pursuit of self-interest.

Fritz is waiting for me outside the newspaper building, worried I might be late. Here they all seem caught up in an anxious chain of responsibilities. Fritz feels I am his; eyes always on me in case something goes wrong and I need help - or is it that I might step out of line in some unknown way? Wolfgang has become my charge, while Heide's has shifted to Heinrich, or someone else. So it goes on.

This is my tenth night shift; my movements are now automatically attuned. Dozing off, I let my newspaper pile go slightly outside the conveyer belt or sit at an incorrect angle, provoking a roar at the far end and a corresponding upright jerk in my body as my eyebrows twitch upwards and the whites of my eyeballs frame the blue iris, as if transfixed by fright. Morning comes grudgingly; at ten to six someone pushes and taps my shoulder. I wriggle it. Still ten minutes, not a second more, to go, and that will be it for the day. But the tapping persists, the pushes provoke. Swivelling round angrily, my eyes meet a stern look and a torrent of German from a stout *frau* on the morning shift. Deftly prised off my seat, I look around for Fritz, somewhat irritated.

'I want to be paid for the last ten minutes she's taken from my shift,' I tell him.

'Of course.' He laughs at my surprise. The morning workers have been, it seems, hired on a contract and are keen to prove their credentials. Too keen, I judge as we shuffle out across the nearby square to our usual breakfast café. It is full.

'Go somewhere more quiet?' Fritz suggests, choosing a small street leading to a scruffier open space. Just as we enter the square, I feel a weight on my shoulder, and twist round to see a policeman behind me. Another is interrogating Fritz and looking repeatedly at me. They're asking for identification documents. I'm not carrying my new passport around with me for fear of losing it again, so Fritz is explaining that I've left it where I'm staying with friends, and all this while I'm staring at the policemen uncomprehendingly. After some minutes and noting down everything about Fritz, not me, the two policemen turn back up the street to the square we have just left.

'Anything important?'

'No,' grumbles my red-haired friend who had seemed a rather undemonstrative type for the ten days we have known each other, 'just we tired and they hear you no German. They told to see people - like me!' he snorts, 'do not pass night with foreigners. I told I pass all night with you - work legal. They go to check.' He laughs. He's not as mild as I thought.

People are reading the first edition of the morning newspapers; not the headlines, but the local news. Fritz translates it for me. On page three, in huge letters, it says a young man has committed suicide in Hamburg. He lived in a basement flat surrounded by clocks which he had meticulously set to raise the alarm - over two hundred of them in unison - an hour after he hanged himself. There was no mention that, having served in the SS from a tender age, whatever he did would be carried out scrupulously.

I am never going to let anyone read it, but the last entry in my journal is about Wolfgang.

CHAPTER 20

Nothing turned out quite as I expected. My parents were pleased to see me back from Hamburg, though they were somewhat preoccupied settling into the flat. I told them a bit about my summer, not enough to disturb them. Events moved fast after my mother - well into her fifties and desperate about their straitened finances - gained a certificate allowing her to teach small children. She started by forming a group soon after they moved to Godalming. A few months later she replied to an advertisement for a qualified person to teach two young children at a country house in the Midlands. The parents wanted her to start almost immediately. A thatched 16th-century stone cottage went with the post.

I was relieved for them. They were too busy to have me with them and I was glad for an excuse to return to Cambridge before the autumn term started. I wanted to change some of the courses I had chosen for my second year before I went to Paris. Inevitably I bumped into Madame Magny. She passed me in a corridor with a slight smile and a whiff of *eau de cologne* impregnated with brandy. Without saying anything, she continued on her way as if she hadn't seen me. I was just another Newnham College undergraduate. It was irritating that I had become irrelevant, but also a relief.

With Mike it was different. I half hoped there wouldn't be a note from him in my pigeon-hole. My feelings had changed, but I wasn't sure in what way. Nothing there. Relief, but also frustrated expectation.

Then, soon after term began, I glimpsed him through a steamed-up café window on King's Parade, but couldn't see who was with him. Should I leave him a note at Clare College? Perhaps, but what could I say?

Unexpectedly, a few days later, there he was coming towards me in front of King's College, still looking cuddly like the

Newfoundland dog in *Peter Pan,* with brown curls draped over his collar, forehead and one eye. He approached me with his familiar lolloping gait and an amiable smile as if we'd been in touch throughout the summer.

An obvious exchange followed: Where have you been? What are you doing? Where are you going? Must meet. Soon. Will call, contact. Must go, late... and so on.

Do I like cuddly but unkempt men? If so, why? If not, what type does suit me?

He lolloped off and I cycled away. Later, to my astonishment, he sent me a message, probably as a joke, proposing marriage! I'd already decided to take a course on Dante taught by a Dominican monk instead of Madame Magny's on nineteenth-century French literature, and to row out alone into the vast unmapped ocean of my future.

EPILOGUE

"There's a feeling of power in reserve, a power that drives right through the bone, like the shiver you sense in the shaft of an axe when you take it into your hand. You can strike, or you can not strike, if you choose to hold back the blow, you can still feel inside you the resonance of the omitted thing."
Hilary Mantel *Wolf Hall* (2009)

Last night I dreamt I returned to Scarperia. Not like the first time when Francesco met me in Florence and took me to the Certosa monastery where we gazed across the Tuscan hills. A thrill. A shiver of recognition. An unrealised memory of olives shimmering silver above russet earth, of leafy tendrils and vines heavy with grapes, of tall cypresses along roads that wind up hillsides to umbrella pines sheltering farmhouses. It already was, and still is, my own image of Tuscany, though I had never been there before.

When I returned to Scarperia last year, I was no longer the student or young mother I had been before. John and I left our house near Lake Trasimeno on a September morning that was shaking off summer in a scurry of raindrops. He didn't ask why I chose this roundabout route along the old road to Bologna from Florence. In any case, on our journey north he preferred to take time and avoid motorway fumes and fury. It was a good idea to explore a new way back, so we set out on a road only used for local traffic after tunnels had threaded the motorway through the Apennines in the 1950s.

That first time in Scarperia, I was lying on a bed reading on a stifling August afternoon. Francesco's mother had shown me to the bedroom Francesco used to share with his two brothers in Via di San Martino. It's off to the right when you face the church in Scarperia. That somnolent stillness in the hush of a close afternoon. Time was suspended, until the iron bed frame suddenly shook me, the window panes rattled and the floor seemed to list. Then nothing. The siesta quiet again, though a dog continued to howl. A wait. Nothing more. I returned to my book, succumbed to the heat and slept. I was woken by another shudder the length of my spine and rushed out of the room.

Francesco was sitting in the kitchen holding a newspaper and staring out of the door.

'They're letting off dynamite. Blasting tunnels through the Apennines.'

'At two o'clock in August?' I said doubtfully. He laughed, slightly condescendingly. What did I understand about such things? Indeed.

When John and I arrived in Scarperia last year, I was disoriented by the ugly suburbs smothering the fields of clover for animal fodder that used to be the setting for romantic assignations. I was surprised too by the new blocks of flats choking the groups of villas built by former farmhands on the outskirts of the historic centre. In the past young women, hair tightly wound over curlers, would chat in the evening while watering flower pots. They had just come home from the convent where, under the direction of the nuns, they were embroidering Grace Kelly's wedding trousseau. Later they would form lively groups in the main square, the town hall clock chaperoning them on one side and the priest at the church door on the other. Youths from the local knife factory used to sprawl at the café tables on a corner of the square to watch the girls. Arm in arm in threes or fours, curls loose over their shoulders, they swung round the square or paused to giggle in huddles, peeping over shoulders invitingly before veering towards the municipal garden on the edge of the town. There Francesco and his youngest brother, Orlando, had played with my small child, tossing him one to the other as he chuckled in delight and I watched in consternation. I can still feel the sting of rivalry in their jokes.

Under low clouds and an imminent drizzle, John and I walked along the deserted main street from the municipal garden to the square. I found myself disturbed by memories and thoughts of what might have been. Everything I saw reminded me of something else, something just out of reach. The castle and stone walls of the clock tower or *campanile* represented a sense of belonging to Scarperia: *campanilismo*. A narrowing of the inhabitants' horizons? I didn't remember the tie-bars like thick black hyphens all over the fortified castle, now town hall and local museum. We bought tickets, both curious to wander among displays of locally-made knives going back to medieval times and antiquated farming implements. The old men smoking outside the café on the corner or lingering at the church door would, we imagined, have enjoyed telling us their story - now curated into history. Ox yokes and painted carts bore silent witness to centuries of unchanging labour; of scythes, of sheaves of hay leaning unsteadily on one another at harvest time; of the antique threshing machine from the local co-operative wheezing away and the long treks from fields to farmhouses in the Mugello, land of the Medici. Their Cosimos and Lorenzos strode out from here. Hill towns spilled over slopes around castles guarding their lands.

The woman who slowly pushed the studded doors of the museum shut behind us looked too young to be in charge of it.

I asked her, 'Do you happen to know anyone in Scarperia called Castelli?' Not perhaps the best way to begin my quest, but I had to start somewhere.

'Why don't you try in the café?' She pointed to the familiar one in the corner of the square.

The Italian miracle has passed this café by unnoticed. The same hard chairs scrape back and forth on the speckled grey *terrazzo* tiles. A basic, resistant surface. There was not a face below sixty except for a portly fiftyish woman fussing our order out of the hissing *cappuccino* machine.

I looked around. 'Does anyone know a family called Castelli?'

Epilogue

Where does the surname Castelli, or castle, come from? Descendents, perhaps, of servants in the castle, now town hall, or of peasants toiling for the lords of the castle in the valley below? If they had not laboured for the Medici, they would have laboured for some other equally ambitious master who had fought his landless family into power and built his own castle.

'*Signora Anna, conosci per caso questa famiglia? Castelli?*' A man hunched in an oversized jacket repeated my question. A V-shaped furrow between her brows, Anna was visibly concentrating on our coffee and my request.

'Try the telephone directory. I think there is a family or two of that name.' The directory was as before lying on the telephone ledge in the far corner. 'Read out what you find there for Castelli, and I'll tell you if I know anyone.'

I found a Silvano Castelli at Sant'Agata, about three kilometres from Scarperia. He might be the middle brother, a quiet, slightly brow-beaten man, already married then with a small daughter. Anna didn't know him. Sant'Agata was, she thought, the epicentre of an earthquake some time ago. Decades even. It happened in September - this month - her mother had told her. She was only a baby then.

I suffer from a mild form of telephone phobia, but forced myself to try this number. A woman replied. It was Silvano's number. Yes, he was Fancesco's brother but her husband Silvano had just died. The woman gulped as she put the receiver down.

"I remember now. I have heard of Silvano Castelli!' Anna exclaimed. 'His daughter, Silvia I think she's called, is a policewoman. Yes, here in town.'

The other two Castellis were linked to surnames I didn't recognise. No Francesco. What about Orlando, the youngest brother, the one who...? A sharp stab of recollection pierced me, of a life that might have been. I found an Orlando Castelli with another surname after it.

'Try it,' John said, rising to the chase and wanting something to happen, unaware of the trail I was following.

I did. A pause at the sound of my voice. One thing uncontroversially mine is my accent when I speak Italian.

'Valeria?' After so many decades, she recognised me. It had to be Marcella, the person I least wanted to see. 'Shall we meet?' I said. She agreed to come to the café.

On my first visit to Scarperia to meet Francesco's mother I was introduced to Orlando, his younger brother, my age. He was already engaged to a gangly blond girl busy embroidering Grace Kelly's trousseau. Everyone was talking about the film star's dream marriage to Prince Rainier of Monaco. I remembered noting Marcella's round, rather prominent eyes that must have been strained. She earned in one week only just enough to buy a shirt for her fiancé, part of her dowry, together with more modestly embroidered sheets, pillowcases and nightdresses.

On another visit Francesco proposed marriage. So did Orlando a few days later. Confused, I returned to Cambridge, where Mike had already done the same. Three tantalising paths into the future lay before me – or I could refuse them all.

Marcella took her time to appear. After we had ordered a second cappuccino followed by a Campari soda she arrived with her daughter, who combined her mother's colouring with Orlando's features. They stayed outside the café declining my offer of refreshment. We all stood awkwardly in the drizzle as it became prematurely dark. Orlando was away, but would return later. They had two children – her daughter here, and a son - both working in the pharmacy in Scarperia, though whether they were qualified pharmacists was unclear. She had found work in the local post office and ended up as the manager. Orlando had retired from the same job he had when I met him, driving a bus. All of them were still living and working where their families had survived for generations. No, they didn't travel much. To Florence, and to the seaside in

Epilogue

August. Good for one's health. Little curiosity about me or the small child Orlando had played with in the municipal garden. Francesco had returned to Scarperia about ten years ago. Until then he lived in Rome; she didn't know what he did there. I tried to avert pangs of memory. After a pause, she added that he had returned to his home town to die.

The drizzle turned into rain and there we were standing under umbrellas, Marcella and her daughter still reluctant to enter the café. Walls have ears. She kept staring at me. A grey curtain of rain swept over us. I shuddered, reliving the lure of paths we both might have taken.

John shook our umbrella and said it was time to leave for Imola. Marcella warned us of the hairpin bends in the road climbing the Apennines and over the Giogo - a pass like the yoke of an ox - into the Po valley. I felt a tremor within, a desire to wait and meet Orlando, but there was no invitation to stay. Better to leave untouched my memory of the athletic young man who loved and proposed and played with the child. His own prearranged path led into the future with patient Marcella.

We set off on the old road over the Apennines. In the fifties I was fascinated by tales of the Allies pushing the Germans north in 1944 and the brothers' surprise at the first black man they had ever seen, an American soldier. As we drove up through the woods, I recalled stories of the brothers picking wild strawberries in May and June and mushrooms in September. Our route north corkscrewed towards our distant destination, Firenzuola, the boundary town between Tuscany, land of the Medici, and Romagna.

Afternoon was fading into dusk when we drove into the main square by the frontier castle. Young people were noisily enjoying themselves in the two bars on the main street. It was time to find a place to eat and sleep. Our meal served in the chilly arcade by the castle was the best we had that summer. The drizzle had stopped and the sky was clearing with a glimpse of stars and the promise of a dry day to come. Inside the restaurant families and friends were boisterously celebrating; we were alone in the lamplit square.

Our room in the *pensione* boasted two iron bedsteads, woollen mattresses, crisp lavender-scented linen sheets and a corner basin, elderly but functioning. Down the corridor a bathroom, basic and spotless. Ours, as there was no one else. I shivered, transported back to the Fifties and resonances of a life that might have been.

Now I realised why Marcella had stared at me. I was wearing red trousers and a dark jersey, just like when we first met. They would have reminded her of that evening long ago when the brothers played with the child while she and I watched with shared apprehension as we faced the future.

Sunlight slanting through the slatted shutters woke John. We ordered coffee and croissants sitting in the arcade before leaving Tuscany on the road to Imola, then Bologna along the Via Romagna. The Romans built it across the Po valley to join routes straddling the mountain passes into Germany, Switzerland and France. Our journey north took my chosen path into the present.

If you have enjoyed this book, you might like to read *In Restoration*, Valerie Thornhill's recent novel about love, loss and reconciliation available on Amazon in paperback and e-book. (It won The People's Book Prize for Fiction 2012.)

She has also published *The Children of Kumbhalgarh and Other Stories,* a collection of short stories set in India, Russia, the USA, Italy, England and Japan.

Her short novel, *The Tycoon's Tale,* freely based on Dickens's *A Christmas Carol* and which predicted the financial crisis, is a wryly humorous account of a captain of industry's triumphs and tribulations.

All are available in e-book and paperback from Pergola Press
www.pergolapress.co.uk
info@pergolapress.co.uk

Pergola Press sends *Cynthia Loves her Fiat 500,* Valerie Thornhill's entertaining short story set in Rome in the Sixties, free with every book order.

Excerpts from Valerie Thornhill's publications can be found on her website: www.valeriethornhill.org.uk